[redacted]

THERMODYNAMICS OF STEADY STATES

THERMODYNAMICS OF STEADY STATES

RALPH J. TYKODI
ASSOCIATE PROFESSOR OF CHEMISTRY
SOUTHEASTERN MASSACHUSETTS
TECHNOLOGICAL INSTITUTE

THE MACMILLAN COMPANY
New York
COLLIER-MACMILLAN LIMITED
London

First Printing

Library of Congress catalog card number: 67–10889

THE MACMILLAN COMPANY, NEW YORK
COLLIER-MACMILLAN CANADA, LTD., TORONTO, ONTARIO
Printed in the United States of America

TO

Mary and Martin Kilpatrick

Preface

This book is both an original monograph and a textbook dealing with the application of thermodynamics to nonequilibrium situations; it represents an attempt to extend and to make rigorous a line of development initiated by William Thomson [1] and pursued by other investigators such as Eastman [2], Wagner [3], and (in a certain sense) Brønsted [4]. Each of the cited authors tried to treat nonequilibrium situations on a par with equilibrium ones, using (essentially) the same severely classical techniques for both types of phenomena. These classical approaches to the treatment of nonequilibrium situations failed to achieve the desired degree of rigor and generality, and a nonclassical method of treatment originating with Onsager [5] has come to the fore in the last few decades [5–9]—it today enjoys great popularity under the title *Thermodynamics of Irreversible Processes.*

Although I did not originally intend it so, this book has ended up being something of a synthesis of the lines of development initiated by William Thomson and by Lars Onsager. The treatment here is along decidedly classical lines (I maintain throughout a global rather than a local view of systems and processes), yet some of the conceptions introduced by Onsager do find a natural place in the development. Before reading this book the reader should be acquainted with the elements of classical thermodynamics.

I have divided the book into three parts: Principles, Applications, and Comments. I lay down the theoretical foundations in the part on Principles and comment on them in the part on Comments. The section on Applications contains analyses of systems I have found to be of interest. I have not attempted to make the coverage in any way exhaustive.

With respect to my earlier work in this area [10], this book shows an improvement in notation (I now indicate special quantities by using a typographical convention instead of German script), and it includes much new material appearing here in print for the first time. In keeping with the textbook function of this work, I have constructed a series of exercises for the reader; the exercises are partly of the theorem-proving type and partly of the data-processing type. In my overall style of presentation I have been influenced by the writings of Michael Polanyi [11]. When developing a logical chain of argument or when introducing routine assumptions, I march shoulder to shoulder with the reader: *if we combine Eqs...., we get...; let us assume that....* When dealing with definitions, speculative assumptions, or matters of opinion, I step forward and assume full responsibility for the presentation: *I here find it convenient to introduce the quantities...; I assume that the system...; I feel that....*

This book does for the class of nonequilibrium situations involving stationary states and steady-rate processes what any good book on ordinary thermodynamics does for equilibrium situations: it develops a series of relations of interest in their own right; it helps the experimentalist plan his experiments efficiently by making use of the necessary interconnections among experimentally determined quantities; it provides the experimenter with some consistency checks on his measurements; and it yields equations interrelating macroscopic quantities—equations that are of use to engineers and that serve as guides for more detailed kinetic theory or statistical mechanical analysis of the phenomena.

I wish to thank those persons who have encouraged me in my work on nonequilibrium thermodynamics: my former associates in the chemistry department of the Illinois Institute of Technology, foremost among whom has been Peter G. Lykos; other colleagues, in particular Ted A. Erikson, Charles K. Hersh, Isadore Hauser, Myron Tribus, Robert G. Parr, James C. M. Li, and L. T. Fan; many friends; and, above all, my wife Lois. I am indebted to the Illinois Institute of Technology for financial support that enabled me to spend part of a summer working on the manuscript.

Acknowledgements

I am indebted in the following ways for permission to reproduce previously published material: to John Wiley and Sons, Inc. (Interscience), for permission to quote from Brønsted's monograph on *Energetics*; to John Chipman and the American Chemical Society for permission to reproduce Figure 8–9; to the American Institute of Physics for permission to reproduce Figure 2–2; and to Ted A. Erikson for permission to include Figures 2–3 through 2–6.

References

1. W. Thomson, *Mathematical and Physical Papers*, Vol. I (Cambridge University Press, Cambridge, 1882), pp. 232–291.
2. E. Eastman, *J. Am. Chem. Soc.*, **48**, 1482 (1926); **49**, 794 (1927).

3. C. Wagner, *Ann. Phys.*, **3**, 629 (1929).
4. J. N. Brønsted, *Principles and Problems in Energetics* (Interscience Publishers, New York, 1955), Chapter 7.
5. L. Onsager, *Phys. Rev.*, **37**, 405 (1931); **38**, 2265 (1931).
6. I. Prigogine, *Etude Thermodynamique des Phenomenes Irreversibles* (Desoer, Liege, 1947).
7. S. de Groot, *Thermodynamics of Irreversible Processes* (North-Holland Publishing Company, Amsterdam, 1951).
8. K. Denbigh, *Thermodynamics of the Steady State* (Methuen and Company, Ltd., London, 1951).
9. I. Prigogine, *Introduction to the Thermodynamics of Irreversible Processes* (Charles C. Thomas, Springfield, Illinois, 1955).
10. R. J. Tykodi and T. A. Erikson, *J. Chem. Phys.*, **31**, 1506–1525 (1959); **33**, 40–49 (1960).
11. M. Polanyi, *Personal Knowledge* (University of Chicago Press, Chicago, 1958).

R. J. T.

List of Primary Symbols

(Italic number following definition indicates the page symbol is first used)

(*)	reference state, *20*.
$\delta/\tilde{\delta}\eta$	partial derivative with respect to η evaluated at the point $\eta = 0$, *27*.
.	(dot over letter)—time derivative, i.e. $\dot{Z} \equiv dZ/dt$.
–	(bar over letter)—property per mole; molar, partial molar, or mean molar property according to context.
$\langle\ \rangle$	average value.
$\langle\ \rangle_t$	time-average value.
[ ]	integral steady-state quantity.
$[\ ]^\partial$	differential steady-state quantity.
$\equiv$	is identically equal to, is by definition equal to.
$\approx$	is approximately equal to.
$\propto$	is proportional to.
a	place designation; activity, *21*; Helmholtz free energy density, *139*.
a_{ij}	element of the determinant A, *36*.
A	Helmholtz free energy, $A \equiv U - TS$, *6*; functional determinant, *36*.
A_{ij}	cofactor of the element a_{ij} in the determinant A, *36*.
$\mathscr{A}$	molar total Helmholtz free energy, i.e., ordinary molar Helmholtz free energy plus additional energy terms, *11*.
b	place designation.
B	interfacial area, *17*; reactant in a chemical reaction, *20*; cross sectional area, *131*; magnitude of the magnetic field vector **B**, *192*.
B	magnetic field vector, *188*.
$[c]$	Thomson-type steady-state function, *66*; Thomson coefficient, *106*.
C	concentration, *18*; heat capacity, *55*; nonreactive component, *148*.
$[C]$	integral molar steady-state heat capacity function, *65*.
$[C]^\partial$	differential molar steady-state heat capacity function, *52*.
D	diffusion coefficient, *18*; product in a chemical reaction, *20*.

E	emf of a cell, *102*.
$\mathbf{f}$	dummy field vector, *188*.
F	the Faraday; number of degrees of freedom, *29*.
$\mathscr{F}$	generalized potential difference, *69*.
g	acceleration due to gravity, *93*; Gibbs free energy density, *138*.
$[\mathbf{g}]$	steady-state Gibbs free energy density function, *142*.
G	Gibbs free energy, $G \equiv H - TS$, *6*.
$[G]$	integral molar steady-state Gibbs free energy function, *50*.
$[G]^{\partial}$	differential molar steady-state Gibbs free energy function, *65*.
$\mathscr{G}$	molar total Gibbs free energy, i.e., ordinary molar Gibbs free energy plus additional energy terms, *11*.
h	running index; height above a reference plane, *93*; enthalpy density, *138*.
$[h]$	molar steady-state linkage function, *49*.
H	enthalpy, *6*.
$[H]$	integral molar steady-state enthalpy function, *49*.
$[H]^{\partial}$	differential molar steady-state enthalpy function, *65*.
$\mathscr{H}$	molar total enthalpy, i.e., ordinary molar enthalpy plus additional energy terms, *11*.
i	running index.
I	electric current, *43*.
$\mathscr{I}$	moment of inertia, *191*.
j	running index.
J	molar flux, *18*; a current other than a heat current, *156*.
k	running index; reaction rate constant, *22*.
$\mathbf{k}_T$	thermal diffusion ratio, *88*.
K	equilibrium constant, *21*; phenomenological coefficient, *31*.
$\mathscr{K}$	molar kinetic energy of macroscopic motion, *41*.
L	phenomenological coefficient, *31*.
m	running index; molality, *94*.
M	molecular weight, *40*.
$[M]$	integral steady-state function, *100*.
$[M]^{\partial}$	differential steady-state function, *100*.
n	number of moles, *6*.
N	torque, *149*.
$[N]$	integral steady-state coefficient, *12*.
$[N]^{\partial}$	differential steady-state coefficient, *12*.
P	pressure.
q	heat gained by the surroundings of a gradient part, *9*.
$\mathbf{q}$	separation factor, *88*.
Q	heat supplied to the system, *6*.
$Q^{(r)}$	heat supplied to a reservoir, *9*.
$[Q]$	integral molar steady-state latent heat function, *65*.

$[Q]^{\partial}$	differential molar steady-state latent heat function, *52*.
$\mathscr{Q}$	activity quotient, *21*.
r	composition ratio, *120*; radial distance, *190*.
$[r]$	coupling coefficient, *41*.
$[r]^{\partial}$	differential coupling coefficient, *42*.
R	the gas constant; electrical resistance, *113*.
$[R]$	steady-state coupling coefficient, *41*.
s	entropy associated with the surroundings of a given linkage, *47*; entropy density, *138*.
$[s]$	molar steady-state linkage function, *49*.
$[\mathbf{s}]$	steady-state entropy density function, *141*.
S	entropy, *6*.
$S^{(r)}$	entropy of a reservoir, *9*.
$[S]$	integral molar steady-state entropy function, *49*.
$[S]^{\partial}$	differential molar steady-state entropy function, *52*.
$\mathbf{S}$	separation, *88*.
t	transference number, *153*; time, *173*.
T	temperature.
$\langle T \rangle$	effective average temperature of the surroundings of a given linkage, *47*.
u	internal energy density, *139*.
U	internal energy, *6*.
$U^{(r)}$	internal energy of a reservoir, *27*.
$\mathscr{U}$	molar total energy, i.e., internal energy plus kinetic energy plus gravitational energy plus . . ., *9*.
V	volume.
W	work supplied to the system, *6*.
W_0	work other than pressure-volume work supplied to the system, *12*.
X	mole fraction, *42*.
Y	generalized steady current, *27*.
z	dummy intensive variable.
Z	dummy variable.
α	place designation.
$\boldsymbol{\alpha}$	thermal diffusion factor, *88*.
β	place designation.
γ	place designation; activity coefficient, *96*.
Γ	Stefan–Boltzmann constant, *140*; thermomagnetic or galvanomagnetic coefficient, *193*.
δ_{jk}	the Kronecker delta symbol, *37*.
$\in$	symbol for set inclusion, *31*.
ζ	dummy variable; figure of merit, *123*.
η	dummy variable; efficiency, *123*.

$[\eta]$	alternative measure of efficiency, *123*.
θ	*measured-to-mean* mass flow ratio, *17*; relative activity, *100*; angular measure, *149*.
ϑ	*measured-to-all tube* mass flow ratio, *17*; fraction, *114*; fractional parameter, *143*.
Θ	rate of entropy production, *11*.
κ	thermal conductivity, *131*.
λ	distance parameter, *41*; wavelength, *139*.
Λ	characteristic length, *41*.
$\mu^{(i)}$	chemical potential of the *i*th species, *6*.
$\bar{\mu}$	electrochemical potential, *109*.
ν	stoichiometric coefficient, *20*; number of steady currents or affinities, *29*; number of components, *94*.
ξ	degree of advancement of a chemical reaction or process, *5*.
π	Peltier heat, *106*.
ρ	running index.
σ	reference thermostatic state, *29*.
$\boldsymbol{\sigma}$	Soret coefficient, *97*.
τ	current ratio (transference number), *117*.
φ	gravitational potential energy per gram, *40*.
χ	dummy variable usually equal to α or β.
ψ	dummy variable; electric potential, *43*.
ω	dummy variable usually equal to α or β.
Ω	generalized affinity, *27*.

Contents

THERMODYNAMICS OF STEADY STATES

PART I: PRINCIPLES

1

Introduction

In the last decade of his life, J. N. Brønsted grew increasingly concerned with the foundations and formulations of classical thermodynamics. His writings on the subject show a keen appreciation of the thermodynamic way of doing things, and his critical analyses of classical procedures will always be of value. In addition to his critical work, he also undertook a general reformulation of the language of thermodynamics in such a way as to stress *processes* rather than *states*; he called his formulation of the principles of thermodynamics by the name *energetics*. Shortly before his death in 1947, he summarized his work in this area in a short monograph entitled *Principles and Problems in Energetics*.

Although this book does not follow Brønsted in the formal part of his energetics, it owes much to his critical writings. It would be difficult to find a clearer statement of the scope and nature of classical thermodynamics than that appearing in the introductory chapter of Brønsted's monograph [1]:

The subject of *energetics* describes ordinary macroscopic phenomena, and attempts from a general point of view to establish the laws governing the changes brought about by these phenomena. It deals with the forms and components of energy, and with its transformations. This field of knowledge is usually termed *thermodynamics*, but in spite of the great importance of thermal phenomena their position in relation to the whole field is hardly sufficiently outstanding to justify the traditional name. On the other hand, the concept of energy is a universal one and provides a natural name for this division of science. The field covered by energetics is, however, limited by the fact that purely mechanical phenomena, including motion, are completely described under the heading of mechanics, and therefore are not usually included in energetics.

It is important to bear in mind that energetics seeks to solve problems solely on the basis of macroscopic observations. In other words, it does not appeal to ideas involving the existence of discrete particles of matter or energy. The introduction of such ideas represents an excursion outside the bounds of pure energetics. This statement does not, of course, seek to question the importance of molecular theory and quantum theory for science as a whole or for the general problems with which energetics is concerned. However, it is of great importance for the clarity of scientific understanding that the different methods of attack should be kept strictly separated from one another. Several serious weaknesses in the existing system of traditional thermodynamics can be attributed to an insufficient appreciation of the value of this prescript.

Historically, the origin of energetics lies in the study of the transformations of energy. Carnot, Robert Mayer, Joule, Clausius, William Thomson, and other pioneers in energetics were concerned with the "motive power of heat" and the "equivalence of different forms of energy." "Heat" and "work" were the practical concepts whose relations were sought. Later developments (notably by Willard Gibbs) led to a system of functional energetics in which a material system is described by means of the functions that are characteristic of its state and that serve to determine its behavior under different conditions. These two tendencies in energetics differ somewhat in that the former emphasizes energetic transformations and the latter, energetic functions. However, both lines of development, in conformity with their historical origin, are based on the study (in the light of experience) of suitably chosen elementary processes, while the principles of energetics are the generalizations arrived at by a logical interpretation of this study.

The Brønsted admonition against inopportunely introducing microscopic considerations into purely thermodynamic discussions reflects a basic feature of a well-established thermodynamic tradition; indeed a thermodynamicist was once heard to remark that thermodynamics is the study of systems with macroscopically describable surroundings—it is the surroundings that are studied in order that the properties of the system may be inferred. This book is imbued with the classical spirit so aptly epitomized by Brønsted; it deals with the *necessary* relations among the macroscopic properties of well-defined systems. Once we have established the set of thermodynamic relations for a given class of phenomena, we usually desire (in this modern age) to "explain" the observed behavior of the quantities and coefficients introduced into the thermodynamic analysis in terms of the properties of atoms and molecules. Evidently, we cannot "explain" a set of experimental facts and necessary relations until we know what the facts and relations are. For the large class of nonequilibrium situations amenable to thermodynamic analysis, the gathering of experimental facts and the establishment of necessary relations among those facts is work for the present; the explanation via statistical mechanical analysis of the patterns revealed by the facts is largely work for the future.

Nonequilibrium Situations

Classical thermodynamics deals primarily with equilibrium (static) states and with quasi-static processes (sequences of equilibrium states). In order to successfully carry through a classical analysis, we must be able to distinguish between the *system* and the *surroundings*, and we must be able to keep track of given amounts of heat, work, and energy exchanged between system and surroundings. Now these requirements are broad enough to encompass not only classical thermodynamics but also a class of nonequilibrium situations involving steady states and quasi-steady processes (sequences of steady states). We can use for steady states procedures analogous to those we use for static states, and as a result we can rigorously derive truly thermodynamic relationships for many nonequilibrium situations. We must take care, however, always to relate derived concepts to the primitive concepts of heat, work, and energy. A common set of concepts and procedures is adequate for the treatment of equilibrium states, quasi-static processes, steady states, and quasi-steady processes. Excluded from this extended classical domain are situations involving rapidly varying values of the parameters of the system;* such situations properly fall in the domain of kinetic theory and statistical mechanics.

It is surprising how easily and naturally classical procedures can be adapted to the treatment of steady-state situations. This book, then, presents a general thermodynamic approach, entirely classical in spirit, to the problems posed by nonequilibrium situations; it analyzes in detail a large number of stationary states and steady-rate processes; and it concerns itself exclusively with the macroscopic features of the investigated phenomena.

The Porous Plug Experiment

For purposes of orientation consider that well-known example of an irreversible process: the flow of a gas across a porous plug (the Joule–Thomson experiment)—gas and plug being thermally insulated from the surroundings. Let the system of interest be marked out as in Figure 1–1, where α and β refer to the high-pressure and low-pressure sides, respectively. Let us assume that the gas is flowing across the plug at a steady rate of $\dot{\xi}$ moles per second, that the gradients in temperature and pressure can be localized in a region in the vicinity of the plug, and that sufficiently far from the plug the thermodynamic state of the gas is characterized by the variables (T_α, P_α) and

* I am referring here to situations that are not even quasi-steady—i.e., to situations for which the concept *macroscopic state of the system* is inapplicable, it being necessary to specify the instantaneous and rapidly varying values of the parameters at each and every point of system.

(T_β, P_β). The system is thus divided into *terminal parts* that are homogeneous in intensive variables and a *gradient part* that contains gradients in intensive variables. Let us further assume that the gradient part remains stationary (i.e., pointwise invariant in time) during the steady-flow process. Now, if we take a definite mass of gas and the porous plug as our system, and if we apply

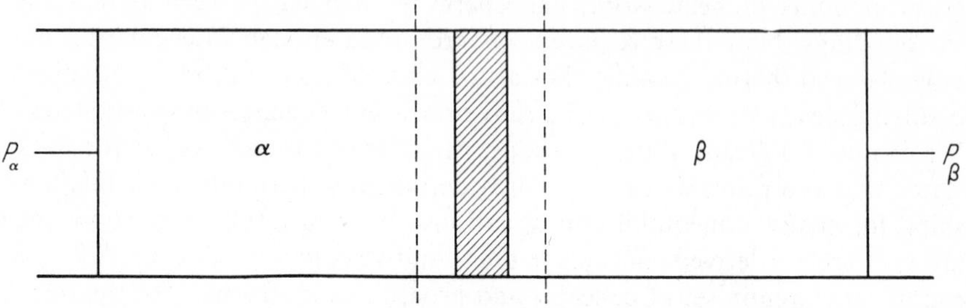

Figure 1–1. A mass of gas in adiabatic flow across a porous plug; $P_\alpha > P_\beta$.

the first law of thermodynamics to the adiabatic steady-flow process, then we obtain the relation*

$$\dot{U}(\text{system}) = \dot{W} = -P_\alpha \dot{V}_\alpha - P_\beta \dot{V}_\beta. \tag{1.1}$$

Since the flow is between terminal parts of the system, we have

$$\dot{U}(\text{system}) = \overline{U}_\alpha \dot{n}_\alpha + \overline{U}_\beta \dot{n}_\beta, \tag{1.2}$$

$$\dot{V}_\omega = \dot{n}_\omega \overline{V}_\omega(T_\omega, P_\omega) \qquad \omega = \alpha, \beta, \tag{1.3}$$

and

$$-\dot{n}_\alpha = \dot{n}_\beta \equiv \dot{\xi}, \tag{1.4}$$

where the overbar indicates a molar property of the gas. The gradient part, being stationary, does not contribute to $\dot{U}$(system). Putting Eqs. (1.1) to (1.4) together (and neglecting kinetic energy contributions to the internal energy), we get

$$(\overline{U}_\beta - \overline{U}_\alpha)\dot{\xi} = (P_\alpha \overline{V}_\alpha - P_\beta \overline{V}_\beta)\dot{\xi} \tag{1.5}$$

and

$$\overline{H}_\beta = \overline{H}_\alpha, \tag{1.6}$$

where $\overline{H} \equiv \overline{U} + P\overline{V}$. Equation (1.6) is the well-known constant enthalpy condition for the porous plug experiment. In deriving it, I made use of

* My choice of symbols for the standard thermodynamic functions is U, H, A, G, and S; Q and W represent heat and work supplied *to* the system; $\mu^{(i)}$ is the chemical potential of the ith species, and n stands for number of moles.

several features characteristic of my version of the thermodynamics of irreversible processes; a listing, therefore, of my primary assumptions is here in order.

Basic Premises

In addition to invoking the laws of ordinary thermodynamics, I assume that

(I) The system is capable of sustaining steady-rate operations under the described conditions.

(II) The system can always be divided into terminal parts and gradient parts, the gradient parts being stationary during steady-flow operations.

(III) Certain nonflow states can be treated as the limit of a sequence of steady-flow states.

I also systematically investigate the consequences of yet another assumption:

(IV) In a *proper* (ordinarily affine*) *sequence* of steady-flow states converging on a nonflow state, the limiting state is a state of minimum rate of entropy production relative to the neighboring flow states.

A fifth assumption appears in Chapter 3.

Assumption I plays the same role here that the analogous assumption plays in equilibrium thermodynamics: it is there always tacitly assumed that equilibrium states can be achieved under the given conditions; if a set of experiments yields conflicting results, we conclude that at some stage we failed to attain equilibrium. It is equally so with steady states: conflicting results imply failure to achieve steady states at some point in the procedure.

Assumption II is one of the distinguishing features of the present approach. The division of the system into terminal parts and gradient parts is especially fruitful when applied to steady states. In a steady state the gradient parts are stationary (pointwise invariant in time) so the change in any thermodynamic property of the system in a given time interval is found by simply summing up the changes in the terminal parts for the appropriate time interval.

Assumption III allows us to embed a nonflow state in a larger class of steady-flow states so as to have some maneuvering room for determining conditions of migrational equilibrium.† Much the same thing is done in equilibrium thermodynamics when variations are taken about an equilibrium state so as to determine the extremum properties of the equilibrium state.

Assumption IV holds when the reference nonflow state is a state of

* I explain the technical significance of this word in Chapter 3.

† A formal definition of the meaning ascribed to this phrase appears later in the chapter.

thermostatic equilibrium;* it is interesting to trace the consequences of this assumption for more general cases. If we could show that a properly generalized form of assumption IV (see the *special fields* section of the Appendix) is always true, the result would be of sufficient importance to merit calling it the Fourth Law of Thermodynamics.

Whereas the meaning of assumptions I and II is fairly clear, the full import of assumptions III and IV can only be appreciated inductively, by examination of a number of special cases. In the succeeding chapters we shall arrive at more precise formulations of assumptions III and IV, and in the concluding chapter we shall again take up assumptions III and IV in the light of the intervening analyses.

Brief Outline

Archimedes of Syracuse, upon having discovered the law of the lever, is reported to have said, "Give me a place to stand and I will move the world." The Archimedean lever with which we set in motion the machinery of thermodynamics is the closed system: the first law of thermodynamics can always be applied in an unambiguous fashion to closed systems. With a little ingenuity we can always manage to encapsulate the system or process of interest inside a closed system; then, starting from the first law of thermodynamics, we can proceed to winnow out the sought-after relations. A brief outline of the method I employ, together with a number of necessary preliminaries, is as follows.

In each case I define the *system* in such a way as to insure that only heat and work can be exchanged between the system and the surroundings; therefore, if we restrict our attention to steady-rate processes, we are always entitled to write

$$\dot{U}(\text{system}) = \dot{Q} + \dot{W} \tag{1.7}$$

for the rate at which the system gains internal energy. I normally divide the system into terminal parts and gradient parts, and I assume that the terminal parts of the system are spatially uniform.

Next, I find it useful to distinguish between *monothermal* and *polythermal* processes (and systems). A monothermal process is one in which the *entire* system is in heat communication with a *single* heat reservoir of temperature T during the process. A polythermal process (or system) is one in which the terminal parts of the system are separately in heat communication with heat reservoirs of temperatures T_i during the process. I allow for heat communication between the surroundings (exclusive of labeled thermostats) and the

* The rate of entropy production is zero in a state of thermostatic equilibrium, whereas in any neighboring steady-flow state the rate of entropy production must be positive definite.

gradient parts in the polythermal case, but I shall not now delve into the details of the analysis.* For a monothermal process then

$$\dot{Q} = -\dot{Q}^{(r)} = -T\dot{S}^{(r)}, \tag{1.8}$$

where $\dot{Q}^{(r)}$ represents the rate of influx of heat into the heat reservoir and $\dot{S}^{(r)}$ represents the rate of accumulation of entropy in the heat reservoir. Similarly, for a polythermal process,

$$\dot{Q} = -\dot{q} - \sum_i \dot{Q}_i^{(r)} = -\dot{q} - \sum_i T_i\dot{S}_i^{(r)}, \tag{1.9}$$

where $\dot{q}$ represents the heat gained per unit time by the surroundings (exclusive of labeled thermostats) via exchange with gradient parts, and $\dot{S}_i^{(r)}$ (e.g.) represents the rate of accumulation of entropy in the ith heat reservoir (which exchanges heat with the ith terminal part of the system).

In those cases for which there is a steady exchange of mass between terminal parts of the system, I assume that the gradient parts of the system are stationary, i.e., the state of the gradient parts is pointwise invariant in time during the steady-flow process. Under such conditions we can write

$$\dot{U}(\text{system}) = \sum_i \mathscr{U}_i\dot{n}_i, \tag{1.10}$$

where $\mathscr{U}_i$ is the total energy per mole (internal energy plus other kinds of energy—kinetic, gravitational, etc.) of the material in the ith terminal part of the system, and $\dot{n}_i$ represents the rate of influx of matter into the ith terminal part. The sum is taken over the terminal parts only, since the gradient parts (being stationary) do not contribute to $\dot{U}$(system) during the steady-flow process.† It is usually possible to arrive at a satisfactory description of any steady-rate process by combining Eqs. (1.7) and (1.10).

In dealing with systems in which there is no flow of a given type, I assume that the nonflow state can be taken as the limit of a sequence of steady-flow states. In addition, I find it necessary to assume that the system is capable of sustaining steady-rate operations under the described conditions. Sometimes I have to introduce new quantities to account for the fact that stationary states and steady-rate processes are, after all, different from static states and quasi-static processes. I introduce such quantities in as operational a manner as possible, using the equations of classical thermostatics as guides.

* The *monothermal*, *polythermal* language reflects the emphasis on the *surroundings* that was mentioned earlier. A system may be immersed in a thermostat and yet, due to going processes inside of it, it may not be uniform in temperature. We could not properly refer to such a system as isothermal. However, the surroundings of such a system would be characterized by a constant, well-defined temperature, and a going process in such a system could be referred to as monothermal.

† From the definition of a terminal part—spatially uniform in intensive properties—it follows that for a steady-flow process $d\mathscr{U}_i/dt = 0$.

The preceding outline forms the basis for treating two types of problems: (i) the steady migration of a given chemical species from one terminal part of the system to another, and (ii) the *migrational equilibrium* of a given chemical species in a spatial field. A chemical species is said to be in migrational equilibrium in a spatial field if there is no macroscopic tendency for the given species to migrate from one place in the field to another. Chemical reactions can be made to fall into classes (i) and (ii) if we consider migration with change of identity—there being a correlation between reactants supplied to or removed from one point of the spatial field and products removed from or supplied to another point. Examples of case (i) are the forced vaporization process and chemical reactions in monothermal fields.* Examples of case (ii) are such polythermal field phenomena as the thermo-molecular pressure effect, the Soret effect, etc.† Of the two sorts of problems, those of type (ii) are much the more important. By introducing migrational equilibrium functions, I try to systematize the treatment of steady states in the same way that Gibbs systematized the treatment of static states in his paper on heterogeneous equilibrium.

Reference

1. J. N. Brønsted, *Principles and Problems in Energetics* (Interscience Publishers, New York, 1955), p. 1.

* See Chapter 2.
† See Chapters 5 and 8.

2

Monothermal Steady-Rate Processes

General Remarks

For a system that is the site of a monothermal steady-rate process (provided that we can split the system into terminal parts and gradient parts), we can write

$$\dot{U}(\text{system}) \equiv \sum \mathscr{U}_i \dot{n}_i = -T\dot{S}^{(r)} + \dot{W}, \tag{2.1}$$

$$\dot{H}(\text{system}) \equiv \sum \mathscr{H}_i \dot{n}_i = -T\dot{S}^{(r)} + \dot{W} + \sum P_i \dot{V}_i, \tag{2.2}$$

$$\dot{A}(\text{system}) \equiv \sum \mathscr{A}_i \dot{n}_i = -T\dot{S}^{(r)} - \sum T_i \bar{S}_i \dot{n}_i + \dot{W}, \tag{2.3}$$

$$\dot{G}(\text{system}) \equiv \sum \mathscr{G}_i \dot{n}_i = -T\dot{S}^{(r)} - \sum T_i \bar{S}_i \dot{n}_i + \dot{W} + \sum P_i \dot{V}_i, \tag{2.4}$$

where $\mathscr{U}_i$ represents the total energy per mole of material in the ith terminal part, $\bar{Z}_i$ represents a molar property of the material in the ith terminal part, $\mathscr{H}_i \equiv \mathscr{U}_i + P_i \bar{V}_i$, $\mathscr{A}_i \equiv \mathscr{U}_i - T_i \bar{S}_i$, $\mathscr{G}_i \equiv \mathscr{H}_i - T_i \bar{S}_i$, $\dot{S}^{(r)}$ represents the rate of accumulation of entropy in the surrounding heat reservoir of temperature T, and $\dot{n}_i$ and $\dot{V}_i$ represent the rate of accumulation of mass and volume, respectively, in the ith terminal part of the system. The sums in Eqs. (2.1) to (2.4) are over the terminal parts only since the gradient parts are stationary during the steady-flow process. The rate of entropy production Θ,

$$\Theta \equiv \dot{S}(\text{system}) + \dot{S}(\text{surroundings}), \tag{2.5}$$

under steady-flow conditions is

$$\Theta = \dot{S}^{(r)} + \sum \bar{S}_i \dot{n}_i. \tag{2.6}$$

In terms of the rate of entropy production Θ and the rate of performance of other-than-pressure-volume work $\dot{W}_0$,

$$\dot{W}_0 \equiv \dot{W} + \sum P_i \dot{V}_i, \tag{2.7}$$

Eqs. (2.1) to (2.4) take the well-known forms

$$\dot{U}(\text{system}) = -T\dot{S}^{(r)} + \dot{W}, \tag{2.8}$$

$$\dot{H}(\text{system}) = -T\dot{S}^{(r)} + \dot{W}_0, \tag{2.9}$$

$$-\dot{A}(\text{system}) = T\Theta - \dot{W} + \sum (T_i - T)\bar{S}_i \dot{n}_i, \tag{2.10}$$

$$-\dot{G}(\text{system}) = T\Theta - \dot{W}_0 + \sum (T_i - T)\bar{S}_i \dot{n}_i. \tag{2.11}$$

For most cases of interest it will be true that $T_i = T$ (however, see Ex. 2–4).

At this point I find it convenient to define coefficients $[N]$ and $[N]^\partial$ such that

$$[N] \equiv \frac{\Theta}{R\dot{n}_k^{\,2}}, \tag{2.12}$$

$$[N]^\partial \equiv [N] + \dot{n}_k \left(\frac{\partial [N]}{\partial \dot{n}_k} \right)_T, \tag{2.13}$$

where R is the gas constant, and $\dot{n}_k$ is a suitably chosen rate parameter. The relationship between the quantities $[N]$ and $[N]^\partial$ is like that between integral molar and differential molar properties for gas-solid adsorption systems [1]: in general, an integral molar property $\bar{Z}$ of the adsorbed molecules is related to a differential molar property Z^∂ via a relation of the form

$$Z^\partial = \bar{Z} + n_a \left(\frac{\partial \bar{Z}}{\partial n_a} \right)_T, \tag{2.14}$$

where n_a represents the number of moles of gas adsorbed on the solid [1]. The similarity in form between Eqs. (2.13) and (2.14) should now be evident.

Equations (2.11) and (2.12) yield

$$-\sum \frac{\mathcal{G}_i \dot{n}_i}{\dot{n}_k} + \frac{\dot{W}_0}{\dot{n}_k} = [N]RT\dot{n}_k + \sum (T_i - T)\bar{S}_i \frac{\dot{n}_i}{\dot{n}_k}. \tag{2.15}$$

If we write $\Delta\mathcal{G}$ for the first sum in Eq. (2.15), we have (for $T_i = T$)

$$-\Delta\mathcal{G} + \frac{\dot{W}_0}{\dot{n}_k} = [N]RT\dot{n}_k. \tag{2.16}$$

Equation (2.16) has the form of Ohm's law: potential difference = resistance × current, with the $[N]RT$ combination playing the role of a thermodynamic resistance. Occasionally it is useful to consider a *specific* rate parameter (i.e., rate parameter per unit area, per unit volume, etc.). Under such circumstances it is convenient to define a corresponding specific coefficient: if the specific rate parameter is $\dot{n}_k/Z$, then the specific coefficient $[N_Z]$ is $[N_Z] \equiv Z[N]$.

Forced Vaporization

Consider the monothermal steady vaporization process (steady vaporization of a liquid *without boiling*) indicated schematically in Figure 2–1. The terminal parts of the system consist of liquid at temperature T and pressure P_0, and vapor at temperature T and pressure P. For convenience let us assume

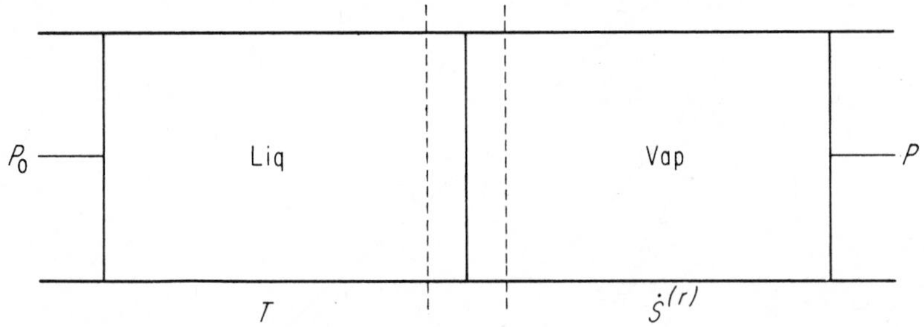

Figure 2–1. Monothermal steady vaporization of a liquid; P_0 = saturated vapor pressure at temperature T; $P \leqslant P_0$.

that the liquid-gas interface is fixed in space and that liquid is brought up to and vapor removed from the interface.

Under steady-flow conditions ($\dot{n}_{\text{liq}} + \dot{n}_{\text{gas}} = 0$) with $\dot{W}_0 = 0$, Eq. (2.16) takes the form

$$-(\mathscr{G}_{\text{gas}} - \mathscr{G}_{\text{liq}}) = [N]RT\dot{n}_{\text{gas}}. \tag{2.17}$$

If we neglect kinetic energy terms, assume that the vapor can be treated as an ideal gas, and write simply $\dot{\xi}$ for $\dot{n}_{\text{gas}}$, then we can rearrange Eq. (2.17) to give

$$\ln P = \ln P_0 - \dot{\xi}[N]. \tag{2.18}$$

More than thirty years ago Alty [2, 3] made some measurements on the rate of vaporization of water and of carbon tetrachloride in an attempt to find out something about the accommodation coefficient [4] at the liquid–vapor interface. His experimental arrangement was such that he could measure the rate of steady vaporization $\dot{\xi}$, the temperature T of the surrounding thermostat, the approximate temperature T_s at the interface, and the pressure P in the gas phase at a moderate distance from the interface. We have at our disposal, then, the variables $\dot{\xi}$, T, T_s, P; and we can form differential coefficients such as $(\partial \ln P/\partial T_s)_T$ and $RT^2(\partial \ln P/\partial T)_{\dot{\xi}}$. From Eq. (2.18) we see that

$$\left(\frac{\partial \ln P}{\partial T_s}\right)_T = -[N]^0\left(\frac{\partial \dot{\xi}}{\partial T_s}\right)_T, \tag{2.19}$$

and

$$RT^2\left(\frac{\partial \ln P}{\partial T}\right)_{\dot{\xi}} = \Delta\overline{H}_{\text{vap}} - \dot{\xi}RT^2\left(\frac{\partial [N]}{\partial T}\right)_{\dot{\xi}}. \tag{2.20}$$

Figure 2–2 exhibits Alty's data in the form of a ln P versus $\dot{\xi}$ plot; for small rates of vaporization the coefficient $[N]$ is independent of the rate parameter $\dot{\xi}$. The carbon tetrachloride data stand out as peculiar: beyond a

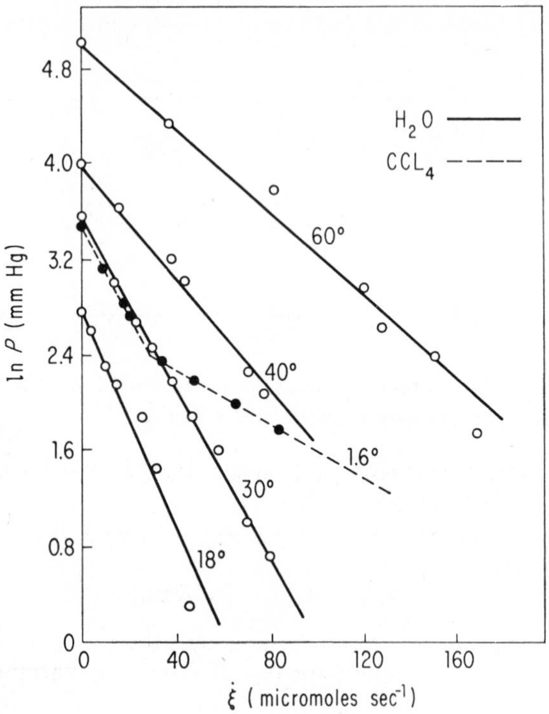

Figure 2–2. Plot of ln P versus $\dot{\xi}$ for the data of Alty. (From the *J. Chem. Phys.*, **31,** 1521 (1959), by permission.)

certain flow rate the slope of the ln P versus $\dot{\xi}$ plot becomes less steep, indicating a *decrease* in flow resistance with *increasing* rate of flow.

Exercise 2–1. Alty investigated the vaporization of water from a certain glass tube at the monothermal temperatures 18, 40, and 60°C. An analysis of Alty's data [5, 6] reveals that over the range 18 to 60°C for flow rates in the range 0 to 40 micromoles per second, the $[N]$ coefficient for the given tube can be roughly represented by the relation

$$[N] = -0.166 + \frac{61.0}{T},$$

where $[N]$ is expressed in seconds per micromole.

Compute the approximate value of the term $-\dot{\xi}RT^2(\partial[N]/\partial T)_{\dot{\xi}}$ for the conditions $\dot{\xi} = 10$ micromoles per second and $T = 298°K$; compare the magnitude of the computed term to that of $\Delta\bar{H}_{vap}$ at 298°K.

T. A. Erikson [7] has made some interesting studies of the steady vaporization process. In a series of measurements he had five glass tubes with differing diameters* hooked up to a common pressure manifold—the entire apparatus being immersed in a thermostat—and he measured the rate of vaporization from each tube for a given liquid at various settings of the

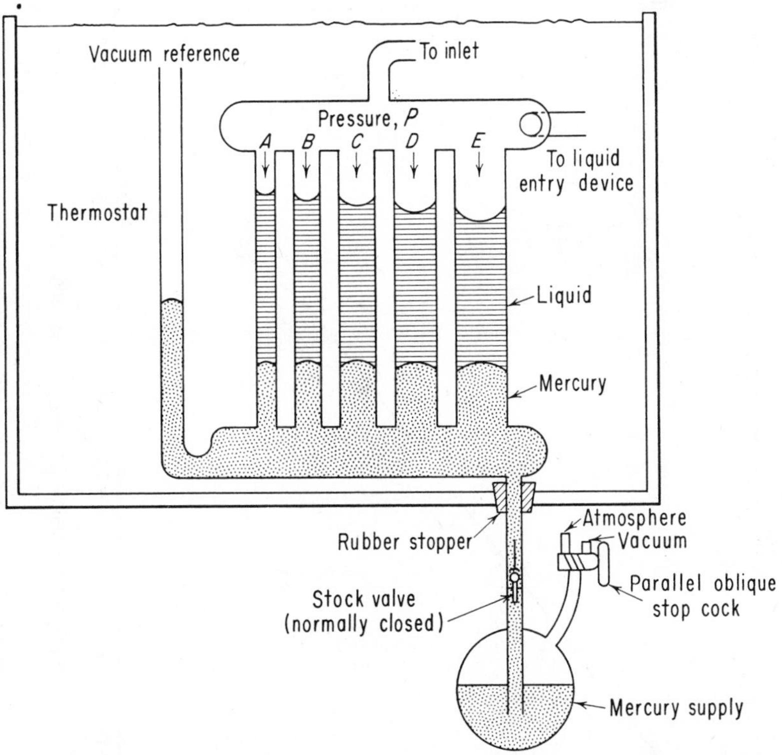

Figure 2–3. Schematic diagram of the forced vaporization equipment.

thermostat temperature T and the manifold pressure P (see Figure 2–3). Erikson presents his data in an interesting fashion: his observations consist of a set of rates of vaporization (for a given liquid at a given temperature) for each tube corresponding to various values of the pressure in the common

* The diameters ranged from 2.8 mm (tube A) to 19.0 mm (tube E).

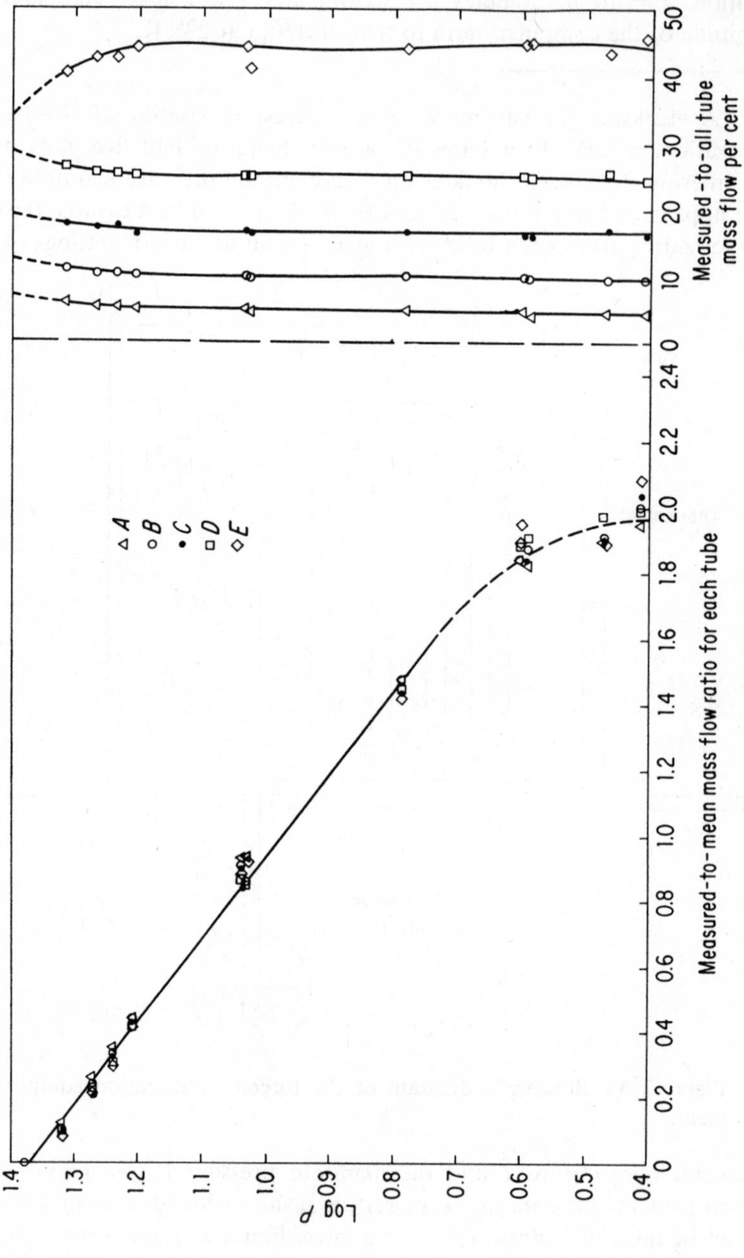

Figure 2–4. Normalized forced vaporization data for water at 25°C.

manifold; he finds it convenient to average the measured rates of vaporization for each tube and to express the rate of vaporization for each tube as a fraction of the average rate of vaporization for that tube, i.e., if at a given temperature there are m different settings of the manifold pressure, and if $\dot{\xi}_j^{(i)}$ is the steady rate of vaporization from the ith tube at the jth setting of the pressure, then Erikson defines a reduced flow rate $\theta_j^{(i)}$ such that

$$\theta_j^{(i)} \equiv \frac{\dot{\xi}_j^{(i)}}{\frac{1}{m}\sum_{k=1}^{m} \dot{\xi}_k^{(i)}} \equiv \frac{\dot{\xi}_j^{(i)}}{\langle \dot{\xi}^{(i)} \rangle}.$$

He also introduces another reduced variable $\vartheta_j^{(i)}$ such that

$$\vartheta_j^{(i)} \equiv \frac{\dot{\xi}_j^{(i)}}{\sum_{i=1}^{5} \dot{\xi}_j^{(i)}},$$

this variable representing the fraction of the total mass vaporized that comes from a given tube at a fixed pressure setting. Erikson calls θ the *measured-to-mean* mass flow ratio, and he calls ϑ the *measured-to-all tube* mass flow ratio.

Figure 2–4 shows Erikson's results for water at 25°C. The usefulness of the θ variable is at once apparent: the data from all the tubes fall very close to a single curve. The behavior of the ϑ variable close to equilibrium is quite interesting: here the relative contribution of tube E (the tube of largest diameter) to the total mass flow varies significantly with the manifold pressure. Erikson calculates the coefficient $[N^{(i)}]$ for the ith tube from a plot of $\log_{10} P$ versus $\theta^{(i)}$ (Figure 2–4) via the relation

$$[N^{(i)}] = \frac{-2.3 \text{ slope}}{\langle \dot{\xi}^{(i)} \rangle} \tag{2.21}$$

for the linear part of the plot. He then defines a specific coefficient $[N_B^{(i)}]$ such that $[N_B^{(i)}] \equiv B^{(i)}[N^{(i)}]$ with $B^{(i)}$ being the area [8] of the liquid meniscus in the ith tube. The $[N_B]$ coefficient defined in this manner depends on the tube diameter. Erikson eliminates this apparatus dependency by extrapolating his results to a tube of infinite diameter* (Figure 2–5). The limiting value $[N_B^{(\infty)}]$ is then a well-defined, apparatus-independent property of the vaporization process for a given liquid at a given temperature. Figure 2–6 shows the temperature dependence of the $[N_B^{(\infty)}]$ coefficient for water; we expect $[N_B^{(\infty)}]$ to approach zero at the critical point.

* In a small diameter tube the meniscus is essentially a spherical cap having an area twice as large as the cross-sectional area of the tube. In a large diameter tube the meniscus is essentially flat and its area coincides with the cross-sectional area of the tube. The ratio of the meniscus area to the cross-sectional area of the tube, $B^{(i)}/B_t$, thus varies from 2 to 1 as the tube diameter goes from 0 to ∞.

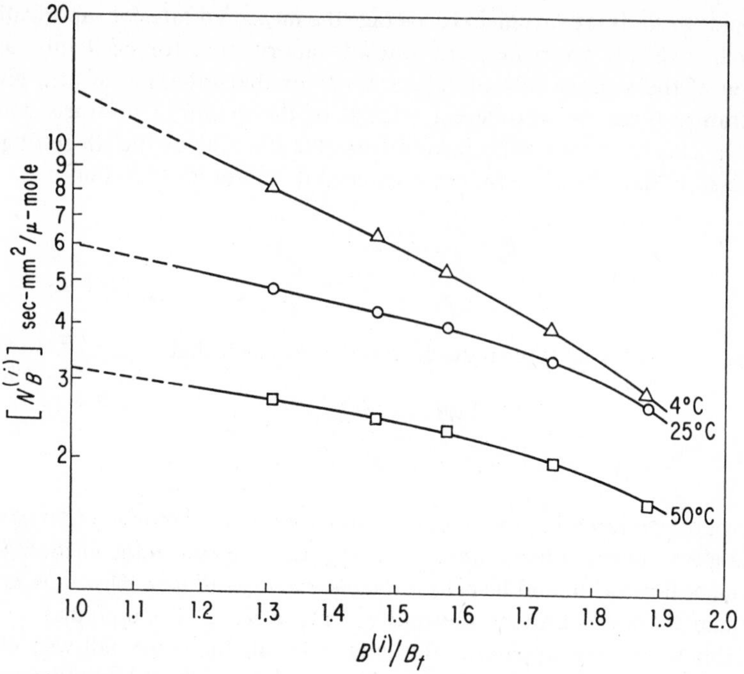

Figure 2–5. Dependence of $[N_B^{(i)}]$ on tube diameter and extrapolation to infinite diameter.

Exercise 2–2. For Erikson's experimental arrangement show that if each separate tube has a linear dependence of $\ln P$ on ξ, i.e., if $\ln P = \ln P_0 - \xi^{(i)}[N^{(i)}]$ with constant $[N^{(i)}]$, then the data from all the tubes fall on a single straight line when plotted in the form $\ln P$ versus $\theta^{(i)}$.

Exercise 2–3. Consider the situation (steady diffusion of a gas through a metal diaphragm) indicated schematically in Figure 2–7 and apply Eq. (2.16) to this situation. Assume approximate equilibrium at the metal–gas interface, a linear concentration gradient in the metal diaphragm, and the applicability of Fick's law of diffusion:

$$J = -D\frac{\partial C}{\partial x},$$

where J is the molar flux (moles sec^{-1} area^{-1}), D is the diffusion coefficient, and C is the molar concentration of the gas dissolved in the metal. Show that given the preceding assumptions

$$D \approx \frac{\Delta x}{B[N]\langle C\rangle},$$

where B is the metal–gas interfacial area and $\langle C\rangle$ is the average concentration of the dissolved gas.

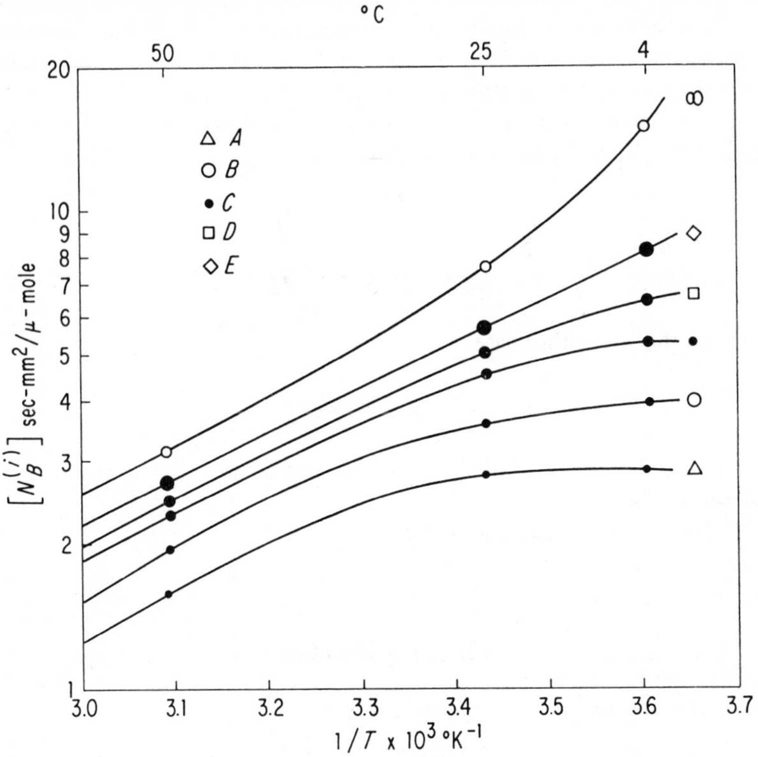

Figure 2–6. Temperature dependence of $[N_B^{(i)}]$.

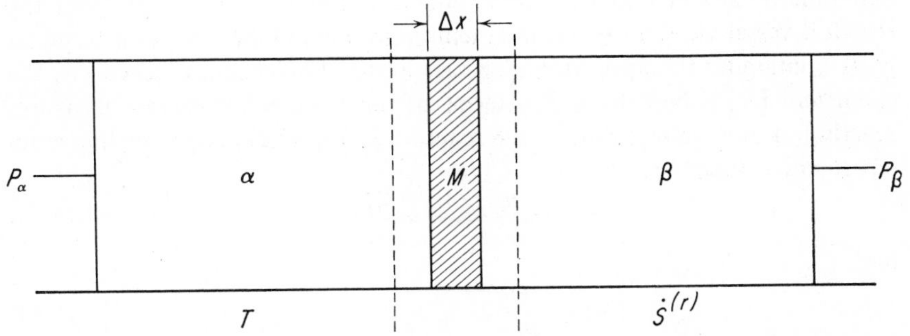

Figure 2–7. Monothermal steady diffusion of a gas through a metal diaphragm.

Exercise 2–4. Suppose that a pure liquid and a pure solid in equilibrium at a temperature $T*$ are heated to a temperature $T > T*$ (the pressure being kept constant)—forced melting of a one-component system. Assume that the liquid takes on the temperature T and that the solid (i) takes on the temperature T, or (ii) remains at the temperature $T*$ during the forced melting process. Show that for both (i) and (ii) $\mu_{\text{solid}} - \mu_{\text{liquid}} > 0$ and that

$$\text{(i)} \qquad \frac{T*}{T} \ln \frac{T}{T*} \approx \frac{\dot{n}_{\text{liq}} [N]_{\text{mel}} R}{\Delta \bar{S}(*)_{\text{mel}}},$$

$$\text{(ii)} \qquad \frac{\Delta T}{T} \approx \frac{\dot{n}_{\text{liq}} [N]_{\text{mel}} R}{\Delta \bar{S}(*)_{\text{mel}}},$$

and hence that for either case

$$\frac{\Delta T}{T} \propto \dot{n}_{\text{liq}},$$

where $\Delta T \equiv T - T*$, and $\Delta \bar{S}(*)_{\text{mel}}$ is the molar entropy of fusion at the temperature $T*$.
Hint: For case (ii) make use of Eq. (2.15).

Chemical Reaction

Consider the reversible chemical reaction

$$\sum \nu_i B_i = \sum \nu_j D_j \tag{2.22}$$

(the reactants B_i being transformed to products D_j with stoichiometric coefficients ν_i and ν_j, respectively) taking place in a steady-flow gradient reactor of volume V in a thermostat of temperature T. Let the reactants be individually supplied to and the products individually removed from the reaction vessel via semipermeable membranes communicating with terminal parts containing the appropriate species alone. For chemical reactions, the coefficient $[N]$ is best defined in terms of the number of reaction measures reacting in unit time $\dot{\xi}$; thus, if the reaction in Eq. (2.22) is proceeding from left to right, then*

$$\dot{\xi} = \frac{-\dot{n}_i}{\nu_i} = \cdots = \frac{\dot{n}_j}{\nu_j} = \cdots, \tag{2.23}$$

and

$$[N] \equiv \frac{\Theta}{R\dot{\xi}^2} = \frac{\Theta \nu_i^2}{R\dot{n}_i^2} = \cdots. \tag{2.24}$$

* Observe that the changes in state discussed in the porous plug experiment and in the forced vaporization experiment can be written in the form of Eq. (2.22); hence the variable $\dot{\xi}$ introduced into those discussions represents but a special case of the use of Eq. (2.23).

I want to point out here two general relations pertaining to reversible chemical reactions taking place in a steady monothermal fashion:

$$\Delta H \equiv \sum \nu_j \bar{H}_j - \sum \nu_i \bar{H}_i = \frac{-T\dot{S}^{(r)}}{\dot{\xi}} = \frac{\dot{Q}}{\dot{\xi}}, \tag{2.25}$$

$$-\Delta G \equiv \sum \nu_i \mu_i - \sum \nu_j \mu_j = \frac{T\Theta}{\dot{\xi}} = [N]RT\dot{\xi} = [N]RT\frac{\dot{n}_k}{\nu_k}, \tag{2.26}$$

where I have neglected kinetic energy terms, have considered only pressure-volume work ($\dot{W}_0 = 0$), have assumed that $T_i = T$, and in the final part of Eq. (2.26) have described the process in terms of the rate parameter $\dot{n}_k$ (the rate of influx of mass into the kth terminal part containing the product species D_k); I compute the change in any thermodynamic property, ΔG for example, relative to the *terminal parts of the system.* Equation (2.25) is an especially clear statement of the physical significance of the enthalpy change ΔH accompanying a chemical reaction.

The Ohm's law type of formulation, Eq. (2.16), for monothermal steady-rate processes normally yields an $[N]$ coefficient that is independent of the rate parameter (for moderate flow rates) under those conditions for which the system is allowed to adjust itself to the promptings of the environment—i.e., the gradient part has a definite structure and a number of natural "back emf's" are induced by the steady-flow process. If we destroy the natural gradient structure of the system (by stirring, e.g.), then the overall $[N]$ coefficient may or may not be independent of the rate parameter. Although processes with a constant $[N]$ coefficient are the most interesting, we can treat *any* monothermal steady-rate process according to the formalism of Eq. (2.16). If we find that the integral coefficient $[N]$ depends markedly on the rate parameter, we can discuss the process in terms of the differential coefficient $[N]^{\partial}$.

If we wish to relate Eq. (2.26) to the formulas of chemical kinetics, we must move down the sequence *gradient reactor*, *stirred-flow reactor*, *batch reactor*. Consider first the stirred-flow reactor (same setup as for the steady-flow gradient reactor, but the contents of the reaction vessel are stirred). Under steady-flow conditions an equation of the form (2.26) holds. If we assume that the change in Gibbs free energy ΔG(out) for the reaction is approximately the same as the free energy change ΔG(in) computed from the chemical potentials *inside* the stirred reactor, we can then write

$$\ln \mathcal{Q} = \ln K - \frac{[N_V]}{\nu_k}\left(\frac{\dot{n}_k}{V}\right) \tag{2.27}$$

where V is the volume of the reactor, $[N_V] \equiv V[N]$, K is the equilibrium constant for the reaction, and $\mathcal{Q} \equiv \Pi a_j^{\nu_j}/\Pi a_i^{\nu_i}$, the activities in the activity quotient being computed for the state of affairs holding inside the stirred reactor.

Consider a further step in the sequence: let the reaction be taking place in a batch reactor, and assume that the changing conditions inside the batch reactor can be treated as equivalent to a sequence of steady-flow states in a stirred-flow reactor—i.e., assume that Eq. (2.27) can be applied to a batch reactor provided that $\dot{C}_k$ (the rate of change of the concentration of the D_k species in the batch reactor) is substituted for the quantity $\dot{n}_k/V$. In the batch reactor, then

$$\ln \mathcal{Q} = \ln K - \frac{[N_V]}{\nu_k}\dot{C}_k. \qquad (2.28)$$

Exercise 2–5. Show that for a first-order reversible reaction $B \rightleftharpoons D$, close to equilibrium,

$$[N_V] \approx \frac{1}{k_b C_D^{(\text{eq})}},$$

where k_b is the backward reaction rate constant, and $C_D^{(\text{eq})}$ is the equilibrium concentration of the D species.

If we apply Eq. (2.28) to a number of well-known kinetic situations, we find that the $[N_V]$ coefficient depends (rather strongly) on the rate parameter. Such a state of affairs can result from any of a number of possibilities:

(i) In the stirred-flow reactor $\Delta G(\text{in})$ may differ significantly from $\Delta G(\text{out})$.

(ii) The states inside a batch reactor may not be comparable to steady-flow states in a stirred-flow reactor.

(iii) In accord with an electrical analogy, it may be the case that capacitance and inductance effects are important.

(iv) It may be that the $[N_V]$ coefficient is independent of the rate parameter in a steady-flow gradient reactor but is not independent of the rate parameter in a stirred-flow reactor or in a batch reactor due to loss of the natural gradients ("back emf's") in the system.

The investigations of Prigogine et al. [9] appear to favor position (iv). Kirkwood and Crawford [10], by injecting some elements of relaxation theory into their description of chemical reactions, have developed an approach somewhat similar to that of position (iii).

Other Monothermal Steady-Rate Processes

I can think of several other (potentially) steady-rate processes that would lead to interesting experimental investigations. Consider the steady monothermal vaporization of water from a saturated solution of a sparingly soluble salt. As the vaporization proceeds, small crystals of the salt will nucleate and grow in a region bordering on the liquid–vapor interface. A steady process is possible provided that the small crystals being precipitated do not clutter up the liquid meniscus and thus interfere with the vaporization process. If a steady process can be achieved, we can analyze the situation by the methods of this chapter, can extract from the analysis an overall $[N]$ coefficient, and can resolve the overall $[N]$ coefficient into a part due to the vaporization process and a part due to the precipitation process.

Consider next a three-phase, 2-component system consisting of solid solvent, solid solute, and solution. Such a collection of phases can coexist in equilibrium at the eutectic temperature $T*$. If we place the three-phase system in a thermostat at some temperature $T > T*$, then the solid phases will pass into solution until at least one of them vanishes. If we assume that dissolution of the solid phases can be made to take place at a steady rate with all terminal parts at temperature T and that the solution phase has a composition approximately corresponding to that of a solution saturated with respect to the solute at temperature T, then we can carry through the standard analysis and can evaluate an $[N]$ coefficient for the process. Here again we can probably break up the overall $[N]$ coefficient into more fundamental pieces. This case is rather interesting in that the progress of the dissolution process can be followed by dilatometry.

A final thought is that it would be interesting to study a chemical reaction proceeding at a steady rate, far from equilibrium, and involving terminal parts and a gradient part. By way of example, consider a steady hydrogen–oxygen flame burning in a water thermostat (Figure 2–8). Let the hydrogen and oxygen be led from storage tanks through volume flow meters (wet-test meters, say), being saturated with water vapor as they pass through the meters; assume that the hydrogen and oxygen each enter the mixing chamber at temperature T and partial pressure $P' \equiv P - P_{H_2O}$, where P_{H_2O} is the saturated vapor pressure of water at temperature T. Consider the case where oxygen is in excess, and let the subscript x stand for properties of the excess oxygen bubbling out of the thermostat into the atmosphere. If we write P_{atm} for atmospheric pressure, then let $P'_{atm} \equiv P_{atm} - P_{H_2O}$.

For the reaction

$$2H_2(g, P', T) + O_2(g, P', T) = 2H_2O(liq, P_{atm}, T) \qquad (2.29)$$

conducted in a steady monothermal fashion with oxygen in excess, it follows that

$$\dot{\xi} = -\tfrac{1}{2}\dot{n}_{H_2}; \qquad \dot{n}_x \equiv -\dot{n}_{O_2} + \tfrac{1}{2}\dot{n}_{H_2}; \qquad \dot{n}_{H_2O} = -\dot{n}_{H_2}. \qquad (2.30)$$

Equations (2.11) and (2.24) yield, in the present instance,

$$-(\dot{n}_{H_2}\mu_{H_2} + \dot{n}_{O_2}\mu_{O_2} + \dot{n}_{H_2O}\mu_{H_2O} + \dot{n}_x\mu_x) = [N]RT\dot{\xi}^2. \qquad (2.31)$$

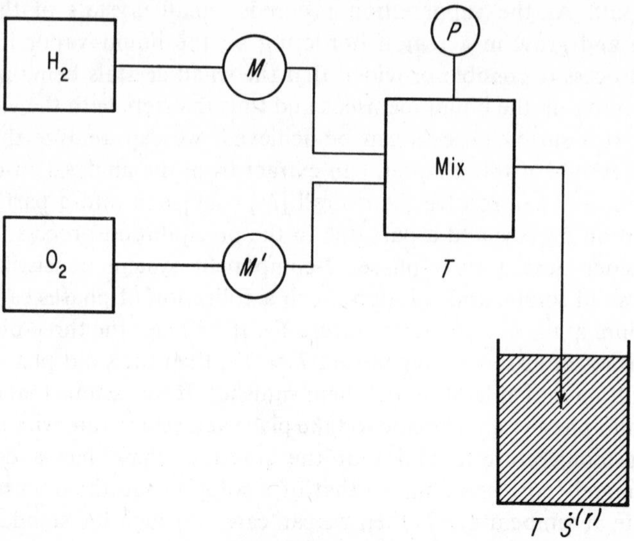

Figure 2–8. Hydrogen–oxygen flame: hydrogen and oxygen from reservoir cylinders pass through flow meters M and M' (wet-test meters, say) into a mixing chamber where the temperature and pressure of the gaseous mixture are T and P, respectively. From the mixing chamber the gaseous mixture goes to a flame at the end of a nozzle immersed in a water thermostat of temperature T.

Equations (2.30) and (2.31) combine to give

$$-\left\{-2\mu_{H_2} - \mu_{O_2} + 2\mu_{H_2O} - \frac{\dot{n}_x}{\dot{\xi}}(\mu_{O_2} - \mu_x)\right\} = [N]RT\dot{\xi}, \tag{2.32}$$

$$-\Delta G + \frac{\dot{n}_x}{\dot{\xi}}(\mu_{O_2} - \mu_x) = [N]RT\dot{\xi}. \tag{2.33}$$

If we use expressions derived from the perfect gas law in Eq. (2.33), we then get

$$3 \ln P' + \frac{\dot{n}_x}{\dot{\xi}} \ln \frac{P'}{P'_{\text{atm}}} = [N]\dot{\xi} + \frac{\Delta G^{(\text{ref})}}{RT}, \tag{2.34}$$

where $\Delta G^{(\text{ref})}$ is defined by $\Delta G \equiv \Delta G^{(\text{ref})} + RT \ln (1/P_{H_2}^2 P_{O_2})$, and I have made use of the condition $P_{H_2} = P_{O_2} = P'$. It would certainly be interesting to evaluate the $[N]$ coefficient for this situation and to see how it varied with changing experimental conditions.

References

1. R. J. Tykodi, *J. Chem. Phys.*, **22**, 1647 (1954).
2. T. Alty, *Proc. Roy. Soc.* (London), **A131**, 554 (1931).

3. T. Alty and F. Nicoll, *Can. J. Research*, **4**, 547 (1931).
4. T. A. Erikson, *J. Phys. Chem.*, **64**, 820 (1960).
5. R. J. Tykodi and T. A. Erikson, *J. Chem. Phys.*, **31**, 1521 (1959).
6. T. A. Erikson, M.S. Thesis, Illinois Institute of Technology (1959).
7. T. A. Erikson, unpublished results.
8. T. A. Erikson, *J. Phys. Chem.*, **69**, 1809 (1965).
9. I. Prigogine, P. Outer, and C. Herbo, *J. Phys. Chem.*, **52**, 321 (1948).
10. J. G. Kirkwood and B. Crawford, Jr., *J. Phys. Chem.*, **56**, 1041 (1952).

3

The Rate of Entropy Production

For the purposes of this text, I classify steady-state situations as either *ordinary* or *special.* Special situations are those involving external magnetic or centrifugal fields; ordinary situations (the vast majority of those of interest) are simply situations *not* involving magnetic or centrifugal fields. The body of the text deals with ordinary situations, and I formulate Eq. (3.5) in a way especially suited to such situations; I discuss the change in formulation needed to deal with special situations in a section of the Appendix.

General Remarks

When a system is the site of one or more steady-rate processes, there are steady rates of accumulation of energy, entropy, volume, mass, chemical reaction measures, electric charge, etc., in terminal parts of the system or in reservoirs adjoined to the system. In steady closed-loop operation there can be a steady accumulation of work in a work reservoir—the rate of accumulation of work in the reservoir being normally factorable into a well-defined "current" and a "potential difference." I choose a set of work-delivering currents and steady rates of accumulation of thermodynamic quantity as a *canonical set*: in equilibrium thermodynamics the fundamental relation

$$dU = T\,dS - P\,dV + \sum \mu^{(j)}\,dn^{(j)} + \cdots \tag{3.1}$$

gives rise to a preferred set of independent variables for both the energy function and the entropy function; thus $U = U(S, V, n^{(j)}, \ldots)$ and $S = S(U, V, n^{(j)}, \ldots)$. In analogy to the equilibrium case, the canonical set consists of quantities of the type $\dot{S}^{(r)}$ or $\dot{U}^{(r)}$, $\dot{V}$, $\dot{n}^{(j)}, \ldots$, where the superscript r refers to an adjoined reservoir. In a heat reservoir of the classical ideal type, $\dot{U}^{(r)} = \dot{Q}^{(r)}$, and I find the choice between $\dot{S}^{(r)}$ and $\dot{Q}^{(r)}$ to be arbitrary and largely a matter of convenience. I refer to the quantities of the canonical set as currents and symbolize them by Y_i, thus $\{Y_i\} = \{\dot{S}^{(r)}$ or $\dot{Q}^{(r)}, \dot{V}, \dot{n}^{(j)}, \ldots\}$. The currents are thus time derivatives of extensive thermodynamic quantities.

By combining the first and second laws of thermodynamics we can always express the rate of entropy production $\Theta \equiv \dot{S}(\text{system}) + \dot{S}(\text{surroundings})$ for a steady-state situation in the form

$$\Theta = \sum_i Y_i \Omega_i, \tag{3.2}$$

with the Y_i forming a subset of *independent* currents chosen from the canonical set, and the Ω_i being *affinities* conjugate to the (independent) currents Y_i. I define the affinities Ω_i via Eq. (3.2), and I note that they are normally combinations of intensive variables.*

Assumption IV

In discussing problems of migrational equilibrium we shall be analyzing the behavior of pertinent parameters of the system for a characteristic limiting operation: we shall be interested in how the values of the pertinent parameters change as a given current or affinity approaches zero along a prescribed path via a sequence of steady states; i.e., symbolically, we shall study the limit of $\{Z(\eta, \ldots) - Z(0, \ldots)\}/\eta$ as $\eta \to 0$, with Z being the pertinent parameter and η being the given current or affinity. These limits, of course, are nothing but partial derivatives evaluated at the point $\eta = 0$ with certain things being held constant:

$$\lim_{\eta \to 0} \frac{Z(\eta, \ldots) - Z(0, \ldots)}{\eta} \equiv \left(\frac{\partial Z}{\partial \eta}\right)_{\ldots}\Bigg|_{\eta = 0,\, z_\omega = z_\omega(*)}, \tag{3.3}$$

where the derivative is evaluated for a *specific steady state*—one for which $\eta = 0$ and for which the intensive variables z_ω of the system have the definite values $z_\omega(*)$. Now, since such derivatives appear over and over again in the text, and since the right-hand side of Eq. (3.3) is rather cumbersome, I propose the following notational convention: let

$$\left(\frac{\delta Z}{\delta \eta}\right)_{\ldots} \equiv \left(\frac{\partial Z}{\partial \eta}\right)_{\ldots}\Bigg|_{\eta = 0,\, z_\omega = z_\omega(*)}. \tag{3.4}$$

* By choosing a canonical set of currents and by defining my affinities via Eq. (3.2), I circumvent Truesdell's objections [1, 2] to other formulations.

I can now state assumption IV in precise mathematical form (however, see the *special fields* section of the Appendix):

$$\left(\frac{\delta\Theta}{\overline{\delta Y_k}}\right)_{\Omega'} = 0, \qquad \left(\frac{\delta^2\Theta}{\overline{\delta Y_k{}^2}}\right)_{\Omega'} > 0, \tag{3.5}$$

where the subscript Ω' indicates that the affinities conjugate to the non-vanishing currents are to be kept constant; i.e., constant Ω_i for each $i \neq k$. I call the sequence of steady states (constant Ω_i for $i \neq k$) used in the limiting operation of Eq. (3.5) an *affine sequence*, and it is this sort of sequence that I had in mind in my earlier (Chapter 1) verbal statement of assumption IV. Perhaps it will help if I put Eq. (3.5) into words:

ASSUMPTION IV: If a system that is the site of $\nu + 1$ steady (independent) currents converges via a sequence of steady states on a state involving ν steady currents in such a way that the affinities conjugate to the ν non-vanishing currents are maintained constant, then the state with ν currents is a state of minimum rate of entropy production relative to the (steady) states with $\nu + 1$ currents.

From Eq. (3.2) we see that

$$\begin{aligned}\left(\frac{\delta\Theta}{\overline{\delta Y_k}}\right)_{\Omega'} &= \sum_i Y_i\left(\frac{\delta\Omega_i}{\overline{\delta Y_k}}\right)_{\Omega'} + \sum_i \Omega_i\left(\frac{\delta Y_i}{\overline{\delta Y_k}}\right)_{\Omega'} \\ &= \sum_i \Omega_i\left(\frac{\delta Y_i}{\overline{\delta Y_k}}\right)_{\Omega'},\end{aligned} \tag{3.6}$$

since in the limiting state $Y_k = 0$ and $(\delta\Omega_i/\overline{\delta Y_k})_{\Omega'} = 0$ for $i \neq k$; hence we can also write assumption IV as

$$0 = \left(\frac{\delta\Theta}{\overline{\delta Y_k}}\right)_{\Omega'} = \sum_i \Omega_i\left(\frac{\delta Y_i}{\overline{\delta Y_k}}\right)_{\Omega'}. \tag{3.7}$$

For just one current Y_1, with the limiting state being one of thermostatic equilibrium, Eq. (3.7) indicates that the conjugate affinity Ω_1 vanishes at equilibrium; i.e., $\Omega_1(0) = 0$. By way of example consider the monothermal steady vaporization process described in Chapter 2. It follows from Eqs. (2.12), (2.17), and (2.18) that

$$\Theta = \frac{\dot{n}_{gas}(\mu_{liq} - \mu_{gas})}{T} = Y_1\Omega_1 \tag{3.8}$$

and that

$$\left(\frac{\delta\Theta}{\overline{\delta\dot{n}_{gas}}}\right)_T = \frac{\mu_{liq} - \mu_{gas}}{T}. \tag{3.9}$$

Thus Eq. (3.7) implies that at thermostatic equilibrium $\mu_{liq} = \mu_{gas}$.

Degrees of Freedom

In order to specify the equilibrium thermodynamic state of the two-phase system H_2O(liq) + H_2O(gas) we only need to know the temperature or the vapor pressure since the system has but 1 degree of freedom. To specify the state of steady vaporization for the same two-phase system, we require considerably more information: we need to know the thermostat temperature, the pressure in the gas phase, and the diameter and nature (glass, metal, etc.) of the tube in which the process is taking place. In general, to describe a steady-state system it is necessary to describe the apparatus, the chemicals (i.e., the contents of the apparatus), and the precise way in which the apparatus interacts energetically with the surroundings. In his forced vaporization work, Erikson (Chapter 2) was able to overcome the apparatus dependence of his steady-state quantities by a clever extrapolation procedure. The apparatus dependence of steady-state quantities should always be kept in mind; and, where possible, explicit extrapolation or limiting procedures should be worked out for obtaining apparatus-independent results.

Continuing our examination of Erikson's experiments on the forced vaporization of water, we see that for a given tube the steady state is completely characterized by the thermostat temperature T and the gas-phase pressure P, thus $\Theta = \Theta(T, P)$, and $\dot{\xi} = \dot{\xi}(T, P)$. Since $(\partial\dot{\xi}/\partial P)_T \neq 0$, we can invert the $\dot{\xi}$ relation to get $P = P(T, \dot{\xi})$ and $\Theta = \Theta(T, \dot{\xi})$. We can thus express the rate of entropy production in terms of a parameter T characteristic of a related state of thermostatic equilibrium and in terms of the steady current $\dot{\xi}$ traversing the system. I should like to extend this idea to other systems. For a given system we can consider any steady state to have been generated from a reference thermostatic (equilibrium) state σ with variables $T_\sigma, P_\sigma, \mu_\sigma^{(i)}, \ldots$, a thermostatic state of F_σ degrees of freedom (in the phase rule sense). Now the primary variables pertaining to a given steady-state system are the intensive variables in each of its terminal parts. I wish to take the set of primary variables and to perform a transformation such that I get an equivalent set of variables dealing with a reference thermostatic state σ and with ν independent currents (or affinities); the Jacobian of the transformation must, of course, have certain desirable properties.* In terms of the new set of variables we can say that a steady state characterized by ν independent currents has $F_\sigma + \nu$ degrees of freedom and that the rate of entropy production Θ, being a function of the (steady) state of the system, requires for its complete determination the specification of $F_\sigma + \nu$ independent variables. In describing a given steady-state system, then, the most convenient set of variables will usually be a set

* I discuss the inversion problem and the properties of the Jacobian in a section of Chapter 15.

of ν independent currents (or affinities) and F_σ parameters characteristic of the reference thermostatic state; thus

$$\Theta = \Theta(Y_j, \sigma) = \Theta(\Omega_j, \sigma), \tag{3.10}$$

$$Y_i = Y_i(\Omega_j, \sigma), \tag{3.11}$$

$$\Omega_i = \Omega_i(Y_j, \sigma), \tag{3.12}$$

where I have rather inelegantly used the symbol σ to stand for the set of variables $T_\sigma, P_\sigma, \mu_\sigma^{(i)}, \ldots$.

The expression $\Theta = \sum_i Y_i \Omega_i$ for the rate of entropy production is symmetric in the currents and affinities; also, we see from Eqs. (3.10) to (3.12) that there is an easy interconvertibility in the roles of currents and affinities. These observations suggest that a *duality principle* may hold for steady-state situations. I here introduce my fifth, and final, basic assumption:

(V) A duality principle holds for steady-state situations: a new theorem results upon the interchange of the roles of currents and affinities in any given theorem, provided that the original theorem deals *solely* with currents, affinities, and the rate of entropy production (in any combination) and makes use of no additional quantities.

An example may help to clarify the preceding material. Consider the (one-dimensional) steady monothermal diffusion [3, 4] of a gas through a metal diaphragm* as indicated schematically in Figure 2–7. In the steady state $\dot{n}_\alpha + \dot{n}_\beta = 0$, and

$$\Theta = \frac{\dot{n}_\beta(\mu_\alpha - \mu_\beta)}{T} = Y_1 \Omega_1. \tag{3.13}$$

The steady state is completely described by the three variables T, P_α, P_β. We may consider this steady state to have originated from any of several thermostatic states. (i) We could have started from the state $[T, P_\alpha = \langle P \rangle, P_\beta = \langle P \rangle]$, where $\langle P \rangle \equiv \frac{1}{2}(P_\alpha + P_\beta)$, and could have reached the steady state in question by letting P_α and P_β approach $P_\alpha(\dot{n})$ and $P_\beta(\dot{n})$, respectively, while keeping $\langle P \rangle$ constant. (ii) We could have started from the state $[T, P_\alpha = P_\alpha(\dot{n}), P_\beta = P_\alpha(\dot{n})]$ and could have reached the final (steady) state by letting P_β approach $P_\beta(\dot{n})$ while keeping P_α constant—in this case the affinity Ω_1 is a measure of the deviation of the final state from the reference thermostatic state. (iii) . . . Each thermostatic reference state has 2 degrees of freedom (T, P) and each steady-flow state has one current $(\dot{n}_\beta)$; hence the number of degrees of freedom of the steady state is $F_\sigma + \nu = 2 + 1 = 3$, and $\Theta = \Theta(\dot{n}_\beta, T, P)$.

* See Ex. 2–3.

From the discussion in Chapter 2, treating the gas as ideal, we get (for a certain range of flow rates)

$$\Theta = \dot{n}_\beta R \ln \frac{P_\alpha}{P_\beta}, \tag{3.14}$$

$$\Theta = R[N(T, P)]\dot{n}_\beta^2, \tag{3.15}$$

$$\Omega_1 = R \ln \frac{P_\alpha}{P_\beta} = R[N(T, P)]\dot{n}_\beta, \tag{3.16}$$

where the "resistance factor" $[N]$ depends on the temperature and on the concentration of dissolved gas in the membrane via the reference state variables T, P.

Reprise

We can make explicit mention of a thermostatic reference state σ in the limiting procedures based on Eq. (3.4); thus, for example, $(\delta/\tilde{\delta}\eta)_{\ldots,\sigma}$ is an operation performed while holding constant F_σ variables characteristic of the reference state, and $(\delta/\tilde{\delta}Y_k)_{\Omega',\sigma}$ is an operation performed via a uniquely specified sequence of steady states: the final state is characterized by F_σ parameters related to the reference thermostatic state, by $\nu - 1$ affinities Ω_i $(i \neq k)$, and by the condition $Y_k = 0$, a total of $F_\sigma + (\nu - 1) + 1$ constraints in all. Hence the final state is fully characterized, and the neighboring states participating in the operation $(\delta/\tilde{\delta}Y_k)_{\Omega',\sigma}$ form a determinate set. Of the many possible sequences of steady states implied by the notation $(\delta/\tilde{\delta}Y_k)_{\Omega'}$, the operation $(\delta/\tilde{\delta}Y_k)_{\Omega',\sigma}$ singles out *one* such sequence and evaluates the derivative $(\partial/\partial Y_k)_{\Omega',\sigma}$ along that sequence. Both forms, the less explicit one $(\delta/\tilde{\delta}Y_k)_{\Omega'}$ and the more explicit one $(\delta/\tilde{\delta}Y_k)_{\Omega',\sigma}$, have their uses and both will appear in the material that follows.

Linear Current-Affinity Relationships

For a given steady-state situation with a number (ν) of independent currents Y_i chosen from the canonical set and with the rate of entropy production expressed in terms of the Y_i—i.e., $Y_i \in \{\dot{S}^{(r)}$ or $\dot{Q}^{(r)}, \dot{V}, \dot{n}^{(j)}, \ldots\}$ and $\Theta = \sum_i Y_i\Omega_i$—we can assume that the currents may be expressed as linear functions of the affinities, and vice versa, in a neighborhood of a thermostatic reference state σ. Let us assume that

$$Y_i = \sum_j L_{ij}(\sigma)\Omega_j, \tag{3.17}$$

$$\Omega_i = \sum_j K_{ij}(\sigma)Y_j, \tag{3.18}$$

given that

$$Y_i \in \{\dot{S}^{(r)} \text{ or } \dot{Q}^{(r)}, \dot{V}, \dot{n}^{(j)}, \ldots\}, \tag{3.19}$$

$$\Theta = \sum_i Y_i \Omega_i \geqslant 0, \tag{3.20}$$

where the Y_i are independent currents. For a fixed reference state σ and constant coefficients $L_{ij}(\sigma)$ and $K_{ij}(\sigma)$, I shall show that

$$0 = \left(\frac{\delta\Theta}{\bar{\delta} Y_k}\right)_{\Omega',\sigma} \leftrightarrow L_{ik}(\sigma) = L_{ki}(\sigma) \quad [\text{and } K_{ik}(\sigma) = K_{ki}(\sigma)]; \tag{3.21}$$

all summations will be over the index i.

We see from Eqs. (3.17) and (3.20) that

$$\left(\frac{\delta\Theta}{\bar{\delta} Y_k}\right)_{\Omega',\sigma} = \Omega_k + \sum_{i\neq k} \Omega_i \left(\frac{\delta Y_i}{\bar{\delta} Y_k}\right)_{\Omega',\sigma}$$
$$= \Omega_k + \sum_{i\neq k} \Omega_i \frac{L_{ik}}{L_{kk}}. \tag{3.22}$$

We also have the condition

$$0 = Y_k = L_{kk}\Omega_k + \sum_{i\neq k} L_{ki}\Omega_i \tag{3.23}$$

with $L_{kk} > 0$ by virtue of the positive definite character of the rate of entropy production (Eq. 3.20). Upon eliminating Ω_k between Eqs. (3.22) and (3.23) we get

$$\left(\frac{\delta\Theta}{\bar{\delta} Y_k}\right)_{\Omega',\sigma} = \sum_{i\neq k} \frac{(L_{ik} - L_{ki})\Omega_i}{L_{kk}}. \tag{3.24}$$

Now, if $L_{ik} = L_{ki}$, then $(\delta\Theta/\bar{\delta} Y_k)_{\Omega',\sigma}$ must equal zero. Conversely, if $(\delta\Theta/\bar{\delta} Y_k)_{\Omega',\sigma} = 0$, then L_{ik} must equal L_{ki}; this is so because Eq. (3.24) holds for a whole set of values Ω_i ($i \neq k$), and if L_{ik} were not equal to L_{ki} then Eq. (3.24) with $(\delta\Theta/\bar{\delta} Y_k)_{\Omega',\sigma} = 0$ would be a demonstration of the linear dependence of the affinities Ω_i. Since we assumed that we were dealing with a set of *independent* affinities, we are forced to conclude that $L_{ik} = L_{ki}$. If the matrix of coefficients L_{ij} is symmetric, then the matrix of coefficients K_{ij} (the reciprocal matrix) is symmetric also.* Thus for ordinary steady states in the region where linear current-affinity relations are expected to hold, assumption IV holds if and only if the Onsager reciprocal relations [5] hold. Note that the coefficients used here are global, not local, ones. I assume that assumption IV holds for any ordinary steady-state situation whatsoever, and I do not limit it to the region of linear current-affinity relationships (see the Appendix).

(As an aside observe that Eqs. (3.16) and (3.18) reveal that $[N] = K_{11}/R$.)

* The dual (assumption V) of Eq. (3.5) is the relation $(\delta\Theta/\bar{\delta}\Omega_k)_{Y'} = 0$; this dual form of Eq. (3.5) leads to a relation analogous to Eq. (3.21):

$$0 = \left(\frac{\delta\Theta}{\bar{\delta}\Omega_k}\right)_{Y',\sigma} \leftrightarrow K_{ik} = K_{ki} \quad (\text{and } L_{ik} = L_{ki}).$$

Observations

Consider the following two sets of relations, sets that I refer to as *petit principles of entropy production* and *grand principles of entropy production.*

Petit *Principles of Entropy Production*

$$\left(\frac{\delta \Theta}{\delta Y_k}\right)_{\Omega', \sigma} = 0, \tag{3.25}$$

$$\left(\frac{\delta^2 \Theta}{\delta Y_k^2}\right)_{\Omega', \sigma} > 0, \tag{3.26}$$

$$\left(\frac{\delta \Omega_k}{\delta Y_k}\right)_{Y', \sigma} \geqslant \left(\frac{\delta \Omega_k}{\delta Y_k}\right)_{\Omega', \sigma} > 0, \tag{3.27}$$

$$0 = \left(\frac{\partial Y_k}{\partial \Omega_j}\right)_{\Omega', \sigma} - \left(\frac{\partial Y_j}{\partial \Omega_k}\right)_{\Omega', \sigma} + \sum_i \Omega_i \left\{\left(\frac{\partial^2 Y_i}{\partial \Omega_j\, \partial \Omega_k}\right)_{\Omega', \sigma} - \left(\frac{\partial^2 Y_i}{\partial \Omega_k^2}\right)_{\Omega', \sigma} \left(\frac{\partial Y_k}{\partial \Omega_j}\right)_{\Omega', \sigma} \left(\frac{\partial Y_k}{\partial \Omega_k}\right)^{-1}_{\Omega', \sigma}\right\} \tag{3.28}$$

at the point where Eqs. (3.25) and (3.26) hold, i.e., at the point where $Y_k = 0$ and $\Omega_i = \Omega_i(*)$ for $i \neq k$. Each of Eqs. (3.25) to (3.28) has a dual. I feel that the *petit* principles of entropy production are of unlimited validity for ordinary steady-state situations.

Grand *Principles of Entropy Production*

$$\left(\frac{\partial^2 \Theta}{\partial Y_k^2}\right)_{\Omega', \sigma} > 0, \tag{3.29}$$

$$\left(\frac{\partial \Omega_k}{\partial Y_k}\right)_{Y', \sigma} \geqslant \left(\frac{\partial \Omega_k}{\partial Y_k}\right)_{\Omega', \sigma} > 0, \tag{3.30}$$

$$\left(\frac{\partial Y_k}{\partial \Omega_j}\right)_{\Omega', \sigma} - \left(\frac{\partial Y_j}{\partial \Omega_k}\right)_{\Omega', \sigma} = 0. \tag{3.31}$$

Each of Eqs. (3.29) to (3.31) has a dual. I feel that the *grand* principles of entropy production have a wide (but perhaps limited) range of validity for ordinary steady-state situations. In the linear current-affinity region Eqs. (3.29) to (3.31) are indistinguishable from Eqs. (3.26) to (3.28).*

Relations (3.29) to (3.31) have a strong intuitive appeal: Eq. (3.29) is of the form of a *haste-makes-waste* principle, the more we "push" a steady

* The *petit* principles of entropy production claim to be valid only at the point $Y_k = 0$, whereas the *grand* principles claim to be valid for *any* value of Y_k; this distinction is immaterial in the linear current-affinity region.

process the greater we make the rate of entropy production; Eq. (3.30) is analogous to the conditions of stability for thermostatic systems; and Eq. (3.31) is of the form of a general reciprocity relation.

Exercise 3–1. Prove that relations (3.29) to (3.31) hold for linear current-affinity relations in ordinary steady-state situations.

Exercise 3–2. Show that assumption IV and Eq. (3.29) lead to the relation (and its dual)

$$Y_k\left(\frac{\partial \Theta}{\partial Y_k}\right)_{\Omega', \sigma} \geqslant 0. \tag{3.32}$$

Explorations

At this point I wish to explore some of the interconnections among the *petit* principles and among the *grand* principles of entropy production. My first observation is that $(\delta^2 \Theta/\bar{\delta} Y_k^2)_{\Omega',\sigma} > 0$ implies that $(\delta\Omega_k/\bar{\delta} Y_k)_{\Omega',\sigma} > 0$. By straightforward differentiation of Eq. (3.20) we see that

$$\left(\frac{\partial^2 \Theta}{\partial Y_k^2}\right)_{\Omega',\sigma} = -\left(\frac{\partial \Omega_k}{\partial Y_k}\right)^3_{\Omega',\sigma}\left(\frac{\partial^2 Y_k}{\partial \Omega_k^2}\right)_{\Omega',\sigma}\left[Y_k + \sum_i \Omega_i\left(\frac{\partial Y_i}{\partial \Omega_k}\right)_{\Omega',\sigma}\right]$$
$$+ \left(\frac{\partial \Omega_k}{\partial Y_k}\right)_{\Omega',\sigma}\left[2 + \left(\frac{\partial \Omega_k}{\partial Y_k}\right)_{\Omega',\sigma} \sum_i \Omega_i\left(\frac{\partial^2 Y_i}{\partial \Omega_k^2}\right)_{\Omega',\sigma}\right] \tag{3.33}$$

and that

$$\left(\frac{\delta^2 \Theta}{\bar{\delta} Y_k^2}\right)_{\Omega',\sigma} = \left(\frac{\delta \Omega_k}{\bar{\delta} Y_k}\right)_{\Omega',\sigma}\left[2 + \left(\frac{\delta \Omega_k}{\bar{\delta} Y_k}\right)_{\Omega',\sigma} \sum_i \Omega_i\left(\frac{\partial^2 Y_i}{\partial \Omega_k^2}\right)_{\Omega',\sigma}\Bigg|_{Y_k=0}\right]. \tag{3.34}$$

In the linear current-affinity region in the neighborhood of the thermostatic reference state σ the relation $0 < L_{kk}^{-1} = (\delta\Omega_k/\bar{\delta} Y_k)_{\Omega',\sigma}$ holds due to the positive definite character of Θ; thus there exists a region for which $(\delta\Omega_k/\bar{\delta} Y_k)_{\Omega',\sigma} > 0$. Now let us vary the affinities Ω_i $(i \neq k)$ so as to move far away from the reference state σ (out of the linear current-affinity region). Since we are assuming that $(\delta\Omega_k/\bar{\delta} Y_k)_{\Omega',\sigma}$ is a continuous function of the affinities Ω_i $(i \neq k)$, it can only change to a negative value by passing through the value zero; but a zero value (see Eq. 3.34) would violate the condition $(\delta^2\Theta/\bar{\delta} Y_k^2)_{\Omega',\sigma} > 0$. Hence $(\delta^2\Theta/\bar{\delta} Y_k^2)_{\Omega',\sigma} > 0$ implies that $(\delta\Omega_k/\bar{\delta} Y_k)_{\Omega',\sigma} > 0$. An analogous treatment of Eq. (3.33) shows that $(\partial^2\Theta/\partial Y_k^2)_{\Omega',\sigma} > 0$ implies that $(\partial \Omega_k/\partial Y_k)_{\Omega',\sigma} > 0$. Since assumption IV thus implies that $(\delta \Omega_k/\tilde{\delta} Y_k)_{\Omega',\sigma} > 0$, we can make use of the observation that

$$\left(\frac{\delta \Theta}{\tilde{\delta} Y_k}\right)_{\Omega',\sigma} = \left(\frac{\delta \Omega_k}{\tilde{\delta} Y_k}\right)_{\Omega',\sigma} \left(\frac{\partial \Theta}{\partial \Omega_k}\right)_{\Omega',\sigma}\Bigg|_{Y_k=0} \tag{3.35}$$

to express assumption IV in the alternative form

$$0 = \left(\frac{\partial \Theta}{\partial \Omega_k}\right)_{\Omega',\sigma}\Bigg|_{Y_k=0} = \sum_i \Omega_i \left(\frac{\partial Y_i}{\partial \Omega_k}\right)_{\Omega',\sigma}\Bigg|_{Y_k=0}. \tag{3.36}$$

Equation (3.36) and its dual are of use in those cases (rare for most experimental situations) where we have explicit expressions of the form (3.11) or (3.12).

Let us now derive Eq. (3.28) from Eq. (3.36). Equation (3.36) says that

$$0 = \sum_i \Omega_i \left(\frac{\partial Y_i}{\partial \Omega_k}\right)_{\Omega',\sigma} \qquad \text{for } Y_k = 0. \tag{3.37}$$

Let us differentiate Eq. (3.37) with respect to one of the other affinities Ω_j keeping Y_k constant:

$$0 = \left(\frac{\partial Y_j}{\partial \Omega_k}\right)_{\Omega',\sigma} + \left(\frac{\partial Y_k}{\partial \Omega_k}\right)_{\Omega',\sigma} \left(\frac{\partial \Omega_k}{\partial \Omega_j}\right)_{\Omega'',Y_k,\sigma}$$
$$+ \sum_i \Omega_i \left\{ \left(\frac{\partial^2 Y_i}{\partial \Omega_j\, \partial \Omega_k}\right)_{\Omega',\sigma} + \left(\frac{\partial^2 Y_i}{\partial \Omega_k^{\,2}}\right)_{\Omega',\sigma} \left(\frac{\partial \Omega_k}{\partial \Omega_j}\right)_{\Omega'',Y_k,\sigma} \right\}, \tag{3.38}$$

where the subscript Ω'' means constant Ω_i for $i \neq j$ or k. The condition $dY_k = 0$ leads to the relation

$$\left(\frac{\partial \Omega_k}{\partial \Omega_j}\right)_{\Omega'',Y_k,\sigma} = -\left(\frac{\partial Y_k}{\partial \Omega_j}\right)_{\Omega',\sigma} \left(\frac{\partial Y_k}{\partial \Omega_k}\right)_{\Omega',\sigma}^{-1}. \tag{3.39}$$

Upon combining Eqs. (3.38) and (3.39) we get Eq. (3.28). Equation (3.28) is thus a direct consequence of assumption IV; in the linear current-affinity region for ordinary steady-state situations Eq. (3.28) reduces to the Onsager reciprocal relations.

Equation (3.37) is equivalent to two simultaneous equations. In deriving Eq. (3.28) I made use of derivatives of the basic simultaneous equations rather than of the basic equations themselves. For those cases where the currents can be displayed as a Taylor's series expansion in the affinities, with a finite number of terms in the expansion, it turns out that the basic simultaneous equations imply the stronger relation (3.31) as well as the relation (3.28). There are, however, some problems connected with a Taylor's series expansion of this type, and I investigate these matters in a section of the Appendix.

Let us next find the relationship between $(\partial\Omega_k/\partial Y_k)_{\Omega',\sigma}$ and $(\partial\Omega_k/\partial Y_k)_{Y',\sigma}$. Let the determinant

$$\begin{vmatrix} \left(\frac{\partial\Omega_1}{\partial Y_1}\right)_{Y',\sigma} & \left(\frac{\partial\Omega_1}{\partial Y_2}\right)_{Y',\sigma} & \cdots & \left(\frac{\partial\Omega_1}{\partial Y_\nu}\right)_{Y',\sigma} \\ \left(\frac{\partial\Omega_2}{\partial Y_1}\right)_{Y',\sigma} & \left(\frac{\partial\Omega_2}{\partial Y_2}\right)_{Y',\sigma} & \cdots & \left(\frac{\partial\Omega_2}{\partial Y_\nu}\right)_{Y',\sigma} \\ \vdots & \vdots & & \vdots \\ \left(\frac{\partial\Omega_\nu}{\partial Y_1}\right)_{Y',\sigma} & \left(\frac{\partial\Omega_\nu}{\partial Y_2}\right)_{Y',\sigma} & \cdots & \left(\frac{\partial\Omega_\nu}{\partial Y_\nu}\right)_{Y',\sigma} \end{vmatrix}$$

be called A, let the elements be called a_{ij}, and let the cofactor of element a_{ij} be called A_{ij}. Also let $\Omega_k = \Omega_k(Y_i, \sigma)$. Then

$$\left(\frac{\partial\Omega_k}{\partial Y_k}\right)_{\Omega',\sigma} = \left(\frac{\partial\Omega_k}{\partial Y_k}\right)_{Y',\sigma} + \sum_{\substack{i=1\\ i\neq k}}^{\nu} \left(\frac{\partial\Omega_k}{\partial Y_i}\right)_{Y',\sigma}\left(\frac{\partial Y_i}{\partial Y_k}\right)_{\Omega',\sigma}. \tag{3.40}$$

From the condition $\Omega_j = \text{constant}$ $(j \neq k)$, we see that

$$\sum_{i=1}^{\nu} \left(\frac{\partial\Omega_j}{\partial Y_i}\right)_{Y',\sigma}\left(\frac{\partial Y_i}{\partial Y_k}\right)_{\Omega',\sigma} = 0 \qquad \begin{matrix} j = 1, 2, \ldots, \nu \\ j \neq k. \end{matrix} \tag{3.41}$$

Relations (3.41) are a set of $\nu - 1$ linear relations in the quantities $(\partial Y_i/\partial Y_k)_{\Omega',\sigma}$ $(i \neq k)$:

$$\sum_{\substack{i=1\\ i\neq k}}^{\nu} a_{ji}\left(\frac{\partial Y_i}{\partial Y_k}\right)_{\Omega',\sigma} = -a_{jk} \qquad \begin{matrix} j = 1, 2, \ldots, \nu \\ j \neq k. \end{matrix} \tag{3.42}$$

These relations can be solved simultaneously for the quantities $(\partial Y_i/\partial Y_k)_{\Omega',\sigma}$:

$$\left(\frac{\partial Y_i}{\partial Y_k}\right)_{\Omega',\sigma} = \frac{A_{ki}}{A_{kk}}. \tag{3.43}$$

Since

$$\sum_{\substack{i=1\\ i\neq k}}^{\nu} \frac{a_{ki}A_{ki}}{A_{kk}} = \frac{A - a_{kk}A_{kk}}{A_{kk}}, \tag{3.44}$$

we see (Eq. 3.40) that

$$\left(\frac{\partial\Omega_k}{\partial Y_k}\right)_{\Omega',\sigma} = \left(\frac{\partial\Omega_k}{\partial Y_k}\right)_{Y',\sigma} + \frac{A - a_{kk}A_{kk}}{A_{kk}}. \tag{3.45}$$

In the linear current-affinity case, $a_{ij} = K_{ij}$, $A > 0$, $A_{kk} > 0$, $a_{kk} > 0$, and [6] $a_{kk}A_{kk} > A$ if the matrix of coefficients is symmetric, whereas $a_{kk}A_{kk} < A$ if the matrix of coefficients is antisymmetric (i.e., $K_{ki} = -K_{ik}$; see the *special fields* section of the Appendix). The preceding argument can, of course, be carried through in dual form to obtain the relationship between $(\partial Y_k/\partial\Omega_k)_{Y',\sigma}$ and $(\partial Y_k/\partial\Omega_k)_{\Omega',\sigma}$.

For formal completeness I list some relations of general validity (but of limited practical importance):

$$\sum_i \left(\frac{\partial Y_k}{\partial \Omega_i}\right)_{\Omega',\sigma} \left(\frac{\partial \Omega_i}{\partial Y_j}\right)_{Y',\sigma} = \delta_{jk}, \tag{3.46}$$

$$Y_i = \sum_j \left\{\left(\frac{\partial \Theta}{\partial Y_j}\right)_{Y',\sigma} - \Omega_j\right\}\left(\frac{\partial Y_j}{\partial \Omega_i}\right)_{\Omega',\sigma}, \tag{3.47}$$

$$\Omega_i = \sum_j \left\{\left(\frac{\partial \Theta}{\partial \Omega_j}\right)_{\Omega',\sigma} - Y_j\right\}\left(\frac{\partial \Omega_j}{\partial Y_i}\right)_{Y',\sigma}, \tag{3.48}$$

where δ_{jk} is the Kronecker delta; i.e., $\delta_{jk} = 0$ if $j \neq k$, and $\delta_{jk} = 1$ if $j = k$.

Exercise 3–3. Show that for linear current-affinity relationships Eqs. (3.47) and (3.48) reduce to Eqs. (3.17) and (3.18).

A final word in clarification of assumption V may be in order. Equations such as (3.16), (3.17), and (3.18) do not possess duals because they contain the "additional quantities" $R[N]$, L_{ij}, and K_{ij}.

Equations of State

The role played by explicit current-affinity relations (Eqs. 3.11, 3.12, 3.17, 3.18, etc.) in the thermodynamics of steady states is analogous to the role played by equations of state in equilibrium thermostatics. In thermostatics it is essential that we have a firm belief in the *existence* of equations of state, but we do not need an *explicit* equation of state in order to establish such basic thermodynamic results as the conditions of equilibrium, the conditions of stability, the phase rule, etc. Explicit equations of state are undeniably useful, but we may erect an elaborate thermodynamic structure upon the mere premise that equations of state exist. In an analogous fashion we merely need a firm belief in the existence of current-affinity relations in order to develop the thermodynamics of steady states. An overemphasis on equations of state in thermostatics sometimes leads students of the subject to conclude (erroneously) that classical thermodynamics applies only to ideal gases. I fear that a corresponding overemphasis on explicit current-affinity relations for steady-state situations may leave the student with the (erroneous) impression that the thermodynamics of steady states is valid only in the linear current-affinity region.

The resolution of the rate of entropy production Θ into currents and affinities generates for us a useful and suggestive language in terms of which we can efficiently state the theorems of the thermodynamics of steady states.

The problem of determining the sign and the magnitude of a given current as a function of the pertinent parameters for a given steady-state situation, however, is more a problem of general physics than of thermodynamics. To insist on displaying the currents as power series in the affinities is to generate needless complications. The functional forms are all wrong: a heat flux depends on grad T and not on grad $(1/T)$, a diffusion flux depends on grad C and not on grad ln C, and so on. Of course, in an infinitesimal neighborhood of a given point, grad $(1/T)$ is proportional to grad T and grad ln C is proportional to grad C. It is to this simple fact that we owe a distressing overemphasis on the linear current-affinity region.

I shall have more to say on these matters in succeeding chapters of the text.

References

1. B. Coleman and C. Truesdell, *J. Chem. Phys.*, **33**, 28 (1960).
2. C. Truesdell, *J. Chem. Phys.*, **37**, 2336 (1962).
3. R. J. Tykodi and T. A. Erikson, *J. Chem. Phys.*, **31**, 1521 (1959).
4. L. S. Darken and R. W. Gurry, *Physical Chemistry of Metals* (McGraw-Hill Book Co., New York, 1953), p. 440.
5. L. Onsager, *Phys. Rev.*, **37**, 405 (1931); **38**, 2265 (1931).
6. H. Cramer, *Mathematical Methods of Statistics* (Princeton University Press, Princeton, 1946), Chapter 11.

4

Migrational Equilibrium in Monothermal Fields

General Considerations and Conditions of Thermostatic Equilibrium

Consider a system in a monothermal field with all terminal parts at temperature T; for a state that is a steady-flow state involving the steady migration of a given chemical substance into the kth terminal part of the system, we observe that

$$\Theta = -\frac{\dot{G}(\text{system})}{T} + \frac{\dot{W}_0}{T}. \tag{4.1}$$

We find the condition for the migrational equilibrium of the given chemical substance in the monothermal field by applying the operation $(\delta/\tilde{\delta}\dot{n}_k)_{\Omega'}$ to Eq. (4.1); for monothermal fields let us take the operation $(\delta/\tilde{\delta}\dot{n}_k)_{\Omega'}$ in the form $(\delta/\tilde{\delta}\dot{n}_k)_T, \ldots$ with the temperature and an appropriate set of free-energy differences being held constant. The application of the operation $(\delta/\tilde{\delta}\dot{n}_k)_T, \ldots$ to Eq. (4.1) leads to

$$\left(\frac{\delta\Theta}{\tilde{\delta}\dot{n}_k}\right)_{T,\ldots} = \frac{1}{T}\left\{-\left(\frac{\delta\dot{G}(\text{system})}{\tilde{\delta}\dot{n}_k}\right)_{T,\ldots} + \left(\frac{\delta\dot{W}_0}{\tilde{\delta}\dot{n}_k}\right)_{T,\ldots}\right\}. \tag{4.2}$$

The application of assumption IV to Eq. (4.2) leads to

$$\sum\left(\frac{\delta(\mathscr{G}_i\dot{n}_i)}{\tilde{\delta}\dot{n}_k}\right)_{T,\ldots} \equiv \left(\frac{\delta\dot{G}(\text{system})}{\tilde{\delta}\dot{n}_k}\right)_{T,\ldots} = \left(\frac{\delta\dot{W}_0}{\tilde{\delta}\dot{n}_k}\right)_{T,\ldots}, \tag{4.3}$$

the sum being over the terminal parts of the system. For a steady exchange of mass between two terminal parts (α, β) of a system with only pressure-volume work being exchanged between system and surroundings (i.e., $\dot{W}_0 = 0$), it follows that $\dot{n}_\alpha + \dot{n}_\beta = 0$, and that

$$\Theta = \frac{\dot{n}_\alpha(\mathcal{G}_\beta - \mathcal{G}_\alpha)}{T} = Y_1\Omega_1, \tag{4.4}$$

$$0 = \left(\frac{\delta\Theta}{\delta\dot{n}_\alpha}\right)_T = \frac{\mathcal{G}_\beta - \mathcal{G}_\alpha}{T} = \Omega_1, \tag{4.5}$$

and, hence, that

$$\mathcal{G}_\beta = \mathcal{G}_\alpha, \tag{4.6}$$

provided that there are no other independent currents traversing the system. Equation (4.6) yields many of the well-known relations pertaining to thermostatic equilibrium. Thus, if α and β refer to two different points in a gravitational field, and φ_α and φ_β refer to the potential energy per gram of some fluid of molecular weight M at the points α and β, then $\mathcal{G} = \mu + M\varphi$, and

$$\mu_\beta + M\varphi_\beta = \mu_\alpha + M\varphi_\alpha. \tag{4.7}$$

Concentration Field

Consider next the problem of migrational equilibrium in a monothermal concentration field—the situation indicated schematically in Figure 4–1. A spatial region marked MIX contains two fluid components, 1 and 2. The MIX region communicates with terminal parts of the system at a and b via membranes permeable to component 1 alone and with terminal parts at α and

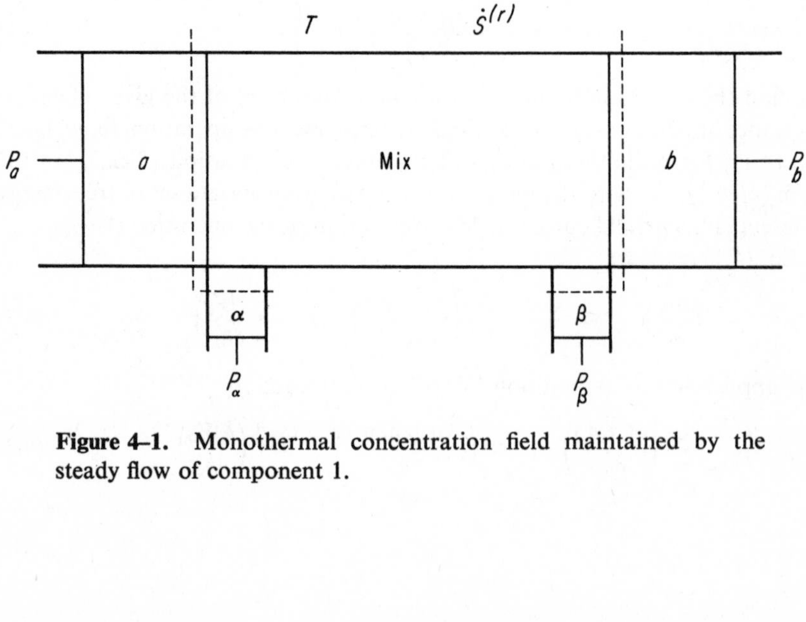

Figure 4–1. Monothermal concentration field maintained by the steady flow of component 1.

β via membranes permeable to component 2 alone. Let us induce a steady flow of component 1 through the MIX region and seek the conditions for the migrational equilibrium of component 2 in the concentration field set up by the flow of component 1. The situation we are considering is such that $\dot{W}_0 = 0$ and all terminal parts are at temperature T. If we establish a steady flow of both components 1 and 2 through the MIX region, then

$$\begin{aligned}\Theta &= -\frac{1}{T}(\mathscr{G}_a\dot{n}_a + \mathscr{G}_b\dot{n}_b + \mu_\alpha\dot{n}_\alpha + \mu_\beta\dot{n}_\beta) \\ &= \dot{n}_a\frac{\mathscr{G}_b - \mathscr{G}_a}{T} + \dot{n}_\alpha\frac{\mu_\beta - \mu_\alpha}{T} \\ &= Y_1\Omega_1 + Y_2\Omega_2,\end{aligned} \tag{4.8}$$

where $\dot{n}_a + \dot{n}_b = 0$, $\dot{n}_\alpha + \dot{n}_\beta = 0$, and $\mathscr{G} \equiv \mu + \mathscr{K}$ with $\mathscr{K}$ being the molar kinetic energy of macroscopic motion. I have neglected kinetic energy terms associated with component 2. The operation $(\delta/\bar{\delta}\dot{n}_\alpha)_{T,\Delta\mathscr{G}^{(1)}}$, where $\Delta\mathscr{G}^{(1)} \equiv \mathscr{G}_b - \mathscr{G}_a$ is of the form $(\delta/\bar{\delta}Y_2)_{\Omega'}$. It follows, then, that

$$T\left(\frac{\delta\Theta}{\bar{\delta}\dot{n}_\alpha}\right)_{T,\Delta\mathscr{G}^{(1)}} = (\mathscr{G}_b - \mathscr{G}_a)\left(\frac{\delta\dot{n}_a}{\bar{\delta}\dot{n}_\alpha}\right)_{T,\Delta\mathscr{G}^{(1)}} + \mu_\beta - \mu_\alpha, \tag{4.9}$$

and, by the application of assumption IV, that

$$\mu_\alpha - \mu_\beta = -[R_{\alpha\beta}](\mathscr{G}_a - \mathscr{G}_b) \tag{4.10}$$

in the state of migrational equilibrium with respect to component 2; $[R_{\alpha\beta}] \equiv (\delta\dot{n}_a/\bar{\delta}\dot{n}_\alpha)_{T,\Delta\mathscr{G}^{(1)}}$. If the flow of the two fluids is coupled ($[R_{\alpha\beta}] \neq 0$), then the flow of component 1 sets up a gradient in the chemical potential of component 2. We can use Eq. (4.10) to test the validity of the relation $(\delta\Theta/\bar{\delta}Y_2)_{\Omega'} = 0$ for the situation considered: we can compare the $[R]$ quantity as computed from Eq. (4.10) to the value computed according to the definition

$$\lim_{\dot{n}_\alpha \to 0} \frac{\Delta\dot{n}_a}{\dot{n}_\alpha} \equiv [R_{\alpha\beta}] \qquad \text{constant } T, \Delta\mathscr{G}^{(1)}. \tag{4.11}$$

By introducing a parameter λ to measure distance in the direction of decreasing $\mathscr{G}$ in the (one-dimensional) concentration field, we can write Eq. (4.10) as

$$\frac{\mu_\beta - \mu_\alpha}{\lambda_\beta - \lambda_\alpha} \equiv \frac{\Delta\mu^{(2)}}{\Delta\lambda} = \frac{\Lambda[R_{\alpha\beta}]}{\Delta\lambda}\left(\frac{\Delta\mathscr{G}}{\Lambda}\right), \tag{4.12}$$

where Λ is a characteristic length (the distance between the semi-permeable membranes at a and b) for the field and $\Delta\mathscr{G} \equiv \mathscr{G}_{\text{source}} - \mathscr{G}_{\text{sink}}$. Upon the introduction of the abbreviation $[r_{\alpha\beta}] \equiv \Lambda[R_{\alpha\beta}]/\Delta\lambda$, we obtain

$$\frac{\Delta\mu^{(2)}}{\Delta\lambda} = [r_{\alpha\beta}]\frac{\Delta\mathscr{G}}{\Lambda}. \tag{4.13}$$

Thus far we have considered two points in the concentration field; we can also compute effects at a given point in the field. For a given point λ, the relations

$$\operatorname{grad} \mu_\lambda^{(2)} \equiv \left(\frac{\partial \mu_\lambda^{(2)}}{\partial \lambda}\right)_{T,\langle 2\rangle}, \tag{4.14}$$

$$[r_\lambda] \equiv \frac{\operatorname{grad} \mu_\lambda^{(2)}}{\Delta\mathscr{G}/\Lambda}, \tag{4.15}$$

are convenient; the subscript $\langle 2\rangle$ means that the *average concentration* (expressed in mole fraction or molality units) of component 2 in the concentration field is to be kept constant. From Eqs. (4.13) and (4.15) we see that

$$[r_{\alpha\beta}] = \frac{1}{\Delta\lambda}\int_\beta^\alpha [r_\lambda]\, d\lambda. \tag{4.16}$$

The coupling coefficients $[r]$ thus far introduced refer to a fixed $\Delta\mathscr{G}/\Lambda$ and are in the nature of integral quantities with respect to $\Delta\mathscr{G}/\Lambda$. For convenience we can also introduce differential coupling coefficients via the definitions

$$[r_{\alpha\beta}]^\partial \equiv \frac{1}{\Delta\lambda}\left(\frac{\partial\, \Delta\mu^{(2)}}{\partial(\Delta\mathscr{G}/\Lambda)}\right)_{T,\langle 2\rangle} \tag{4.17}$$

and

$$[r_\lambda]^\partial \equiv \left(\frac{\partial \operatorname{grad} \mu_\lambda^{(2)}}{\partial(\Delta\mathscr{G}/\Lambda)}\right)_{T,\langle 2\rangle}. \tag{4.18}$$

An equation similar to (4.16) holds between the differential coupling coefficients.

The application of the Gibbs–Duhem relation to the points of the concentration field yields

$$\bar{S}_\lambda \operatorname{grad} T_\lambda - \bar{V}_\lambda \operatorname{grad} P_\lambda + X_\lambda^{(1)} \operatorname{grad} \mu_\lambda^{(1)} + X_\lambda^{(2)} \operatorname{grad} \mu_\lambda^{(2)} = 0, \tag{4.19}$$

where $\bar{Z}_\lambda$ is a mean molar property of the 2-component system evaluated at a point λ in the concentration field, and $X_\lambda^{(i)}$ is the mole fraction of component i at the point λ. Now if $(\Delta\mathscr{G}/\Lambda) \approx -\operatorname{grad} \mu_\lambda^{(1)}$, then

$$[r_\lambda] \approx -\frac{\operatorname{grad} \mu_\lambda^{(2)}}{\operatorname{grad} \mu_\lambda^{(1)}} = \frac{X_\lambda^{(1)}}{X_\lambda^{(2)}} + \frac{\bar{S}_\lambda}{X_\lambda^{(2)}}\left(\frac{\operatorname{grad} T_\lambda}{\operatorname{grad} \mu_\lambda^{(1)}}\right) - \frac{\bar{V}_\lambda}{X_\lambda^{(2)}}\left(\frac{\operatorname{grad} P_\lambda}{\operatorname{grad} \mu_\lambda^{(1)}}\right). \tag{4.20}$$

Now quite clearly there will be gradients in temperature and pressure inside the MIX region due to the flow process and, consequently, $[r_\lambda] \neq (X_\lambda^{(1)}/X_\lambda^{(2)})$. I feel, however, that there is a good chance that the relation $[r_\lambda] \approx \langle X^{(1)}\rangle/\langle X^{(2)}\rangle$ will be close to the truth. We sorely need experimental investigations of concentration fields so as to be able to demonstrate the dependence of the various coupling coefficients on suitable parameters of the system (T, $\langle 2\rangle$, $\Delta\mathscr{G}/\Lambda$, etc.).

Electrokinetic Relations

If we separate two portions of a fluid by a porous membrane and if we place an inert electrode on either side of the membrane, then we find that the flow of fluid through the membrane gives rise to an electrical potential difference across the electrodes and, conversely, that a potential difference applied to the electrodes gives rise to a fluid flow or to a pressure difference across the membrane. The various phenomena that I have just described give rise to relations called *electrokinetic effects* [1, 2]. The situation is indicated schematically in Figure 4–2.

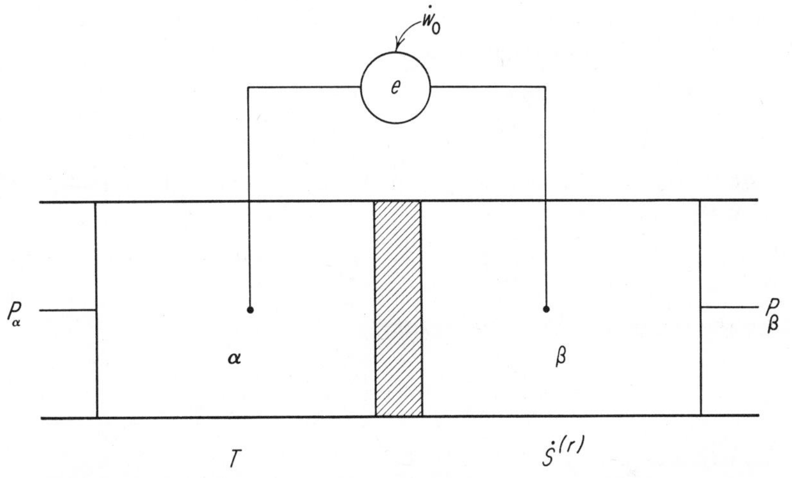

Figure 4–2. Electrokinetic apparatus, schematic; the electric engine at *e* receives work at the rate $\dot{W}_0$ and drives a current *I* around the circuit; $P_\alpha \geqslant P_\beta$.

Consider a state in which there is a steady flow of fluid across the membrane and a steady flow of electric current through the auxiliary circuit:

$$\Theta = -\frac{1}{T}(\dot{n}_\alpha\mu_\alpha + \dot{n}_\beta\mu_\beta) + \frac{\dot{W}_0}{T}. \tag{4.21}$$

Let us treat the fluid as incompressible, replacing $\dot{n}_\beta(\mu_\beta - \mu_\alpha)$ by

$$-\dot{V}_\beta(P_\alpha - P_\beta) \equiv -\dot{V}\Delta P,$$

and let us replace $\dot{W}_0$ by $I(\psi' - \psi'')$, where I is the negative electric current expressed in conventional units (amperes, say) and $\Delta\psi \equiv \psi' - \psi''$ is the difference in electrical potential between the binding posts of the electric engine at *e*. It is necessary to decide upon a sign convention for the direction of flow of negative electric current so as to be able to label (′ or ″) the binding posts of the electric engine properly.* Equation (4.21) thus takes the form

$$\Theta = \dot{V}\left(\frac{\Delta P}{T}\right) + I\left(\frac{\Delta\psi}{T}\right) = Y_1\Omega_1 + Y_2\Omega_2. \tag{4.22}$$

The application of the operation $(\delta/\tilde{\delta}I)_{T,\Delta P}$, which is of the form $(\delta/\tilde{\delta}\,Y_2)_{\Omega'}$, to Eq. (4.22) and the use of assumption IV lead to the relation

$$\left(\frac{\Delta\psi}{\Delta P}\right)_{T,I=0} = -\left(\frac{\delta\dot{V}}{\tilde{\delta}I}\right)_{T,\Delta P}. \tag{4.23}$$

If the right-hand side of Eq. (4.23) is independent of ΔP (as it is in the region of linear current-affinity relations [1]), then we can evaluate it by measuring the volume flow induced by unit electric current in the state for which $\Delta P = 0$; thus, for such circumstances,

$$\left(\frac{\Delta\psi}{\Delta P}\right)_{T,I=0} = -\left(\frac{\dot{V}}{I}\right)_{T,\Delta P=0}. \tag{4.24}$$

In a similar fashion, the operation $(\delta/\tilde{\delta}\dot{V})_{T,\Delta\psi}$ performed on Eq. (4.22) leads to the relations

$$\left(\frac{\Delta P}{\Delta\psi}\right)_{T,\dot{V}=0} = -\left(\frac{\delta I}{\tilde{\delta}\dot{V}}\right)_{T,\Delta\psi} \tag{4.25}$$

and (in the linear current-affinity region)

$$\left(\frac{\Delta P}{\Delta\psi}\right)_{T,\dot{V}=0} = -\left(\frac{I}{\dot{V}}\right)_{T,\Delta\psi=0}. \tag{4.26}$$

Exercise 4–1. Consider the linear current-affinity relations

$$\dot{V} = L_{11}\left(\frac{\Delta P}{T}\right) + L_{12}\left(\frac{\Delta\psi}{T}\right) \tag{4.27}$$

$$I = L_{21}\left(\frac{\Delta P}{T}\right) + L_{22}\left(\frac{\Delta\psi}{T}\right) \tag{4.28}$$

relative to the thermostatic reference state $(T, P_\beta, \Delta\psi = 0)$, treating the coefficients $L_{ik}(T, P_\beta)$ as constant for a given temperature T and reference pressure P_β. Show that

$$\left(\frac{\delta\dot{V}}{\tilde{\delta}I}\right)_{T,P_\beta,\Delta P} = \lim_{I\to 0}\left(\frac{(\partial\dot{V}/\partial\,\Delta\psi)_{T,P_\beta,\Delta P}}{(\partial I/\partial\,\Delta\psi)_{T,P_\beta,\Delta P}}\right)$$

is independent of ΔP and is in fact equal to $(\dot{V}/I)_{T,P_\beta,\Delta P=0}$.

* If it were necessary for us to be explicit about the sign convention, we could, for example, take the spontaneous direction of negative electric current flow for a small positive ΔP as the positive flow direction.

Exercise 4–2. Rather than struggle with the sign convention implicit in Eqs. (4.23) to (4.26), let us shift to absolute values. Thus, e.g.,

$$\left|\left(\frac{\Delta\psi}{\Delta P}\right)_{T,I=0}\right| = \left|\left(\frac{\dot{V}}{I}\right)_{T,\Delta P=0}\right|. \tag{4.29}$$

D. R. Briggs [3] made some measurements of the electrical potential difference developed across a cellulose plug and also across a glass capillary tube when conductivity water was forced through the plug or capillary at a steady rate. His data are listed in Table 4–1.

Table 4–1

Streaming Potential Data of Briggs [3]

ΔP (cm Hg)	$\Delta\psi$ (mv)	*Rate of Flow* (cm^3 sec^{-1})	
55.2	141	0.481	
47.9	122	0.424	
38.7	100	0.343	
28.2	75	0.238	cellulose
17.8	48.6	0.149	
7.5	21.5	0.060	
47.5	118.0	0.424	
38.4	98.0	0.338	
30.5	4370	1.56	
22.0	3100	1.21	capillary
14.4	2140	0.89	

Compute the ratio $(\Delta\psi/\Delta P)_{T,I=0}$ for each set of data. A nearly constant value for the ratio implies that Eqs. (4.27) and (4.28) are adequate representations of the data. From the computed values of the ratio $(\Delta\psi/\Delta P)_{T,I=0}$ and Eq. (4.29) calculate the volume flow (cm^3 sec^{-1}) that would accompany an electric current flow of 1 mamp for the case $\Delta P = 0$; make the calculation for both the cellulose and the capillary cases, paying especial attention to the choice of a consistent set of physical units in which to express the results. Also calculate for the case $\Delta P = 0$ the electric current that would be required to induce a volume flow of 1 cm^3 sec^{-1} across the cellulose plug; do the same for the capillary tube.

References

1. G. N. Lewis and M. Randall, *Thermodynamics*, 2nd edition, edited by K. Pitzer and G. Brewer (McGraw-Hill Book Co., New York, 1961), p. 458.
2. D. MacInnes, *The Principles of Electrochemistry* (Reinhold Publishing Co., New York, 1939), Chapter 23.
3. D. R. Briggs, *J. Phys. Chem.*, **32**, 641 (1928).

5

Migrational Equilibrium in Polythermal Fields: The Thermomolecular Pressure Effect

Let us turn now to the study of systems containing temperature gradients. In such systems we maintain a steady flow of heat in the system by controlling the action of the surroundings, and we look for the conditions of migrational equilibrium for given chemical species in such an environment. The necessary ideas are best illustrated by taking an example: consider the case of the thermomolecular pressure effect.

Thermomolecular Pressure Effect

Consider the system shown schematically in Figure 5–1: a 1-component gaseous substance is distributed through two chambers and a connecting capillary linkage, each chamber being in heat communication with a thermostat. If under conditions of no mass flow we find that $P_\alpha \neq P_\beta$ when $T_\alpha \neq T_\beta$, we say that a thermomolecular pressure effect exists. A study of the functional relatedness of the variables T_α, P_α, T_β, P_β (for states of no mass flow) for various gases and various kinds of capillary tubes is important for fields such as precision gas thermometry [1] and low temperature gas-solid adsorption [2]. In analyzing this situation, I divide the system into terminal parts (α, β) and a gradient part, the gradient part being stationary during steady-flow operations. Under conditions of steady heat flow alone, the relation

$$\begin{aligned}\dot{U}(\text{system}) &= -\dot{Q}_\alpha^{(r)} - \dot{Q}_\beta^{(r)} - \dot{q}(\alpha\beta) \\ &= -T_\alpha \dot{S}_\alpha^{(r)} - T_\beta \dot{S}_\beta^{(r)} - \dot{q}(\alpha\beta) = 0 \end{aligned} \tag{5.1}$$

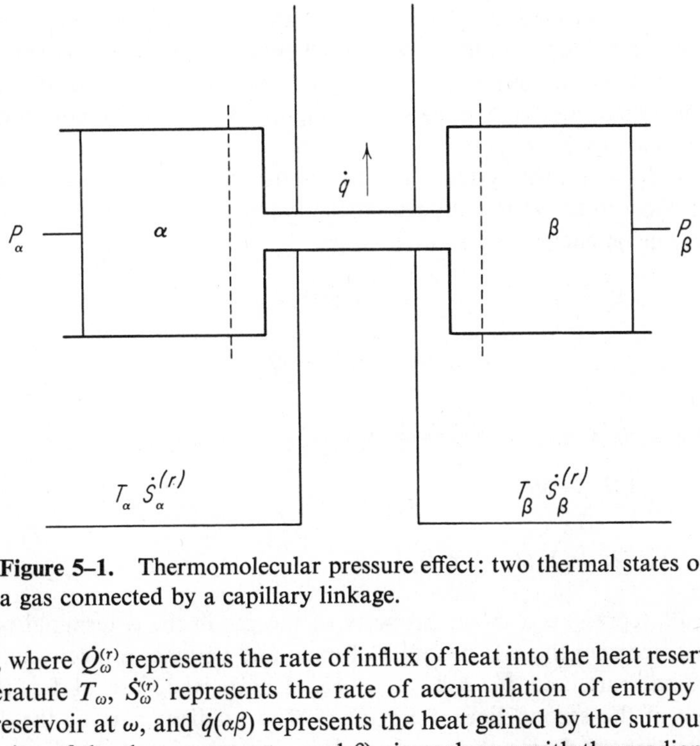

Figure 5–1. Thermomolecular pressure effect: two thermal states of a gas connected by a capillary linkage.

holds, where $\dot{Q}_\omega^{(r)}$ represents the rate of influx of heat into the heat reservoir of temperature T_ω, $\dot{S}_\omega^{(r)}$ represents the rate of accumulation of entropy in the heat reservoir at ω, and $\dot{q}(\alpha\beta)$ represents the heat gained by the surroundings (exclusive of the thermostats at α and β) via exchange with the gradient part. I call the section of the gradient part that falls outside the two thermostats the *link* or the *linkage*. The heat quantity $\dot{q}(\alpha\beta)$ represents the rate at which heat leaks across the lateral surface of the link to parts of the surroundings other than the thermostats at α and β. In order that the process described in Eq. (5.1) take place at a steady rate, it is necessary that the parts of the surroundings involved in the heat transfer $\dot{q}(\alpha\beta)$ be at fixed temperatures; i.e.,

$$\dot{q}(\alpha\beta) = \sum \dot{Q}_x^{(r)} = \sum T_x \dot{S}_x^{(r)} = \langle T(\alpha\beta)\rangle \dot{s}(\alpha\beta), \tag{5.2}$$

$$\dot{s}(\alpha\beta) \equiv \sum \dot{S}_x^{(r)}, \tag{5.3}$$

$$\langle T(\alpha\beta)\rangle \equiv \frac{\sum T_x \dot{S}_x^{(r)}}{\sum \dot{S}_x^{(r)}} = \frac{\dot{q}(\alpha\beta)}{\dot{s}(\alpha\beta)}. \tag{5.4}$$

The quantity $\langle T(\alpha\beta)\rangle$ is an effective average temperature for the surroundings to which heat is being leaked at the rate $\dot{q}(\alpha\beta)$. Two cases that frequently occur are (i) $\langle T(\alpha\beta)\rangle$ = ambient temperature (room temperature), and (ii) $\langle T(\alpha\beta)\rangle$ = the average over an infinite number of heat reservoirs ranging in temperature from T_α to T_β (a series of *Thomson reservoirs*). If both $\dot{q}(\alpha\beta) = 0$ and $\dot{s}(\alpha\beta) = 0$, I define $\langle T(\alpha\beta)\rangle$ as the limit of $\dot{q}(\alpha\beta)/\dot{s}(\alpha\beta)$ as $\dot{q}(\alpha\beta) \to 0$ for those cases where the limit is physically evident.*

In my analysis of polythermal fields, then, I give the various parts of the surroundings unequal emphasis: I give essential temperatures and heat reservoirs individual emphasis, whereas I lump together less essential ones and treat them in terms of "averaged" or "effective" parameters. In addition, when there is no danger of ambiguity, I shorten the notation $\dot{q}(\alpha\beta)$, $\langle T(\alpha\beta)\rangle$, etc., to $\dot{q}$, $\langle T\rangle$, etc.

Consider again the system shown in Figure 5–1. Induce a steady flow of matter between the terminal parts of the system such that $\dot{n}_\alpha + \dot{n}_\beta = 0$ and neglect kinetic energy terms; we then get,

$$\dot{n}_\alpha \overline{U}_\alpha + \dot{n}_\beta \overline{U}_\beta = -\dot{Q}_\alpha^{(r)} - \dot{Q}_\beta^{(r)} - \dot{q} - P_\alpha \dot{V}_\alpha - P_\beta \dot{V}_\beta, \tag{5.5}$$

$$\dot{n}_\alpha \overline{H}_\alpha + \dot{n}_\beta \overline{H}_\beta + \dot{Q}_\alpha^{(r)} + \dot{Q}_\beta^{(r)} + \dot{q} = 0, \tag{5.6}$$

$$\begin{aligned}\Theta &= \dot{n}_\alpha \overline{S}_\alpha + \dot{n}_\beta \overline{S}_\beta + \frac{\dot{Q}_\alpha^{(r)}}{T_\alpha} + \frac{\dot{Q}_\beta^{(r)}}{T_\beta} + \frac{\dot{q}}{\langle T\rangle} \\ &= \dot{n}_\alpha\left(\frac{\overline{H}_\beta - \overline{H}_\alpha}{T_\beta} + \overline{S}_\alpha - \overline{S}_\beta\right) + \dot{Q}_\alpha^{(r)}\left(\frac{1}{T_\alpha} - \frac{1}{T_\beta}\right) + \dot{q}\left(\frac{1}{\langle T\rangle} - \frac{1}{T_\beta}\right) \\ &= Y_1\Omega_1 + Y_2\Omega_2 + Y_3\Omega_3,\end{aligned} \tag{5.7}$$

where $\overline{Z}_\omega$ represents a molar property of the gas in the ω terminal part, $\dot{n}_\omega$ and $\dot{V}_\omega$ represent the rate of influx of mass and volume, respectively, to the ω terminal part, and $\overline{H}_\omega \equiv \overline{U}_\omega + P_\omega \overline{V}_\omega$. I have made use of Eq. (5.6) in arriving at the second line of Eq. (5.7). The gradient part of the system, being stationary during the steady-flow process, does not contribute to the left-hand side of Eq. (5.5). To find the condition for migrational equilibrium in the polythermal field we investigate the behavior of Eqs. (5.6) and (5.7) under the operation $(\delta/\delta\dot{n}_\alpha)_{T_\alpha, T_\beta, \langle T\rangle}$, which is of the form $(\delta/\delta Y_1)_{\Omega'}$:

$$\overline{H}_\alpha - \overline{H}_\beta + \left(\frac{\delta(\dot{Q}_\alpha^{(r)} + \dot{Q}_\beta^{(r)} + \dot{q})}{\delta\dot{n}_\alpha}\right)_{T_\alpha, T_\beta, \langle T\rangle} = 0, \tag{5.8}$$

* If, for example, the link is efficiently insulated so that $\dot{q}(\alpha\beta) = 0$ and $\dot{s}(\alpha\beta) = 0$, and if removal of the insulation would lead to heat exchange with a room of temperature T_R, then it is clear that removal of the insulation followed by step-by-step restoration would lead to $\lim \dot{q}(\alpha\beta)/\dot{s}(\alpha\beta) = T_R$, regardless of the exact way in which the insulation was applied to the link.

$$\begin{aligned}\left(\frac{\delta \Theta}{\tilde{\delta}\dot{n}_\alpha}\right)_{\Omega'} &= \bar{S}_\alpha - \bar{S}_\beta + \left(\frac{\delta(\dot{S}_\alpha^{(r)} + \dot{S}_\beta^{(r)} + \dot{s})}{\tilde{\delta}\dot{n}_\alpha}\right)_{T_\alpha, T_\beta, \langle T\rangle} \\ &= \frac{\bar{H}_\beta - \bar{H}_\alpha}{T_\beta} + \bar{S}_\alpha - \bar{S}_\beta \\ &\quad + \left(\frac{\delta \dot{Q}_\alpha^{(r)}}{\tilde{\delta}\dot{n}_\alpha}\right)_{T_\alpha, T_\beta, \langle T\rangle}\left(\frac{1}{T_\alpha} - \frac{1}{T_\beta}\right) \\ &\quad + \left(\frac{\delta \dot{q}}{\tilde{\delta}\dot{n}_\alpha}\right)_{T_\alpha, T_\beta, \langle T\rangle}\left(\frac{1}{\langle T\rangle} - \frac{1}{T_\beta}\right). \end{aligned} \tag{5.9}$$

In equilibrium thermostatics a heat effect in a heat reservoir surrounding a system that is undergoing a reversible isothermal isopiestic change in state can be related to an enthalpy change in the system. Consider, for example, the reversible isothermal vaporization of a liquid: the amount of heat $-dQ^{(r)}$ lost by the reservoir for the vaporization of dn moles of liquid is related to the enthalpy change $\bar{H}_{\text{gas}} - \bar{H}_{\text{liq}}$ by the relation $-dQ^{(r)} = dn(\bar{H}_{\text{gas}} - \bar{H}_{\text{liq}})$ or $dQ^{(r)}/dn = \bar{H}_{\text{liq}} - \bar{H}_{\text{gas}}$. I use this observation as a guide in setting up a number of useful steady-state definitions:*

$$\left(\frac{\delta \dot{Q}_\omega^{(r)}}{\tilde{\delta}\dot{n}_\omega}\right)_{T_\alpha, T_\beta, \langle T\rangle} \equiv [H_\omega] - \bar{H}_\omega, \tag{5.10}$$

$$\left(\frac{\delta \dot{S}_\omega^{(r)}}{\tilde{\delta}\dot{n}_\omega}\right)_{T_\alpha, T_\beta, \langle T\rangle} \equiv [S_\omega] - \bar{S}_\omega, \tag{5.11}$$

$$\left(\frac{\delta \dot{q}}{\tilde{\delta}\dot{n}_\omega}\right)_{T_\alpha, T_\beta, \langle T\rangle} \equiv -[h(\chi\omega)], \tag{5.12}$$

$$\left(\frac{\delta \dot{s}}{\tilde{\delta}\dot{n}_\omega}\right)_{T_\alpha, T_\beta, \langle T\rangle} \equiv -[s(\chi\omega)]. \tag{5.13}$$

Equations (5.10) to (5.13) are definitions of the steady-state square-bracketed quantities.† The quantity $[H_\omega]$, e.g., is an "effective" molar enthalpy for the gas at the point where it crosses the boundary of the heat reservoir. The application of the definitions (5.10) to (5.13) to Eqs. (5.8) and (5.9) yields the relations

$$[H_\alpha] - [H_\beta] - [h(\beta\alpha)] = 0, \tag{5.14}$$

* I am here using the less explicit limiting operation $(\delta/\tilde{\delta} Y_i)_{\Omega'}$; see Chapter 3. I could use an explicit reference state σ and the explicit operation $(\delta/\tilde{\delta} Y_i)_{\Omega',\sigma}$, adapting the notation accordingly: thus, e.g., I could write Eq. (5.10) as

$$\left(\frac{\delta \dot{Q}_\omega^{(r)}}{\tilde{\delta}\dot{n}_\omega}\right)_{\Omega',\sigma} \equiv [H_\omega]_\sigma - \bar{H}_\omega.$$

Inasmuch as the eye easily tires of the rococo richness of the symbolism, I deem it more merciful to deal (where possible) with the less explicit form $(\delta/\tilde{\delta} Y_i)_{\Omega'}$.

† Note that according to Eqs. (5.12) and (5.13) $[h(\beta\alpha)] = -[h(\alpha\beta)]$ and $[s(\beta\alpha)] = -[s(\alpha\beta)]$.

$$\left(\frac{\delta\Theta}{\bar{\delta}\dot{n}_\alpha}\right)_{\Omega'} = [S_\alpha] - [S_\beta] - [s(\beta\alpha)]$$

$$= \frac{\bar{H}_\beta - [H_\beta]}{T_\beta} + \bar{S}_\alpha - \bar{S}_\beta + \frac{[H_\alpha] - \bar{H}_\alpha}{T_\alpha} - \frac{[h(\beta\alpha)]}{\langle T\rangle}. \quad (5.15)$$

In addition, since $\dot{Q}_\omega^{(r)} = T_\omega \dot{S}_\omega^{(r)}$ and $\dot{q} = \langle T\rangle\dot{s}$, it follows from definitions (5.10) to (5.13) that

$$[H_\omega] = \mu_\omega + T_\omega[S_\omega], \quad (5.16)$$

$$[h(\chi\omega)] = \langle T\rangle[s(\chi\omega)], \quad (5.17)$$

where $\mu_\omega \equiv \bar{H}_\omega - T_\omega\bar{S}_\omega$. Upon combining other equations with it, we can write Eq. (5.14) in the alternative forms

$$\mu_\alpha + T_\alpha[S_\alpha] - \mu_\beta - T_\beta[S_\beta] - [h(\beta\alpha)] = 0, \quad (5.18)$$

$$\mu_\alpha + [S_\alpha]\{T_\alpha - \langle T\rangle\} - \mu_\beta - [S_\beta]\{T_\beta - \langle T\rangle\} = -\langle T\rangle\left(\frac{\delta\Theta}{\bar{\delta}\dot{n}_\alpha}\right)_{\Omega'}, \quad (5.19)$$

$$\frac{[G_\beta] - [G_\alpha]}{\langle T\rangle} = \left(\frac{\delta\Theta}{\bar{\delta}\dot{n}_\alpha}\right)_{\Omega'}, \quad (5.20)$$

where

$$[G_\omega] \equiv [H_\omega] - \langle T\rangle[S_\omega]. \quad (5.21)$$

In definition (5.21) I have again been guided by equilibrium thermostatic considerations. Assumption IV implies that

$$[S_\alpha] - [S_\beta] - [s(\beta\alpha)] = 0 \quad (5.22)$$

and that

$$[G_\beta] - [G_\alpha] = 0. \quad (5.23)$$

Now compare Eqs. (4.2), (4.5), (4.9), and (5.20). Observe that in each case the condition of migrational equilibrium, based on assumption IV, takes the form of a conservation condition for the spatial field in question: $\mathscr{G}$ = constant, $\mu + [R]\mathscr{G}$ = constant, $[G]$ = constant. These results are the generalization of Gibbs' fundamental result for isothermal heterogeneous equilibrium: $\mu^{(i)}$ = constant for all phases in which i is an actual component. This treatment of migrational equilibrium under steady-state conditions is thus as closely analogous to Gibbs' classical procedures as I can make it.

Consider now the special case where the connecting linkage between terminal parts α and β is efficiently insulated so that $\dot{q} = 0$. Under such conditions $[h(\beta\alpha)]$ and $[s(\beta\alpha)]$ are zero and the quantity $\langle T\rangle$ need not enter into any of the calculations. If the physical situation, however, permits us to define $\langle T\rangle$ as $\lim(\dot{q}/\dot{s})$ (see the earlier footnote on this subject), setting it equal to T_R, say, then we can define a $[G]$ function for this case also, and Eqs. (5.20), (5.21), and (5.23) will continue to hold. It is of course possible to have $\dot{q} \neq 0$ and yet $[h(\beta\alpha)] \equiv (\delta\dot{q}/\bar{\delta}\dot{n}_\alpha)_{T_\alpha,T_\beta,\langle T\rangle} = 0$. Under such circumstances $\Delta[H] = 0$ and, according to assumption IV, $\Delta[G] = 0$ and $\Delta[S] = 0$ also.

I have defined the steady-state bracketed quantities in such a way as to make them appear to be pseudo-properties of the gas under consideration, but they in fact depend on the nature of the linkage between the terminal parts of the system, on how that linkage is coupled energetically to the surroundings, and on the path used in the basic limiting operation $(\delta/\delta\dot{n}_\omega)$.* It is now necessary for me to discuss the properties of the linkage between the terminal parts of the system and the effect of those properties on the bracketed quantities thus far introduced.

Owing to the interchange of heat between the system and the surroundings in the state of no mass flow, we can distinguish three situations: (i) full-flux linkage—heat is exchanged only with the constant temperature reservoirs at T_α and T_β, i.e., $\dot{q} = 0$; (ii) zero-flux linkage—heat is exchanged only across the lateral surface of the linkage, i.e., $\dot{Q}_\omega^{(r)} = 0$ (an infinite number of heat reservoirs are coupled to the linkage); (iii) partial-flux linkage—heat is exchanged in such a way that $\dot{Q}_\omega^{(r)} \neq 0$ and $\dot{q} \neq 0$.

Full-Flux Linkage

We can approximate full-flux linkages in the laboratory by means of efficient thermal lagging. For a full-flux linkage $[h(\chi\omega)] = 0$, $[s(\chi\omega)] = 0$, and $\langle T\rangle$, although not needed anywhere in the analysis, can sometimes be set equal to a physically obvious reference temperature T_R.

Partial-Flux Linkage

Partial-flux linkages represent a common laboratory situation where there is *some* lateral leakage of heat from the link to the surroundings. The most common situation is that for which heat leaks to the room of temperature T_R. Under such circumstances $\langle T\rangle = T_R$, and in general, neither of the lower-case bracketed quantities are equal to zero.

Zero-Flux Linkage

The zero-flux linkage with its infinite set of heat reservoirs is a theoretical construct often used to maintain a fixed temperature gradient during steady-flow operations. For the zero-flux linkage $[H_\omega] = \bar{H}_\omega$, $[S_\omega] = \bar{S}_\omega$, $[G_\omega] = \bar{H}_\omega - \langle T\rangle\bar{S}_\omega$, $[h(\chi\omega)] = \bar{H}_\omega - \bar{H}_\chi$, $[s(\chi\omega)] = \bar{S}_\omega - \bar{S}_\chi$, and $\langle T\rangle = \Delta\bar{H}/\Delta\bar{S}$. Now it is often the case that

$$\bar{H}_\alpha - \bar{H}_\beta = \int_{T_\beta}^{T_\alpha} \frac{d\bar{H}}{dT}\,dT = \left\langle \frac{d\bar{H}}{dT} \right\rangle (T_\alpha - T_\beta) \tag{5.24}$$

* See Chapter 6 for a discussion of this point.

and that

$$\bar{S}_\alpha - \bar{S}_\beta = \int_{T_\beta}^{T_\alpha} \frac{d\bar{H}}{dT}\, d\ln T = \left\langle \frac{d\bar{H}}{dT} \right\rangle \ln \frac{T_\alpha}{T_\beta}. \tag{5.25}$$

Under such circumstances $\langle T\rangle = (T_\alpha - T_\beta)/\ln (T_\alpha/T_\beta)$; i.e., $\langle T\rangle$ is just the well-known log-mean temperature used in heat conductivity studies [3].

More Definitions

Consider again the system described in Figure 5–1. Under migrational equilibrium conditions $[G_\alpha] = [G_\beta]$; thus thermomolecular pressure phenomena* are characterized by the constancy of the function $[G]$. I could express the differential thermomolecular pressure effect in terms of the $[G]$ function:

$$\bar{V}\left(\frac{\partial P}{\partial T}\right)_{[G]} = \bar{S} - \left(\frac{\partial\{[S](T - \langle T\rangle)\}}{\partial T}\right)_{[G]} \tag{5.26}$$

in a manner analogous to the usual treatment of the differential Joule–Thomson effect; however, it seems better to me to proceed in a different fashion. I now introduce a new set of steady-state functions that are related to the previous set of functions in a manner analogous to that in which differential thermostatic adsorption quantities are related to integral thermostatic adsorption quantities:†

$$[S_\omega]^\partial \equiv -\left(\frac{\partial \mu_\omega}{\partial T_\omega}\right)_{\chi, \dot{n}_\omega = 0}, \qquad \langle [S]^\partial \rangle \equiv -\frac{\mu_\omega - \mu_\chi}{T_\omega - T_\chi}, \tag{5.27}$$

$$[C_{\omega\omega}]^\partial \equiv T_\omega\left(\frac{\partial [S_\omega]^\partial}{\partial T_\omega}\right)_{\chi, \dot{n}_\omega = 0}, \qquad [C_{\chi\omega}]^\partial \equiv T_\chi\left(\frac{\partial [S_\chi]^\partial}{\partial T_\omega}\right)_{\chi, \dot{n}_\omega = 0}, \tag{5.28}$$

$$[Q_\omega]^\partial \equiv T_\omega(\bar{S}_\omega - [S_\omega]^\partial), \tag{5.29}$$

where the subscript χ on the differential coefficients means that the thermodynamic state at χ is to be kept constant; i.e., all the intensive variables at $\chi - T_\chi$, P_χ, etc., are to be kept constant. It is usually quite clear from the context when states of migrational equilibrium are being considered; hence I normally drop the explicit subscript notation $\dot{n}_\omega = 0$. From the definition of $[S_\omega]^\partial$ we see that

$$\bar{V}_\omega\left(\frac{\partial P_\omega}{\partial T_\omega}\right)_\chi = \bar{S}_\omega - [S_\omega]^\partial; \tag{5.30}$$

* When $\dot{n}_\omega = 0$ and $P_\alpha \neq P_\beta$ for the case $T_\alpha \neq T_\beta$, we say that a thermomolecular pressure effect exists.

† See Chapter 2 for the pertinent discussion.

thus (for $\dot{n}_\omega = 0$) the two conditions $P_\alpha \neq P_\beta$ for $T_\alpha \neq T_\beta$ and $[S_\omega]^\partial \neq \bar{S}_\omega$ mutually imply one another.*

In discussing the next series of operations I find it necessary (in certain integrals) for the sake of clarity to distinguish between the names of thermodynamic states (α, β) and the names of terminal parts (a, b). The thermodynamic state α is characterized by the set of parameters T_α, P_α, etc.; the terminal part at a will usually be in state α ($T_a = T_\alpha, P_a = P_\alpha$, etc.), but such need not always be the case (however, the ambiguity in notation is not serious, except in the case of integrals, and I normally use the same symbol (α, say) both for the name of the state and the name of the terminal part). Consider a series of operations in which the terminal parts of the system start out in the same thermodynamic state (α, say), then the condition of one of the terminal parts (b, say) is changed in such a manner as always to maintain the migrational equilibrium condition while keeping the state of the a terminal part fixed. For such a series of operations we can write

$$\mu_b - \mu_a = \mu_\beta - \mu_\alpha = -\int_{T_b = T_\alpha}^{T_b = T_\beta} [S_b]^\partial \, dT_b = T_\alpha[S_\alpha] - T_\beta[S_\beta] - [h(\beta\alpha)]$$

$$= -\langle [S]^\partial \rangle (T_\beta - T_\alpha), \tag{5.31}$$

$$\left\langle \frac{\bar{S}_\beta - [S_\beta]^\partial}{R} \right\rangle_\alpha = \frac{\ln (P_\beta^{(2)}/P_\beta^{(1)})}{\ln (T_\beta^{(2)}/T_\beta^{(1)})} \text{ (ideal gas)}, \tag{5.32}$$

where $\langle (\bar{S}_\beta - [S_\beta]^\partial)/R \rangle_\alpha$ represents the average value of $(\bar{S}_b - [S_b]^\partial)/R$ as terminal part b passes between states 1 and 2—the state (α) of terminal part a remaining constant during the process. Evidently we can reach the state of affairs for which terminal part a is in state α and part b is in state β, either by starting out with the entire system in state α and carrying b to state β in a proper fashion or by starting out in state β and operating on part a. If we bring these considerations to bear upon Eq. (5.31), we see that

$$\mu_\beta - \mu_\alpha = -\int_{T_\alpha}^{T_\beta} [S_b]^\partial \, dT_b = \int_{T_\beta}^{T_\alpha} [S_a]^\partial \, dT_a. \tag{5.33}$$

The application of the operation $(\partial/\partial T_\beta)_\alpha$ to the second equality of Eq. (5.33) yields the relation†

$$-[S_b]^\partial = -[S_a(\beta)]^\partial, \tag{5.34}$$

* In terms of the notation that I introduce in the next paragraph, we have

$$P_\alpha - P_\beta = \int_{T_a = T_\beta}^{T_a = T_\alpha} \frac{\bar{S}_a - [S_a]^\partial}{\bar{V}_a} \, dT_a.$$

† In the final integral of Eq. (5.33) the value of the integrand at the lower limit is $[S_a(\beta)]^\partial$ since the integration starts from the state in which both terminal parts are in state β. (In terms of the "ambiguous" notation, $[S_b]^\partial \equiv [S_\beta]^\partial$.)

where $[S_a(\beta)]^\partial$ represents the value of $[S_a]^\partial$ for the state in which $T_a = T_b = T_\beta$, $P_a = P_b = P_\beta$, etc. Now since

$$[S_\beta]^\partial = [S_b(\beta)]^\partial + \int_{T_a=T_\beta}^{T_a=T_\alpha} \left(\frac{\partial [S_b]^\partial}{\partial T_a}\right)_\beta dT_a$$
$$= [S_b(\beta)]^\partial + \int_{T_\beta}^{T_\alpha} \frac{[C_{ba}]^\partial}{T_\beta}\, dT_a, \tag{5.35}$$

we see that

$$[S_a(\beta)]^\partial - [S_b(\beta)]^\partial = \int_{T_\beta}^{T_\alpha} \frac{[C_{ba}]^\partial}{T_\beta}\, dT_a. \tag{5.36}$$

The left-hand side of Eq. (5.36) is independent of T_α, whereas the right-hand side is a function of T_α; consistency requires that

$$[C_{\beta\alpha}]^\partial = 0 \tag{5.37}$$

and hence that $[S_a(\beta)]^\partial = [S_b(\beta)]^\partial$. Equation (5.37) is also a direct consequence of Eq. (5.34).

Treatment of Experimental Results

Consider again the situation indicated in Figure 5–1. If we confine our experiments to mass-static measurements (measurements under migrational equilibrium conditions), then the best that we can do is to produce an experimental equation of correlation* $P_\alpha = P_\alpha(T_\alpha, T_\beta, P_\beta, \langle T\rangle)$ for a given gas and linkage; from the equation of correlation we can then compute differential quantities such as $[S_\omega]^\partial$, $[C_{\omega\omega}]^\partial$, etc., or average quantities like those exhibited in Eqs. (5.27) and (5.32). From mass-static measurements alone we cannot say much about the integral quantities $[S_\omega]$, $[C_{\omega\omega}]$, etc. The preceding thermodynamic considerations impose a constraint on the equation of correlation. We see from Eqs. (5.34) and (5.37) that the quantity $[S_\omega]^\partial$ is a function of the ω state variables only (for a given gas and a given linkage), regardless of the nature of the linkage (full, partial, or zero flux); i.e., $[S_\omega]^\partial = [S_\omega]^\partial(T_\omega, P_\omega)$.† It follows from Eq. (5.30), then, that $(\partial P_\omega/\partial T_\omega)_\chi$ must be expressible as a function of the ω state variables only (for a given gas and linkage); this result limits the possible forms of the equation of correlation: in fact the equation of correlation must have the symmetric form $f(T_\alpha, P_\alpha) = f(T_\beta, P_\beta)$.

* It is customary to assume that $(\partial P_\alpha/\partial\langle T\rangle)_{\beta,T\alpha} = 0$; however I know of no experimental information bearing on this point. This assumption has far-reaching consequences, and I shall, for purposes of identification, refer to it as *assumption Q*.

† If assumption Q did not hold, the quantity $[S_\omega]^\partial$ would depend on $\langle T\rangle$ as well as on T_ω and P_ω.

For a given gas, linkage, and temperatures T_α, T_β, I call the plot of P_α versus P_β or of $(P_\alpha - P_\beta)$ versus P_ω the *bithermal relation* or the *bitherm.* In the case of a perfect gas and a Knudsen linkage (molecules pass through the capillary linkage without exchanging energy with its walls or with other molecules; a Knudsen linkage is thus one for which $[h(\chi\omega)] = 0$), the equation of correlation is especially simple, namely $P_\alpha/P_\beta = (T_\alpha/T_\beta)^{1/2}$, and the bitherms are straight lines.

Exercise 5–1. Show that the Knudsen equation $P_\omega/P_\chi = (T_\omega/T_\chi)^{1/2}$ and the ideal gas relation together imply that (i) $\bar{S}_\omega - [S_\omega]^\partial = R/2$, (ii) $[Q_\omega]^\partial = RT_\omega/2$, (iii) $[C_{\omega\omega}]^\partial = \bar{C}_P - (R/2)$, and (iv) $[C_{\chi\omega}]^\partial = 0$. Result (iii) is suggestive: it seems to say that the gas loses 1 degree of freedom while passing through the capillary tube.

Exercise 5–2. (i) Show that for a given bitherm—the (T_ω, T_χ) bitherm, say—involving an ideal gas with an arbitrary linkage the relation

$$\frac{\bar{S}_\omega - \langle [S]^\partial \rangle}{R} = \frac{\bar{C}_P}{R} - \frac{T_\chi}{T_\chi - T_\omega}\left(\frac{\bar{C}_P}{R}\ln\frac{T_\chi}{T_\omega} - \ln\frac{P_\chi}{P_\omega}\right) \tag{5.38}$$

holds (assume $\bar{C}_P$ independent of T). (ii) Note that

$$\bar{S}_\omega - \langle [S]^\partial \rangle - (\bar{S}_\chi - \langle [S]^\partial \rangle) = \bar{S}_\omega - \bar{S}_\chi;$$

show that the right-hand side of Eq. (5.38) is consistent with this observation.

Exercise 5–3. Liang [4] proposed the following equation for treating the thermomolecular pressure effect between states 1 and 2:

$$\frac{P_1}{P_2} = \frac{\boldsymbol{\alpha}(x/\mathbf{f})^2 + \boldsymbol{\beta}(x/\mathbf{f}) + (T_1/T_2)^{1/2}}{\boldsymbol{\alpha}(x/\mathbf{f})^2 + \boldsymbol{\beta}(x/\mathbf{f}) + 1} \tag{5.39}$$

where $\boldsymbol{\alpha}$ and $\boldsymbol{\beta}$ are empirical constants, $\mathbf{f}$ (the pressure-shifting factor) is a constant characteristic of the gas under study, and $x \equiv P_2 d$ with d being the diameter of the tube. Show that Eq. (5.39) is illegitimate as an equation of correlation.

Hint: The derivative $(\partial P_\omega/\partial T_\omega)_\chi$ must be expressible as a function of the variables T_ω and P_ω only for a proper equation of correlation; show that such is not the case for Eq. (5.39). Note also that Eq. (5.39) cannot be put into the symmetric form $f(1) = f(2)$. There have been several attempts to improve upon Liang's equation [5–8]. It sometimes happens that an empirical equation violates the laws of thermodynamics. Such an empirical relation, although it cannot have any *general* validity, may nevertheless prove useful for recording and correlating data over a restricted range of conditions.

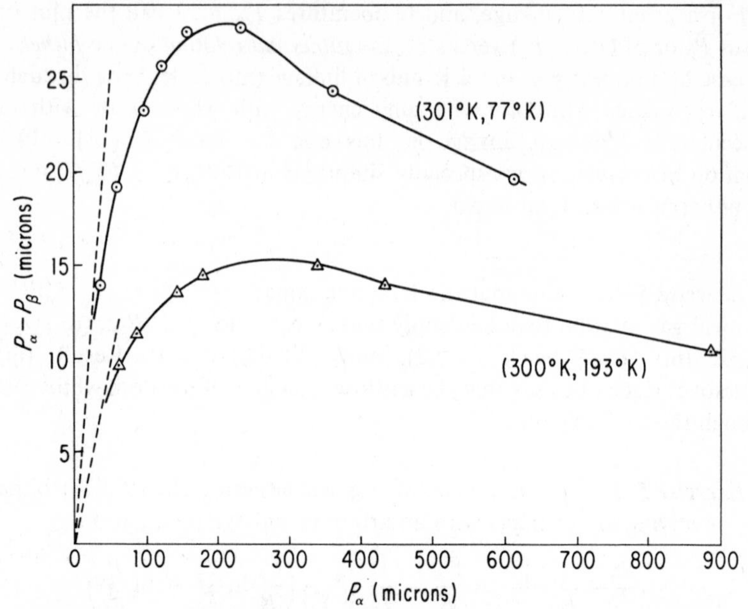

Figure 5–2. Experimental bitherms for argon with a Tru-bore capillary linkage 0.0510 cm in diameter (data of Los and Ferguson).

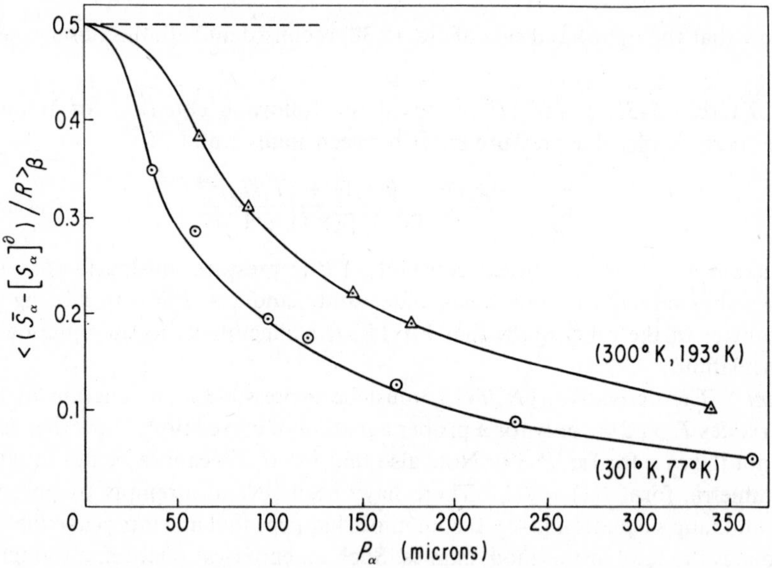

Figure 5–3. Plot of $\langle(\bar{S}_\alpha - [S_\alpha]^\partial)/R\rangle_\beta$ versus P_α as computed from the argon data, averages being taken over the ranges 301–77°K and 300–193°K; $T_\alpha > T_\beta$ in each case.

In terms of experimental data, if we wished to compute, e.g., $\bar{S}_\alpha - [S_\alpha]^\partial$ for a given gas and capillary linkage at some point (P_α, P_β) on the (T_α, T_β) bitherm, say the (298°K, 90°K) bitherm, then we should like to have data for the bitherms (303°K, 90°K), (298°K, 90°K), (293°K, 90°K) so as to be able to use an equation of the form (5.32) with $T_\alpha^{(1)} = 293$°K and $T_\alpha^{(2)} = 303$°K and to associate the resultant quantity $\langle(\bar{S}_\alpha - [S_\alpha]^\partial)/R\rangle_\beta$ with the point (P_α, P_β) on the (298°K, 90°K) bitherm. Families of related bitherms are almost nonexistent in the chemical literature; however, Erikson and I did make some crude calculations for argon and helium [9, 10]. To illustrate some of the conceptions thus far developed, I have taken the data of Los and Ferguson [2] pertaining to argon and a Tru-bore capillary linkage 0.0510 cm in diameter and have made a few sample calculations. Results are displayed in Figures 5–2 to 5–4, where the dashed lines indicate the behavior expected from the Knudsen limiting equation $P_\alpha/P_\beta = (T_\alpha/T_\beta)^{1/2}$.

We see in Figure 5–2 that the experimental data tend toward the Knudsen relation at low pressures and toward a uniform pressure distribution at high pressures; at intermediate pressures the difference $P_\alpha - P_\beta$ reaches a maximum

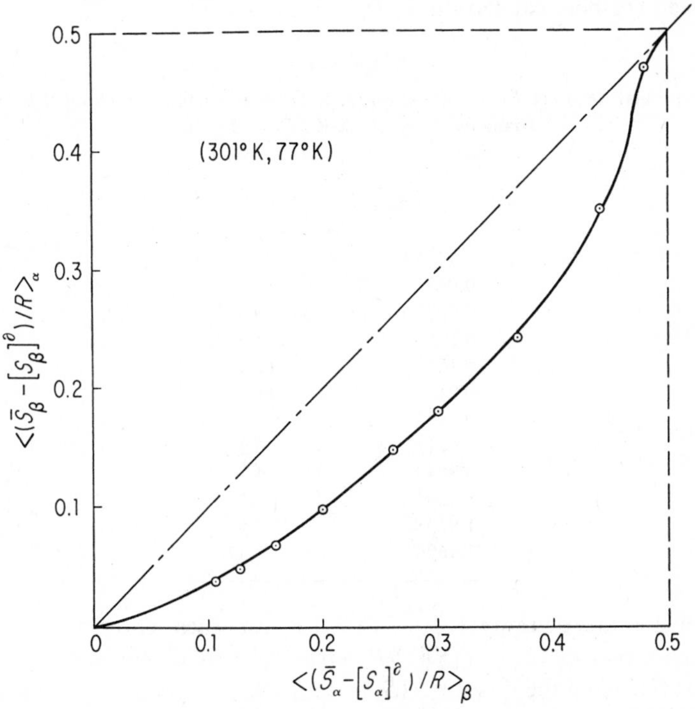

Figure 5–4. Relative plot of $\langle(\bar{S}_\beta - [S_\beta]^\partial)/R\rangle_\alpha$ versus $\langle(\bar{S}_\alpha - [S_\alpha]^\partial)/R\rangle_\beta$ for the argon case, the pairings being made according to the pressure pairings on the (301°K, 77°K) bitherm.

value, the size and position of which are characteristic of the temperatures T_α, T_β, the nature of the gas, and the diameter of the capillary linkage. I wish I could have displayed the quantities $(\bar{S}_\alpha - [S_\alpha]^\theta)/R$ and $(\bar{S}_\beta - [S_\beta]^\theta)/R$ as functions of P_ω for the (301°K, 77°K) bitherm, but the data are insufficient for this purpose; I have, instead, used equations of the form (5.32) to compute average values $\langle(\bar{S}_\omega - [S_\omega]^\theta)/R\rangle_\chi$ over the complete temperature ranges 301–77°K and 300–193°K, and in Figure 5–3 I plot these average quantities versus the pressure P_α at the high temperature side of the capillary linkage. By combining the data for the two bitherms I have constructed the approximate (193°K, 77°K) bitherm, and in Figure 5–4 I have taken the average values $\langle(\bar{S}_\omega - [S_\omega]^\theta)/R\rangle_\chi$ computed for the temperature ranges 301–193°K and 77–193°K and have made a direct intercomparison via the pressure pairings on the (301°K, 77°K) bitherm. Figure 5–4 indicates that for this case the difference $(\bar{S} - [S]^\theta)/R$ is larger (at intermediate pressures) at the high temperature end of the capillary than at the low temperature end.

Exercise 5–4. In Table 5–1 I list the data of Los and Ferguson for argon in another Tru-bore capillary linkage.

Table 5–1

Thermomolecular Pressure Effect for Argon in a Tru-bore Capillary Linkage 0.1018 cm **in Diameter** $T_\alpha = 301.2$°K; $T_\beta = 77.3$°K
(Data of Los and Ferguson[2])

$\frac{1}{2}(P_\alpha + P_\beta)$(mm)	$(P_\alpha - P_\beta)(\mu)$
0.0295	9.9
0.0491	12.2
0.0873	13.3
0.1067	13.5
0.1612	12.5
0.2196	11.4
0.3495	9.1
0.6023	6.3
0.8841	4.7
1.4595	3.2
1.9158	2.5
1.9694	2.37

(i) Calculate the quantity $(\bar{S}_\alpha - \langle[S]^\theta\rangle)/R$ for each entry in the table and make a plot of $(\bar{S}_\alpha - \langle[S]^\theta\rangle)/R$ versus P_β; take $\bar{C}_P$ for argon equal to $5R/2$. (ii) Calculate the quantity $\langle(\bar{S}_\alpha - [S_\alpha]^\theta)/R\rangle_\beta$, averaging over the entire range 301–77°K, for each entry in the table and make a plot of

$$\langle(\bar{S}_\alpha - [S_\alpha]^\theta)/R\rangle_\beta$$

versus P_β.

(iii) Write down an analytic expression for the difference

$$[(\bar{S}_\alpha - \langle[S]^\partial\rangle)/R] - \langle(\bar{S}_\alpha - [S_\alpha]^\partial)/R\rangle_\beta$$

and evaluate the difference for the two limiting cases $P_\alpha/P_\beta = (T_\alpha/T_\beta)^{1/2}$ and $P_\alpha = P_\beta$.

Conditions of Stability

The conditions of stability for thermostatic equilibrium states are relations such as $\bar{C}_V > 0$ and $(\partial\bar{V}/\partial P)_T < 0$. There exist analogous conditions of stability for steady states also. For the system shown in Figure 5–1 it is intuitively evident that the following relations must hold for steady states:

$$\left(\frac{\partial \dot{n}_\alpha}{\partial P_\alpha}\right)_{\beta,\langle T\rangle,T_\alpha} < 0, \qquad \left(\frac{\partial \dot{Q}_\alpha^{(r)}}{\partial T_\alpha}\right)_{\beta,\langle T\rangle,\dot{n}_\alpha = 0} < 0. \tag{5.40}$$

Thus, if we keep fixed the thermodynamic state at β and keep fixed the temperatures T_α, $\langle T\rangle$, then upon increasing the pressure P_α we can only decrease the rate of influx of matter ($\dot{n}_\alpha$) into the α terminal part. Similarly, if we maintain a condition of no mass flow, keeping fixed the thermodynamic state at β and the temperature $\langle T\rangle$, then upon increasing the temperature T_α we can only decrease the rate of influx of heat ($\dot{Q}_\alpha^{(r)}$) into the heat reservoir at α. Whereas relations such as Eq. (5.40) are intuitively evident, the considerations mentioned in Chapter 3 enable us systematically to produce conditions of stability, some of which are not intuitively obvious. In Chapter 3 I showed that there was a neighborhood of a given thermostatic reference state σ for which the relation $(\partial\Omega_k/\partial Y_k)_{\Omega',\sigma} > 0$ held; I now wish to apply this condition to the currents and affinities described in Eq. (5.7) (taking state β as the thermostatic reference state):

$$\begin{aligned}\left(\frac{\partial\Omega_1}{\partial Y_1}\right)_{\Omega',\beta} &= \left(\frac{\partial\{T_\beta^{-1}(\bar{H}_\beta - \bar{H}_\alpha) + \bar{S}_\alpha - \bar{S}_\beta\}}{\partial\dot{n}_\alpha}\right)_{\beta,\langle T\rangle,T_\alpha} \\ &= -\frac{1}{T_\beta}\left(\frac{\partial P_\alpha}{\partial\dot{n}_\alpha}\right)_{\beta,\langle T\rangle,T_\alpha}\left\{\bar{V}_\alpha - T_\alpha\left(\frac{\partial\bar{V}_\alpha}{\partial T_\alpha}\right)_{P_\alpha} + T_\beta\left(\frac{\partial\bar{V}_\alpha}{\partial T_\alpha}\right)_{P_\alpha}\right\},\end{aligned} \tag{5.41}$$

$$\left(\frac{\partial\Omega_2}{\partial Y_2}\right)_{\Omega',\beta} = \left(\frac{\partial(T_\alpha^{-1} - T_\beta^{-1})}{\partial\dot{Q}_\alpha^{(r)}}\right)_{\beta,\langle T\rangle,\Omega_1} = -\frac{1}{T_\alpha^2}\left(\frac{\partial T_\alpha}{\partial\dot{Q}_\alpha^{(r)}}\right)_{\beta,\langle T\rangle,\Omega_1}, \tag{5.42}$$

$$\left(\frac{\partial\Omega_3}{\partial Y_3}\right)_{\Omega',\beta} = \left(\frac{\partial(\langle T\rangle^{-1} - T_\beta^{-1})}{\partial\dot{q}}\right)_{\alpha,\beta} = -\frac{1}{\langle T\rangle^2}\left(\frac{\partial\langle T\rangle}{\partial\dot{q}}\right)_{\alpha,\beta}. \tag{5.43}$$

The condition $(\partial \Omega_k/\partial Y_k)_{\Omega',\beta} > 0$ requires, then, that

$$\left\{\overline{V}_\alpha - T_\alpha\left(\frac{\partial \overline{V}_\alpha}{\partial T_\alpha}\right)_{P_\alpha} + T_\beta\left(\frac{\partial \overline{V}_\alpha}{\partial T_\alpha}\right)_{P_\alpha}\right\}\left(\frac{\partial P_\alpha}{\partial \dot{n}_\alpha}\right)_{\beta,\langle T\rangle,T_\alpha} < 0, \tag{5.44}$$

$$\left(\frac{\partial T_\alpha}{\partial \dot{Q}_\alpha^{(r)}}\right)_{\beta,\langle T\rangle,\Omega_1} < 0, \tag{5.45}$$

$$\left(\frac{\partial \langle T\rangle}{\partial \dot{q}}\right)_{\alpha,\beta} < 0. \tag{5.46}$$

Equations (5.44) to (5.46), when evaluated at the points $Y_k = 0$, represent applications of the *petit* principles of entropy production; when evaluated for arbitrary points Y_k, they represent applications of the *grand* principles of entropy production. Relation (5.46) is intuitively reasonable: we expect that increasing the quantity $\langle T\rangle$ while keeping the thermodynamic states at α and β constant will result in a *decrease* in the rate of heat leakage ($\dot{q}$) *to* the surroundings. Relation (5.45), although similar to relation (5.40), is difficult to appreciate intuitively because of the fact that Ω_1 is to be held constant; i.e., the temperature and pressure at α must vary in such a way as to maintain constant the combination $\overline{S}_\alpha - \overline{H}_\alpha T_\beta^{-1}$.

Relation (5.44) presents us with a serious problem. If the factor marked off by the braces { } is positive for all physically compatible pairs of states (α, β) then relation (5.44) implies that $(\partial P_\alpha/\partial \dot{n}_\alpha)_{\beta,\langle T\rangle,T_\alpha} < 0$, which is very reassuring. If, on the other hand, the factor { } were ever to become negative for some physically compatible pairs of states (α, β), then it would be impossible to satisfy, in a physically reasonable way, the condition $(\partial \Omega_1/\partial Y_1)_{\Omega',\beta} > 0$ for such states, and as a consequence some of the discussions in Chapter 3 pertaining to entropy production would be of limited validity. Now it is clear that the factor { } will be positive for states such that $T_\beta > T_\alpha$ and also for states such that $[\overline{V}_\alpha - T_\alpha(\partial \overline{V}_\alpha/\partial T_\alpha)_{P_\alpha}] \geqslant 0$. The only states for which { } might conceivably be negative are states for which $T_\beta < T_\alpha$ and at the same time $[\overline{V}_\alpha - T_\alpha(\partial \overline{V}_\alpha/\partial T_\alpha)_{P_\alpha}] < 0$. The quantity $[\overline{V}_\alpha - T_\alpha(\partial \overline{V}_\alpha/\partial T_\alpha)_{P_\alpha}]$ satisfies the relation

$$\overline{V}_\alpha - T_\alpha\left(\frac{\partial \overline{V}_\alpha}{\partial T_\alpha}\right)_{P_\alpha} = -\left(\frac{\partial T_\alpha}{\partial P_\alpha}\right)_{\overline{H}_\alpha} \overline{C}_P(\alpha) \tag{5.47}$$

with $(\partial T_\alpha/\partial P_\alpha)_{\overline{H}_\alpha}$ being the Joule–Thomson coefficient for the gas. We wish to investigate, then, that region of the P,T plane for which the Joule–Thomson coefficient is positive. The part of the P,T plane for which the Joule–Thomson coefficient is positive is a bounded region, bounded by the inversion curve and the temperature axis [11]. It is in the region inside the inversion curve, then, that we should look if we hope to find states such that { } < 0. Since $\{T_\beta(\partial \overline{V}_\alpha/\partial T_\alpha)_{P_\alpha} - (\partial T_\alpha/\partial P_\alpha)_{\overline{H}_\alpha}\overline{C}_P(\alpha)\}$ varies *roughly* as

$$[T_\beta(R/P_\alpha) - (\partial T_\alpha/\partial P_\alpha)_{\overline{H}_\alpha}\overline{C}_P(\alpha)],$$

the best combination for getting { } < 0 would seem to be a small value of T_β coupled to a large value of P_α, with α being a point inside the inversion curve.

If we are considering the *petit* principle of entropy production $(\delta\Omega_1/\delta Y_1)_{\Omega',\beta} > 0$, then the states α and β that appear in the quantity { } must be states that can coexist in a condition of migrational equilibrium; hence we cannot indiscriminately vary the quantities T_β and P_α. If we take P_α higher than the critical pressure P_c for the gas, then we must take T_β greater than the critical temperature T_c; if we take $P_\alpha < P_c$, then we must take T_β greater than or equal to the appropriate temperature on the vapor pressure (liquid or solid) curve. There is no use in our letting T_β approach 0°K, either: as $T \to 0$ the vapor pressure of a condensed phase approaches zero also; hence if we let $T_\beta \to 0$ we should have $(\partial\bar{V}_\alpha/\partial T_\alpha)_{P_\alpha} \to (R/P_\alpha) \to \infty$, and the product $T_\beta(\partial\bar{V}_\alpha/\partial T_\alpha)_{P_\alpha}$ would become indeterminate. Although it is not evident that { } *will* always be positive when we deal with the *petit* principle of entropy production, it is at least plausible that it *may* be so.* On the other hand, the *grand* principle of entropy production $(\partial\Omega_1/\partial Y_1)_{\Omega',\beta} > 0$ purports to hold for all values of Y_1, not just the value $Y_1 = 0$, and it seems likely that for some pairs of states (α, β) with $Y_1 \neq 0$ the quantity { } may very well be negative. The *grand* principle would thus seem to have a limited range of validity. I have more to say on this matter, however, in Chapter 15.

I introduced in Chapter 3 the additional *grand* principle of entropy production $(\partial Y_i/\partial\Omega_k)_{\Omega',\sigma} = (\partial Y_k/\partial\Omega_i)_{\Omega',\sigma}$ for ordinary steady-state situations. For the system shown in Figure 5–1 these reciprocity relations take the following forms:

$$T_\beta\left(\frac{\partial \dot{Q}_\alpha^{(\tau)}}{\partial P_\alpha}\right)_{\beta,\langle T\rangle,T_\alpha} = T_\alpha^2\left\{\bar{V}_\alpha - T_\alpha\left(\frac{\partial\bar{V}_\alpha}{\partial T_\alpha}\right)_{P_\alpha} + T_\beta\left(\frac{\partial\bar{V}_\alpha}{\partial T_\alpha}\right)_{P_\alpha}\right\}\left(\frac{\partial\dot{n}_\alpha}{\partial T_\alpha}\right)_{\beta,\langle T\rangle,\Omega_1}, \quad (5.48)$$

$$T_\beta\left(\frac{\partial \dot{q}}{\partial P_\alpha}\right)_{\beta,\langle T\rangle,T_\alpha} = \langle T\rangle^2\left\{\bar{V}_\alpha - T_\alpha\left(\frac{\partial\bar{V}_\alpha}{\partial T_\alpha}\right)_{P_\alpha} + T_\beta\left(\frac{\partial\bar{V}_\alpha}{\partial T_\alpha}\right)_{P_\alpha}\right\}\left(\frac{\partial\dot{n}_\alpha}{\partial\langle T\rangle}\right)_{\beta,T_\alpha,\Omega_1}, \quad (5.49)$$

$$T_\alpha^2\left(\frac{\partial\dot{q}}{\partial T_\alpha}\right)_{\beta,\langle T\rangle,\Omega_1} = \langle T\rangle^2\left(\frac{\partial\dot{Q}_\alpha^{(\tau)}}{\partial\langle T\rangle}\right)_{\beta,T_\alpha,\Omega_1}. \quad (5.50)$$

The condition of constant Ω_1 makes these relations difficult to interpret; I have nothing useful to say about them.

* An examination of the data of Roebuck and Osterberg pertaining to the Joule–Thomson coefficient for argon [12] and for nitrogen [13] reveals that everywhere inside the inversion curve, for each of the two gases, the quantity $[T_\beta(R/P_\alpha) - (\partial T_\alpha/\partial P_\alpha)_{\bar{H}_\alpha}\bar{C}_P(\alpha)]$ is positive for pairs of states (α, β) compatible with the migrational equilibrium constraint.

Linkage Classes

Thus far we have considered the linkage between terminal parts in its heat-transfer function (full, partial, or zero flux) only. We can, however, consider the linkage between two terminal parts in a polythermal field from another point of view. In a certain sense a linkage is that device (apparatus, piece of hardware) that permits certain classes of thermodynamic states (α, β) to be in contact with one another under the migrational equilibrium constraint. Consider the system shown in Figure 5–1. For a given state $\alpha(T_\alpha, P_\alpha)$ the linkage establishes a class of states $\{\beta(i)\}$ ($T_{\beta(1)}, P_{\beta(1)}; T_{\beta(2)}, P_{\beta(2)}; \ldots; T_{\beta(i)}, P_{\beta(i)}; \ldots$) each of which can coexist in a condition of migrational equilibrium across the given linkage with state α; there is such a class $\{\beta(i)\}$ for each state $\alpha(j)$. Now the cataloging of the classes $\{\beta(i)\}$ that can coexist in migrational equilibrium with states $\alpha(j)$ for a given gas and linkage is the thermodynamic way of describing the relevant properties of the linkage—the information is recorded neatly in the equation of correlation $(fT_\alpha, P_\alpha, T_\beta, P_\beta, \langle T \rangle) = 0$. The physical properties of the linkage are, of course, reflected in the structure of the linkage classes $\alpha(j)|\{\beta(i)\}$.

This way of looking at linkages gives rise to an interesting speculation. Consider Figure 5–1 again (full-flux linkage): let terminal parts *a* and *b* start out in state α; then, maintaining migrational equilibrium, change the state of *b* in a well-defined series of operations to some final state β. As terminal part *b* moves from state α to state β, it generates a linkage class $\{\beta(i)\}$ consistent with state α at terminal part *a*. Suppose now, with terminal part *a* in state α and part *b* in state β, it becomes possible to probe the interior of the linkage at some arbitrary point λ and to determine the values T_λ, P_λ. Now does each arbitrary interior point (T_λ, P_λ) of the linkage belong to the linkage class $\{\beta(i)\}$ generated by *b* in going from state α to state β? That is, for a given T_λ, P_λ can we find a point $\beta(k)$ of the set $\{\beta(i)\}$ such that $T_\lambda = T_{\beta(k)}$ and $P_\lambda = P_{\beta(k)}$?

Although the preceding question is a fundamental one, I see no simple way of answering it.

References

1. W. H. Keesom, *Helium* (Elsevier Publishing Co., Amsterdam, 1942), Section 2.74.
2. J. M. Los and R. R. Ferguson, *Trans. Faraday Soc.*, **48**, 730 (1952).
3. R. C. L. Bosworth, *Heat Transfer Phenomena* (John Wiley and Sons, New York, 1952), p. 129.
4. S. Liang, *J. Phys. Chem.*, **57**, 910 (1953).
5. M. Bennett and F. Tompkins, *Trans. Faraday Soc.*, **53**, 185 (1957).
6. H. Podgurski and F. Davis, *J. Phys. Chem.*, **65**, 1343 (1961).

7. E. A. Mason, R. B. Evans, III, and G. M. Watson, *J. Chem. Phys.*, **38**, 1808 (1963).
8. T. Takaishi and Y. Sensui, *Trans. Faraday Soc.*, **59**, 2503 (1963).
9. T. A. Erikson, M.S. Thesis, Illinois Institute of Technology (1959).
10. R. J. Tykodi and T. A. Erikson, *J. Chem. Phys.*, **31**, 1510 (1959).
11. M. Saha and B. Srivastava, *A Treatise on Heat*, fourth edition (The Indian Press Private, Ltd., Allahabad, 1958), Chapter 12.
12. J. R. Roebuck and H. Osterberg, *Phys. Rev.*, **46**, 785 (1934).
13. J. R. Roebuck and H. Osterberg, *Phys. Rev.*, **48**, 450 (1935).

6

Migrational Equilibrium in Polythermal Fields: General Relations

In this chapter I consider a number of more abstract relations and definitions pertaining to the thermomolecular pressure effect and to other steady-state bithermal systems.

Definitions and Theorems

I collect here a number of useful definitions aimed primarily at the thermomolecular pressure effect but useful for other bithermal phenomena as well. In order not to have to write similar formulas twice, once with subscript α and again with subscript β, I use the noncommittal subscripts ω and χ—each formula then yields two relations obtained by replacing ω,χ with either α,β or β,α throughout.*

$$[S_\omega]^\partial \equiv -\left(\frac{\partial \mu_\omega}{\partial T_\omega}\right)_{\chi,\dot{n}_\omega=0}, \qquad \langle [S]^\partial \rangle \equiv -\frac{\mu_\omega - \mu_\chi}{T_\omega - T_\chi}, \tag{6.1}$$

where the subscript χ on the differential coefficient means that the thermodynamic state at χ is to be kept constant; i.e., all the intensive variables at χ

* I have included, for the sake of symmetry, a few quantities that are not strictly definitions but rather theorems derived from other definitions.

(T_χ, P_χ, etc.) are to be kept constant, and the subscript $\dot{n}_\omega = 0$ shows that the coefficient refers to states of migrational equilibrium. Since it is usually quite clear from the context when states of migrational equilibrium are being considered, I do not normally show the subscript $\dot{n}_\omega = 0$ explicitly; after all, we do not always tack on a subscript *eq* in classical thermostatics to show that equilibrium states are intended.

$$[H_\omega] \equiv \mu_\omega + T_\omega[S_\omega], \quad [H_\omega]^\partial \equiv \mu_\omega + T_\omega[S_\omega]^\partial, \tag{6.2}$$

$$[G_\omega] \equiv [H_\omega] - \langle T\rangle[S_\omega], \quad [G_\omega]^\partial \equiv [H_\omega]^\partial - \langle T\rangle[S_\omega]^\partial, \tag{6.3}$$

$$[C_{\omega\omega}] \equiv T_\omega\left(\frac{\partial[S_\omega]}{\partial T_\omega}\right)_\chi, \quad [C_{\omega\omega}]^\partial \equiv T_\omega\left(\frac{\partial[S_\omega]^\partial}{\partial T_\omega}\right)_\chi, \tag{6.4}$$

$$[C_{\omega\chi}] \equiv T_\omega\left(\frac{\partial[S_\omega]}{\partial T_\chi}\right)_\omega, \quad [C_{\omega\chi}]^\partial \equiv T_\omega\left(\frac{\partial[S_\omega]^\partial}{\partial T_\chi}\right)_\omega, \tag{6.5}$$

$$[Q_\omega] \equiv T_\omega(\bar{S}_\omega - [S_\omega]), \quad [Q_\omega]^\partial \equiv T_\omega(\bar{S}_\omega - [S_\omega]^\partial), \tag{6.6}$$

$$[h(\chi\omega)] \equiv \langle T\rangle[s(\chi\omega)], \quad [h(\chi\omega)] \equiv -[h(\omega\chi)], \quad [s(\chi\omega)] \equiv -[s(\omega\chi)]. \tag{6.7}$$

I have, of course, been guided in these definitions by the analogous equations of classical thermostatics. From Eqs. (6.1) to (6.7) and the results of Chapter 5 we can readily deduce the following theorems:

$$\langle[S]^\partial\rangle = \frac{T_\chi[S_\chi] - T_\omega[S_\omega] + [h(\chi\omega)]}{T_\chi - T_\omega}, \tag{6.8}$$

$$[S_\omega]^\partial = [S_\omega] + [C_{\omega\omega}] - [C_{\chi\omega}] - \left(\frac{\partial[h(\chi\omega)]}{\partial T_\omega}\right)_\chi, \tag{6.9}$$

$$\left(\frac{\partial[H_\omega]}{\partial T_\omega}\right)_\chi = [C_{\chi\omega}] + \left(\frac{\partial[h(\chi\omega)]}{\partial T_\omega}\right)_\chi, \quad \left(\frac{\partial[H_\omega]}{\partial T_\chi}\right)_\omega = [C_{\omega\chi}], \tag{6.10}$$

$$\left(\frac{\partial[H_\omega]^\partial}{\partial T_\omega}\right)_\chi = [C_{\omega\omega}]^\partial, \quad \left(\frac{\partial[H_\omega]^\partial}{\partial T_\chi}\right)_\omega = [C_{\omega\chi}]^\partial, \tag{6.11}$$

$$\left(\frac{\partial[G_\omega]}{\partial T_\omega}\right)_\chi = [C_{\chi\omega}]\left(1 - \frac{\langle T\rangle}{T_\chi}\right) - [S_\chi]\left(\frac{\partial\langle T\rangle}{\partial T_\omega}\right)_\chi, \tag{6.12}$$

$$\left(\frac{\partial[G_\omega]}{\partial T_\chi}\right)_\omega = [C_{\omega\chi}]\left(1 - \frac{\langle T\rangle}{T_\omega}\right) - [S_\omega]\left(\frac{\partial\langle T\rangle}{\partial T_\chi}\right)_\omega, \tag{6.13}$$

$$\left(\frac{\partial[G_\omega]^\partial}{\partial T_\omega}\right)_\chi = [C_{\omega\omega}]^\partial\left(1 - \frac{\langle T\rangle}{T_\omega}\right) - [S_\omega]^\partial\left(\frac{\partial\langle T\rangle}{\partial T_\omega}\right)_\chi, \tag{6.14}$$

$$\left(\frac{\partial[G_\omega]^\partial}{\partial T_\chi}\right)_\omega = [C_{\omega\chi}]^\partial\left(1 - \frac{\langle T\rangle}{T_\omega}\right) - [S_\omega]^\partial\left(\frac{\partial\langle T\rangle}{\partial T_\chi}\right)_\omega, \tag{6.15}$$

$$[Q_\omega] = \bar{H}_\omega - [H_\omega], \quad [Q_\omega]^\partial = \bar{H}_\omega - [H_\omega]^\partial. \tag{6.16}$$

Note that apparently $(\partial[H_\omega]/\partial T_\omega)_\chi \neq [C_{\omega\omega}]$, $(\partial[G_\omega]/\partial T_\omega)_\chi \neq -[S_\omega]$, and $(\partial[G_\omega]^\partial/\partial T_\omega)_\chi \neq -[S_\omega]^\partial$.

Exercise 6–1. Establish the correctness of the relations (6.8) to (6.16).

Exercise 6–2. Investigate the consequences of the assumptions that

$$(\partial[H_\omega]/\partial T_\omega)_\chi = [C_{\omega\omega}], \quad (\partial[G_\omega]/\partial T_\omega)_\chi = -[S_\omega], \quad (\partial[G_\omega]^\partial/\partial T_\omega)_\chi = -[S_\omega]^\partial.$$

Consider yet one more definition (this type of definition will be useful in discussing the thermocouple later on):

$$\left(\frac{\delta(\dot{Q}_\alpha^{(r)} + \dot{Q}_\beta^{(r)} + \dot{q})}{\delta\dot{n}_\alpha}\right)_{T_\alpha, T_\beta, \langle T\rangle} \equiv -\int_{T=T_\alpha}^{T=T_\beta} [c]\, dT. \tag{6.17}$$

We see from Eq. (5.8) that

$$\left(\frac{\delta(\dot{Q}_\alpha^{(r)} + \dot{Q}_\beta^{(r)} + \dot{q})}{\delta\dot{n}_\alpha}\right)_{T_\alpha, T_\beta, \langle T\rangle} = -(\bar{H}_\alpha - \bar{H}_\beta). \tag{6.18}$$

Thus

$$[c] = \frac{d\bar{H}}{dT} \tag{6.19}$$

and, for a perfect gas,

$$[c] = \bar{C}_P. \tag{6.20}$$

Note that

$$[c_\omega] = \left(\frac{\partial\bar{H}_\omega}{\partial T_\omega}\right)_\chi = \bar{S}_\omega - [S_\omega]^\partial + T_\omega\left(\frac{\partial\bar{S}_\omega}{\partial T_\omega}\right)_\chi \cdot \tag{6.21}$$

In discussing this next series of operations, it is necessary (in certain integrals) for the sake of clarity to distinguish between the names of thermodynamic states (α, β) and the names of terminal parts (a, b).*

Consider a series of operations in which the terminal parts of the system start out in the same thermodynamic state (α say); then the condition of one of the terminal parts (b say) is changed in such a manner as to maintain migrational equilibrium while keeping the state of the a terminal part fixed. For such a series of operations we can write

$$\begin{aligned}[S_\beta] &= [S_b(\alpha)] + \int_{T_b=T_\alpha}^{T_b=T_\beta} \left(\frac{\partial[S_b]}{\partial T_b}\right)_\alpha dT_b \\ &= [S_b(\alpha)] + \int_{T_\alpha}^{T_\beta} \frac{[C_{bb}]}{T_b}\, dT_b,\end{aligned} \tag{6.22}$$

and from similar considerations,

$$\begin{aligned}[S_\beta] &= [S_b(\beta)] + \int_{T_a=T_\beta}^{T_a=T_\alpha} \left(\frac{\partial[S_b]}{\partial T_a}\right)_\beta dT_a \\ &= [S_b(\beta)] + \int_{T_\beta}^{T_\alpha} \frac{[C_{ba}]}{T_\beta}\, dT_a.\end{aligned} \tag{6.23}$$

* See the discussion in Chapter 5.

The quantity $[S_b(\alpha)]$, e.g., represents the value of $[S_b]$ for the state in which $T_a = T_b = T_\alpha$, $P_a = P_b = P_\alpha$, etc.

The equithermal state, the state, e.g., for which $T_a = T_b = T_\beta$, $P_a = P_b = P_\beta, \ldots$, is an interesting one; for such an equithermal state the following relations hold (provided that assumption IV and assumption Q hold):

$$T_\beta\{[S_a(\beta)] - [S_b(\beta)]\} = [h(ba|\beta)], \tag{6.24}$$

$$[S_a(\beta)] - [S_b(\beta)] = [s(ba|\beta)], \tag{6.25}$$

$$\{T_\beta - \langle T(ab|\beta)\rangle\}\{[S_a(\beta)] - [S_b(\beta)]\} = 0, \tag{6.26}$$

where $[h(ba|\beta)]$, $[s(ba|\beta)]$, and $\langle T(ab|\beta)\rangle$ are the appropriate values of $[h(\beta\alpha)]$, $[s(\beta\alpha)]$, and $\langle T\rangle$ for the given equithermal state.

Exercise 6–3. Establish the validity of relations (6.24) to (6.26).

In the case of full- and partial-flux linkages $\langle T(ab|\beta)\rangle \neq T_\beta$ (in general); so, by Eqs. (6.24) to (6.26), it follows that $[S_a(\beta)] = [S_b(\beta)]$, $[s(ba|\beta)] = 0$, and $[h(ba|\beta)] = 0$. The same set of relations holds for zero-flux linkages in spite of the fact that $\langle T(ab|\beta)\rangle = T_\beta$ for such linkages. From Eq. (5.11) we see that in the zero-flux case* $[S_a(\beta)] = \bar{S}_a(\beta)|_{\text{in}}$ and $[S_b(\beta)] = \bar{S}_b(\beta)|_{\text{in}}$. If we place the thermostats symmetrically about the linkage, then $\bar{S}_a(\beta)|_{\text{in}} = \bar{S}_b(\beta)|_{\text{in}}$.

The general relation (6.9)

$$[S_\beta]^\partial = [S_\beta] + T_\beta\left(\frac{\partial[S_\beta]}{\partial T_\beta}\right)_\alpha - T_\alpha\left(\frac{\partial[S_\alpha]}{\partial T_\beta}\right)_\alpha - \left(\frac{\partial[h(\alpha\beta)]}{\partial T_\beta}\right)_\alpha$$

and Eq. (5.34) together yield yet another useful result:

$$\begin{aligned}
[S_\beta]^\partial &= [S_b(\beta)]^\partial \\
&= [S_b(\beta)] + T_\beta \lim_{T_b \to T_\beta}\left(\frac{[S_b] - [S_b(\beta)]}{T_b - T_\beta}\right)_{a=\beta} \\
&\qquad - T_a \lim_{T_b \to T_\beta}\left(\frac{[S_a] - [S_a(\beta)]}{T_b - T_\beta}\right)_{a=\beta} - \left(\frac{\partial[h(\alpha\beta)]}{\partial T_\beta}\right)_{a=\beta} \\
&= [S_b(\beta)] + T_\beta \lim_{T_b \to T_\beta}\left(\frac{[S_b] - [S_a]}{T_b - T_\beta}\right)_{a=\beta} - \left(\frac{\partial[h(\alpha\beta)]}{\partial T_\beta}\right)_{a=\beta} \\
&= [S_b(\beta)] + T_\beta\left(\frac{\partial[s(\alpha\beta)]}{\partial T_\beta}\right)_{a=\beta} - \left(\frac{\partial[h(\alpha\beta)]}{\partial T_\beta}\right)_{a=\beta} \\
&= [S_b(\beta)] + \{T_\beta - \langle T(ab|\beta)\rangle\}\left(\frac{\partial[s(\alpha\beta)]}{\partial T_\beta}\right)_{a=\beta},
\end{aligned} \tag{6.27}$$

* In the zero-flux case the thermostat at ω does not participate in a heat conduction process (i.e., $\dot{Q}_\omega^{(r)} = 0$ for $\dot{n}_\omega = 0$); hence the limiting operation $(\delta\dot{S}_\omega^{(r)}/\bar{\delta}\dot{n}_\omega)_{T_\alpha, T_\beta, \langle T\rangle}$ represents the isothermal reversible change in molar entropy in taking the gas from the point at which it crosses the boundary of the thermostat at ω to a point adjacent to the piston face at the other end of the ω terminal part; i.e.,

$$(\delta\dot{S}_\omega^{(r)}/\bar{\delta}\dot{n}_\omega)_{T_\alpha, T_\beta, \langle T\rangle} = \bar{S}_\omega|_{\text{in}} - \bar{S}_\omega|_{\text{piston}}.$$

where I have used assumption IV in the form of Eq. (5.22). We see that for full-* or zero-flux† linkages Eq. (6.27) easily reduces to

$$[S_\beta]^\partial = [S_b(\beta)]. \tag{6.28}$$

Since full- and zero-flux linkages are but the two extreme forms of partial-flux linkage, it would be most surprising if Eq. (6.28) did not hold for partial-flux linkages. To establish Eq. (6.28) for partial-flux linkages, however, we must be able to show that $0 = (\partial[s(\alpha\beta)]/\partial T_\beta)_{\alpha=\beta}$. Although I cannot give a direct proof of this relation, it is clear that it must hold, otherwise Eq. (6.27) would be inconsistent: the left-hand side of Eq. (6.27) is a function of the variables T_β, P_β only, whereas the right-hand side, if $(\partial[s(\alpha\beta)]/\partial T_\beta)_{\alpha=\beta}$ were not equal to zero, would be a function of the variables T_β, P_β, and $\langle T(ab|\beta)\rangle$. The entire argument, however, depends on our acceptance of assumption Q. We conclude, then, that Eq. (6.28) holds generally, regardless of the nature of the linkage, whenever assumption IV and assumption Q hold, and it follows that (for the system of Figure 5–1)

$$\left(\frac{\partial P_\beta}{\partial T_\beta}\right)_\alpha = \frac{\bar{S}_\beta - [S_\beta]^\partial}{\bar{V}_\beta} = \frac{\bar{S}_\beta - [S_b(\beta)]}{\bar{V}_\beta} = \frac{[Q_b(\beta)]}{T_\beta \bar{V}_\beta}, \tag{6.29}$$

where $[Q_b(\beta)] \equiv T_\beta(\bar{S}_\beta - [S_b(\beta)])$. Equation (6.29) shows that for the case considered a polythermal ($T_\alpha \neq T_\beta$) temperature coefficient is determined by a set of equithermal ($T_\alpha = T_\beta$) relations.

Exercise 6–4. According to the duality principle mentioned in Chapter 3, the dual of assumption IV is

$$0 = \left(\frac{\delta\Theta}{\bar{\delta}\Omega_k}\right)_{Y'}. \tag{6.30}$$

Show that for the system of Figure 5–1, full-flux linkage, Eq. (6.28) can be derived from Eq. (6.30).

Hint: Use Eq. (6.30) in the form $0 = (\delta\Theta/\bar{\delta}\Omega_2)_{Y_1,\beta}$ (see Eq. 5.7) and pass to the appropriate limit.

---

* $\dfrac{\partial[s(\alpha\beta)]}{\partial T_\beta} = 0.$

† $T_\beta = \langle T(ab|\beta)\rangle$.

Alternative Considerations

When a heat reservoir of temperature T encompasses a region constituting an open system in such a way that masses crossing the boundaries of the region enter from or leave to adjacent regions of the same temperature T, and all mass transfers take place in a reversible fashion, then

$$\dot{S}^{(r)} + \dot{S}(\text{region}) + \dot{S}(\text{out}) - \dot{S}(\text{in}) = 0, \tag{6.31}$$

where, in the steady state, $\dot{S}(\text{region}) = \sum_\rho \dot{S}_\rho$ [summation over all phases ρ of the region], $\dot{S}_\rho = \sum_i \dot{n}_\rho^{(i)} \bar{S}_\rho^{(i)}$ [summation over the components of phase ρ], and $\dot{S}(\text{in})$, e.g., is the convective flow of entropy into the region per unit time; i.e., $\dot{S}(\text{in}) = \dot{n}\bar{S}(\text{in})$. In the limit of vanishing transfer of mass, Eq. (6.31) takes the form

$$\frac{\delta \dot{S}^{(r)}}{\delta \dot{n}} + \sum_\rho \frac{\delta \dot{S}_\rho}{\delta \dot{n}} + \frac{\delta \dot{S}(\text{out})}{\delta \dot{n}} - \frac{\delta \dot{S}(\text{in})}{\delta \dot{n}} = 0. \tag{6.32}$$

In the limit of vanishing mass flow we can maintain the *form* of Eq. (6.32) for *any* heat reservoir by making use of the following conventions: Represent the value of $\dot{S}^{(r)}$ when the rate parameter has the value $\dot{n}$ by $\dot{S}^{(r)}(\dot{n})$; then, if $\dot{S}^{(r)}(0) = 0$, set $\delta\dot{S}(\text{in})/\delta\dot{n} = \bar{S}(\text{in})$; and if $\dot{S}^{(r)}(0) \neq 0$ [the heat reservoir is participating in a heat conduction process], set $(\delta\dot{S}(\text{in})/\delta\dot{n})_{\Omega'} \equiv [S(\text{in})]$. This definition of $[S]$ is entirely equivalent to that used in Eq. (5.11).

Now for a system composed of a number of terminal parts (running index j), a number of heat reservoirs (running index k), and a number of linkages of arbitrary type, it follows that in the steady state

$$\dot{U}(\text{system}) = \sum_j \dot{U}_j = -\sum_k T_k \dot{S}_k^{(r)} - \sum \dot{q}(kh) + \dot{W}, \tag{6.33}$$

$$\dot{H}(\text{system}) = \sum_j \dot{H}_j = -\sum_k T_k \dot{S}_k^{(r)} - \sum \dot{q}(kh) + \dot{W}_0, \tag{6.34}$$

$$\dot{G}(\text{system}) = \sum_j \dot{G}_j = -\sum_k T_k \dot{S}_k^{(r)} - \sum_j \sum_\rho T_\rho \dot{S}_\rho - \sum \dot{q}(kh) + \dot{W}_0, \tag{6.35}$$

$$\Theta = \sum_j \dot{S}_j + \sum_k \dot{S}_k^{(r)} + \sum \dot{s}(kh), \tag{6.36}$$

$$\dot{W}_0 = \sum_x \dot{W}_{0x} = \sum_x Y_{0x} \mathscr{F}_{0x}, \tag{6.37}$$

where $\mathscr{F}_{0x}$ represents the generalized "potential difference" appropriate to work of the type W_{0x}. We can recast Eq. (6.36) into other useful forms: let one of the thermostat temperatures (T_m say) be chosen as a reference temperature; then, on combining Eq. (6.34) or (6.35) with Eq. (6.36), we can write

$$\Theta = \sum_x Y_{0x} \frac{\mathscr{F}_{0x}}{T_m} - \sum_j \frac{\dot{H}_j - T_m \dot{S}_j}{T_m} + \sum_{\substack{k \\ k \neq m}} \dot{Q}_k^{(r)} \left(\frac{1}{T_k} - \frac{1}{T_m} \right)$$
$$+ \sum \dot{q}(kh) \left(\frac{1}{\langle T(kh) \rangle} - \frac{1}{T_m} \right)$$
$$= \sum_x Y_{0x} \frac{\mathscr{F}_{0x}}{T_m} - \frac{1}{T_m} \left\{ \sum_j \sum_\rho \sum_i \mathscr{G}_\rho^{(i)} \dot{n}_\rho^{(i)} + \sum_j \sum_\rho \sum_i (T_\rho - T_m) \bar{S}_\rho^{(i)} \dot{n}_\rho^{(i)} \right\}$$
$$+ \sum_{\substack{k \\ k \neq m}} \dot{Q}_k^{(r)} \left(\frac{1}{T_k} - \frac{1}{T_m} \right) + \sum \dot{q}(kh) \left(\frac{1}{\langle T(kh) \rangle} - \frac{1}{T_m} \right). \quad (6.38)$$

We can eliminate the dependent currents in Eq. (6.38) via the steady-state equations of constraint and via any stoichiometric relations pertaining to the given situation; the resultant equation will be in the form $\Theta = \sum_h Y_h \Omega_h$.

For a state of vanishing mass flow (with respect to a rate parameter $\dot{n}$) we have

$$\sum_j \sum_\rho \sum_i \mathscr{G}_\rho^{(i)} \left(\frac{\delta \dot{n}_\rho^{(i)}}{\tilde{\delta} \dot{n}} \right)_{\Omega'} + \sum_k T_k \left\{ \left(\frac{\delta \dot{S}_k(\text{in})}{\tilde{\delta} \dot{n}} \right)_{\Omega'} - \left(\frac{\delta \dot{S}_k(\text{out})}{\tilde{\delta} \dot{n}} \right)_{\Omega'} \right\}$$
$$+ \sum \left(\frac{\delta \dot{q}(kh)}{\tilde{\delta} \dot{n}} \right)_{\Omega'} = \left(\frac{\delta \dot{W}_0}{\tilde{\delta} \dot{n}} \right)_{\Omega'}, \quad (6.39)$$

$$0 = \left(\frac{\delta \Theta}{\tilde{\delta} \dot{n}} \right)_{\Omega'} = \sum_k \left\{ \left(\frac{\delta \dot{S}_k(\text{in})}{\tilde{\delta} \dot{n}} \right)_{\Omega'} - \left(\frac{\delta \dot{S}_k(\text{out})}{\tilde{\delta} \dot{n}} \right)_{\Omega'} \right\} + \sum \left(\frac{\delta \dot{s}(kh)}{\tilde{\delta} \dot{n}} \right)_{\Omega'}, \quad (6.40)$$

where I have made use of Eq. (6.32) with attendant conventions (the heat reservoirs either communicate with terminal parts or they encompass regions through which mass flows but in which mass does not accumulate). Equations (6.39) and (6.40), taken together, are equivalent to the equation resulting from the application of the operation $(\delta/\tilde{\delta}\dot{n})_{\Omega'}$ to Eq. (6.38).

The equations of this section are basic ones for the analysis of several polythermal situations.

Exercise 6–5. Show that for the thermomolecular pressure case (Figure 5–1) Eq. (6.39) yields Eq. (5.18) directly.

Assumption IV

Assumption IV has some far-reaching consequences for polythermal field effects and is especially important in the treatment of thermocouples and thermocells. For the case considered in the preceding section (Eqs. 6.36 and

6.40) the terms of Eq. (6.40) combine in such a way as to leave quantities of the type $[S_k]$ and $[s(kh)]$, one set of such quantities for each link. If there are m (series-connected) links in the system and $[S_m(\text{out})]$ represents the $[S]$ quantity at the place where mass flows out of the link,* then we can write Eq. (6.40) as

$$0 = \sum_m [S_m(\text{out})] - [S_m(\text{in})] - [s_m(\text{in–out})]. \tag{6.41}$$

The systems investigated are normally constructed so that the separate linkages are independent of one another; therefore assumption IV requires that for *each* (series-connected) linkage in the system

$$[S_m(\text{out})] - [S_m(\text{in})] - [s_m(\text{in–out})] = 0. \tag{6.42}$$

Similar considerations imply that for each (series-connected) linkage in the system

$$[H_m(\text{out})] - [H_m(\text{in})] - [h_m(\text{in–out})] = 0 \tag{6.43}$$

and

$$[G_m(\text{out})] - [G_m(\text{in})] = 0. \tag{6.44}$$

Exercise 6–6. Linkages

(i) Series-Connected Linkages

Consider two series-connected full-flux linkages connecting three terminal parts (α, β, γ) with α and γ serving as mass source and sink, respectively—see Figure 6–1—(for definiteness let the effect be the thermomolecular pressure

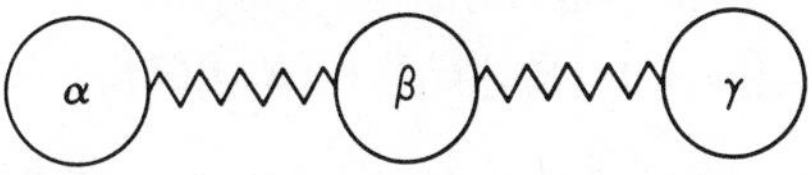

Figure 6–1. Two series-connected full-flux linkages.

effect). Let the steady-flow condition be that $\dot{n}_\alpha + \dot{n}_\gamma = 0$. Show that in the state of migrational equilibrium

$$[H_\alpha] - [H_\gamma] = T_\beta\{[S_\alpha] - [S_\gamma]\}. \tag{6.45}$$

Equation (6.45) is of the form of Eq. (5.14) with $[h(\gamma\alpha)] = T_\beta\{[S_\alpha] - [S_\gamma]\}$; it follows then that $\langle T(\alpha\gamma)\rangle = T_\beta$ and that in a certain sense $\Delta[H] = \int T\, d[S]$, where the integral is a path integral over the flow path.

(ii) Branched Linkages

Consider a branched partial-flux linkage connecting three terminal parts (α, β, γ) as in Figure 6–2 (let the effect be the thermomolecular pressure effect

* If the m link butts on to the k thermostat, then $(\delta\dot{S}_k(\text{in})/\delta\dot{n})_{\Omega'} \equiv [S_m(\text{out})]$.

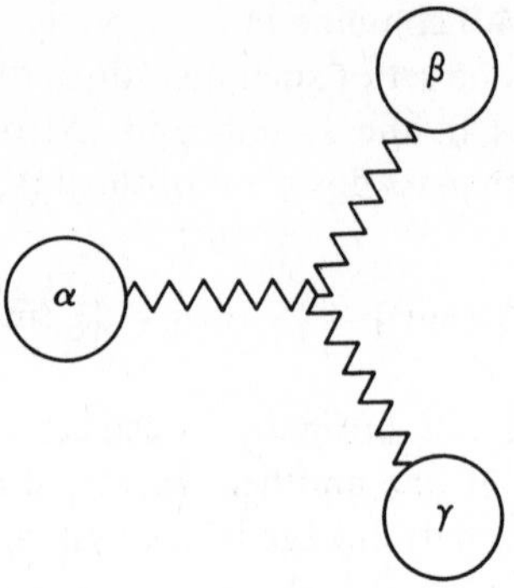

Figure 6–2. A branched, partial-flux linkage.

for definiteness). Let the steady-flow condition be that $\dot{n}_\alpha + \dot{n}_\beta + \dot{n}_\gamma = 0$. Show that for the state of migrational equilibrium the relations

$$[R_{\alpha\chi}][H_\alpha] + [R_{\beta\chi}][H_\beta] + [R_{\gamma\chi}][H_\gamma] = [h(\psi\omega\chi)], \tag{6.46}$$

$$[R_{\alpha\chi}][S_\alpha] + [R_{\beta\chi}][S_\beta] + [R_{\gamma\chi}][S_\gamma] = [s(\psi\omega\chi)], \tag{6.47}$$

$$[R_{\alpha\chi}] + [R_{\beta\chi}] + [R_{\gamma\chi}] = 0, \tag{6.48}$$

hold with $[R_{\omega\chi}] \equiv (\delta\dot{n}_\omega/\delta\dot{n}_\chi)_{\Omega'}$; one of the mass flows $\dot{n}_\alpha$, $\dot{n}_\beta$, or $\dot{n}_\gamma$ has been chosen as rate parameter and has been called $\dot{n}_\chi$.

By making use of the relation

$$[h(\psi\omega\chi)] = \langle T(\alpha\beta\gamma)\rangle[s(\psi\omega\chi)] \tag{6.49}$$

devise a definition for quantities $[G_\omega]$ such that

$$[R_{\alpha\chi}][G_\alpha] + [R_{\beta\chi}][G_\beta] + [R_{\gamma\chi}][G_\gamma] = 0. \tag{6.50}$$

Exercise 6–7. For the situation described in Ex. 6–6(i), any steady state is completely specified when the variables T_α, P_α, T_β, P_γ, T_γ are known for a given gas and apparatus; the steady state is thus characterized by 5 degrees of freedom (see Chapter 3). Similarly, the situation described in Ex. 6–6(ii) is characterized by 7 degrees of freedom: T_α, P_α, T_β, P_β, T_γ, P_γ, $\langle T(\alpha\beta\gamma)\rangle$. Take the state γ as reference thermostatic state for the two situations, and show that in each case the number of degrees of freedom is correctly given by the expression $F_\gamma + \nu$ (see Chapter 3).

Assumption III

Enough material is now at hand so that I can make further remarks concerning assumption III. Assumption III implies that the properties of the state of migrational equilibrium are independent of the exact path used in the $\delta/\bar{\delta} Y_k$ operation. Thus in the case of the thermomolecular pressure effect (Figure 5–1, full-flux linkage) we can, say, hold T_α, P_β, T_β constant and can approach the state of migrational equilibrium by varying P_α [the symbolic operation is $(\delta/\bar{\delta}\dot{n}_\alpha)_{\beta,T_\alpha}$], or we can hold P_α, P_β, T_β constant and can vary T_α [the symbolic operation in this case is $(\delta/\bar{\delta}\dot{n}_\alpha)_{\beta,P_\alpha}$]. Assumption III implies that the same *overall* result is obtained in either case:

$$\bar{H}_\alpha - \bar{H}_\beta + \frac{\delta \dot{Q}_\alpha^{(r)}}{\bar{\delta}\dot{n}_\alpha} + \frac{\delta \dot{Q}_\beta^{(r)}}{\bar{\delta}\dot{n}_\alpha} = 0, \tag{6.51}$$

the requirement being that the quantity $\delta(\dot{Q}_\alpha^{(r)} + \dot{Q}_\beta^{(r)})/\bar{\delta}\dot{n}_\alpha$ be independent of the path used in arriving at the state of migrational equilibrium. For the case being considered we shall see that $\delta(\dot{Q}_\alpha^{(r)} + \dot{Q}_\beta^{(r)})/\bar{\delta}\dot{n}_\alpha$ yields the same result for the two paths but that $(\delta\dot{Q}_\omega^{(r)}/\bar{\delta}\dot{n}_\alpha)_{\beta,T_\alpha} \neq (\delta\dot{Q}_\omega^{(r)}/\bar{\delta}\dot{n}_\alpha)_{\beta,P_\alpha}$.

With respect to the thermomolecular pressure effect any steady state involving a given gas and full-flux linkage is completely specified by the four variables T_α, P_α, T_β, P_β; therefore we can say that $\dot{Q}_\omega^{(r)} = \dot{Q}_\omega^{(r)}(T_\alpha, P_\alpha, T_\beta, P_\beta)$, and that $\dot{n}_\alpha = \dot{n}_\alpha(T_\alpha, P_\alpha, T_\beta, P_\beta)$, and hence that $\dot{Q}_\omega^{(r)} = \dot{Q}_\omega^{(r)}(T_\alpha, P_\beta, T_\beta, \dot{n}_\alpha)$. It is easy to see, then, that

$$\left(\frac{\delta\dot{Q}_\omega^{(r)}}{\bar{\delta}\dot{n}_\alpha}\right)_{\beta,P_\alpha} = \left(\frac{\delta\dot{Q}_\omega^{(r)}}{\bar{\delta}\dot{n}_\alpha}\right)_{\beta,T_\alpha} + \left(\frac{\delta T_\alpha}{\bar{\delta}\dot{n}_\alpha}\right)_{\beta,P_\alpha}\left(\frac{\partial\dot{Q}_\omega^{(r)}}{\partial T_\alpha}\right)_{\beta,\dot{n}_\alpha=0} \tag{6.52}$$

and that in general $(\delta\dot{Q}_\omega^{(r)}/\bar{\delta}\dot{n}_\alpha)_{\beta,P_\alpha} \neq (\delta\dot{Q}_\omega^{(r)}/\bar{\delta}\dot{n}_\alpha)_{\beta,T_\alpha}$. On the other hand, we see from Eq. (6.52) that

$$\left(\frac{\delta(\dot{Q}_\alpha^{(r)} + \dot{Q}_\beta^{(r)})}{\bar{\delta}\dot{n}_\alpha}\right)_{\beta,P_\alpha} = \left(\frac{\delta(\dot{Q}_\alpha^{(r)} + \dot{Q}_\beta^{(r)})}{\bar{\delta}\dot{n}_\alpha}\right)_{\beta,T_\alpha} + \left(\frac{\delta T_\alpha}{\bar{\delta}\dot{n}_\alpha}\right)_{\beta,P_\alpha}\left(\frac{\partial(\dot{Q}_\alpha^{(r)} + \dot{Q}_\beta^{(r)})}{\partial T_\alpha}\right)_{\beta,\dot{n}_\alpha=0}. \tag{6.53}$$

When $\dot{n}_\alpha = 0$, it follows that* $\dot{Q}_\alpha^{(r)} + \dot{Q}_\beta^{(r)} = 0$ and that

$$\left(\frac{\partial(\dot{Q}_\alpha^{(r)} + \dot{Q}_\beta^{(r)})}{\partial T_\alpha}\right)_{\beta,\dot{n}_\alpha=0} = 0;$$

hence Eq. (6.53) reduces to

$$\left(\frac{\delta(\dot{Q}_\alpha^{(r)} + \dot{Q}_\beta^{(r)})}{\bar{\delta}\dot{n}_\alpha}\right)_{\beta,P_\alpha} = \left(\frac{\delta(\dot{Q}_\alpha^{(r)} + \dot{Q}_\beta^{(r)})}{\bar{\delta}\dot{n}_\alpha}\right)_{\beta,T_\alpha}. \tag{6.54}$$

It is clear, then, that overall equations such as (6.51) are independent of the path used in the limiting operation but that separate terms of the type $\delta Y_i/\bar{\delta} Y_k$ do depend on the path. As far as assumption III is concerned, there is no reason to favor one path over another, and any well-defined sequence of steady states is allowable in the limiting operation. If we desire to resolve

* Remember that we are dealing with the full-flux case; see Eqs. (5.1) and (5.6) with $\dot{q} = 0$ and $\dot{n}_\alpha = 0$.

the separate terms $\delta Y_i/\tilde{\delta} Y_k$ into an ordinary part $\bar{Y}$ and an extraordinary part $[Y]$, then we get in general a different extraordinary part $[Y]_{\text{path}}$ for each different limiting path. Note, however, the following two points: (i) The differential quantities $[Z]^{\partial}$ do not depend on the limiting operation $(\delta/\tilde{\delta}\dot{n})_{\text{path}}$; hence they are functions of the terminal states only and show no path dependence whatsoever. (ii) Although the integral quantities $[Z]$ do have a path dependence based on the definitional relations (5.10) to (5.13), the *form* of each relation involving integral quantities is invariant—i.e., independent of the exact path used in the basic definitional relations.* Assumption IV supplies the motivation for singling out a special path (or a class of special paths) for consideration, and I calculate explicitly in the body of the text only extraordinary parts $[Y]_{\Omega'}$ associated with affine sequences. In using affine sequences for the limiting operation $\delta/\tilde{\delta} Y_k$ it is always possible to proceed in two stages: we can first apply the operation $(\delta/\tilde{\delta} Y_k)_{\Omega'}$ to the First Law equation $\dot{U}(\text{system}) = \dot{Q} + \dot{W}$ (or to an equation derived from it), and we can then combine the resultant equation with the equation $(\delta\Theta/\tilde{\delta} Y_k)_{\Omega'} = 0$ to get a final equation. The first equation depends only on the laws of ordinary thermodynamics and on assumptions I to III; the final equation depends in addition on assumption IV.

* Consider, e.g., two different limiting paths (′) and (″) used to define the quantities $[H']$, $[H'']$, etc. In spite of differences in path, it will still be true that $[H'] = \mu + T[S']$, $[H''] = \mu + T[S'']$, $[H_\alpha'] - [H_\beta'] = [h(\beta\alpha)']$, $[H_\alpha''] - [H_\beta''] = [h(\beta\alpha)'']$, etc. Remember, however, that there is in general only *one* path for which $(\delta\Theta/\tilde{\delta} Y_k) = 0$ if the final state $(Y_k = 0)$ is not one of thermostatic equilibrium.

7

Thermodynamics: The Well-Tempered Science

Macroscopic thermodynamics is a science that matches well the human temperament—R. T. Cox has summed it all up very well [1]:

> Classical thermodynamics is an admirable theory, unpretentious and consoling to common sense. The quantities with which it deals lie in the scale of ordinary measurement, and the laws on which it is based are verified in commonplace experience. As a logical system it is marvelous in the economy of its means. Its concepts and principles are never superfluous, its limits are clearly stated, and within these limits it is, humanly speaking, perfect, with nothing left out and nothing left over.

That thermodynamics has an *extra*-scientific appeal for many of its practitioners is clear from the steady stream of books and expository articles devoted to the subject each year. It seems as though each successful practitioner of the subject reformulates the meaning of the basic postulates of thermodynamics in terms of his own experience and then tries to tell the world about his own personal way of looking at the subject.

Thermodynamics, then, is very much a part of the human scene, and it continues to be a congenial, viable science in spite of the fact that technically it should have been swallowed up by statistical mechanics a long time ago; thermodynamics has so many features that appeal to human needs that it seems likely to go on leading an independent existence for a long time to come. The congeniality of thermodynamics is truly amazing: although, as I think of it, it finds its natural expression in the picturesque language of engineering—heat baths, piston-and-cylinder arrangements, etc.—it has been treated from points of view as diverse as those of Planck [2], Brønsted [3], Tisza [4], Landsberg [5], Hatsopoulos and Keenan [6], and Tribus [7]. This infectious congeniality of thermodynamics will, of course, drive its practitioners to extend its domain to the widest possible class of phenomena—hence the spate of books on nonequilibrium thermodynamics.

The Utility of Thermodynamics

Thermodynamics is par excellence a language for describing experiment. One of its useful language functions is the efficient storage and encoding of experimental information; the experimental information can then be processed (reflected into a number of different perspectives) so as to reveal different facets of the phenomena since some ways of looking at a given set of data are more useful than others. Thus, for example, pH scales and activity coefficients enable us to describe a wide range of phenomena via a comfortable range of numbers, and we may break down Gibbs free energy changes into enthalpy changes and entropy changes. I made use of this storage and encoding function of thermodynamics, e.g., in defining the coefficients $[N]$ and $[S]^{\partial}$; these coefficients merely represent efficient ways of recording data for the forced vaporization process and for, e.g., the thermomolecular pressure effect; the processing of the data then yields quantities such as $[C_{\omega\omega}]^{\partial}$ and $[Q_{\omega}]^{\partial}$.

In addition to merely describing experiments, thermodynamics also makes some positive statements about the systems experimented upon: it says that energy is conserved, that isolated systems tend toward states of equilibrium, and that systems in internal equilibrium show a characteristic form of behavior in the vicinity of 0°K. This factual content of the laws of thermodynamics results in some necessary relations among the quantities introduced in the descriptive stage of thermodynamics; the language of thermodynamics is thus *cross-referenced* (by Maxwell's relations, e.g.), and it is possible to determine some quantities indirectly instead of directly. Thus, e.g., by measuring vapor pressure as a function of temperature we can determine indirectly the heat of vaporization. The cross-referencing also enables us to check the consistency of our measurements; the separate partial pressures of the components in a multicomponent mixture, e.g., must satisfy the Gibbs–Duhem relation. In dealing with steady states, I introduced enough quantities so as to be able to *describe* the steady phenomena in sufficient detail. The laws of thermostatics (equilibrium thermodynamics) supply a certain amount of cross-referencing for the steady-state language. They imply, e.g., that $[C_{\chi\omega}]^{\partial} = 0$; the result, then, is a weakly cross-referenced thermodynamic language that is adequate for dealing with steady states.*

If we make a positive statement about the rate of entropy production in the system (assumption IV), we introduce an additional amount of cross-referencing into the steady-state language, and we make things easier for the experimenter by allowing him to determine some quantities indirectly instead of directly† and by giving him some consistency checks for his data.‡ Note that assumption IV is in no sense *necessary* for the successful establishment of a thermodynamic language for treating steady states; when assumption IV holds, it merely makes life that much easier for the experimenter.

Historical Conspectus

I now wish to make some remarks about the historical growth of thermodynamics. I distinguish three phases in the evolution of thermodynamics: (i) There was first an area of interest. In the period 1800–1850 there was a widespread interest in the workings of the steam engine, in problems of efficiency, and in the interrelations among heat, work, and energy. (ii) In the second stage a suitable language (the work of men such as Thomson, Clausius, Gibbs, and Planck) was developed for describing and dealing with the phenomena in the area of interest. The quantities introduced by the language were studied to determine how they varied with the experimental conditions. (iii) Finally, the quantities introduced and studied in stage (ii) were given an atomic interpretation through the invention of statistical mechanics (Maxwell, Boltzmann, Gibbs, Fowler, etc.).

I should like to see the thermodynamics of steady states develop in the same orderly fashion. That there is a class of nonequilibrium phenomena—an area of interest—to which we would like to apply the concepts and techniques of thermodynamics is shown by the early work of Thomson on the thermocouple and by the continuing interest we have in such nonequilibrium phenomena as the Soret effect, the thermomolecular pressure effect, thermoösmosis, and concentration cells with transference. The area of interest is certainly there; we need next an adequate language for describing the phenomena and for exhibiting the necessary relations among the phenomena. We need to study the phenomena in terms of our language so as to learn how the various quantities and coefficients depend on the experimental variables. After we have learned what to expect experimentally, we need to explain the experimental behavior in terms of atoms and molecules; i.e., we need to invent a statistical mechanics of nonequilibrium states.

* Up to this point I am considering only assumptions I to III; I am not yet considering assumption IV.

† See, e.g., Eqs. (4.9) to (4.11) and Eq. (6.29).

‡ See, e.g., Ex. 5–3 and Eq. (8.45).

Consider the following case in point. The term *activity coefficient* was introduced into the study of electrolytic solutions by Noyes and Bray [8] in 1911. In the period 1911 to 1923, activity coefficients were accepted as a useful way of recording data and were intensively studied. A great deal was learned empirically about the dependence of activity coefficients of electrolytes on fractional powers of the molality and on the ionic strength of the solution; this empirical information is summarized very well in the 1923 text of Lewis and Randall [9]. Then in 1923 Debye and Hückel [10] succeeded in rationalizing some of the experimental information by giving the limiting behavior of the solution an atomistic interpretation. I take this case as a paradigm for the thermodynamics of steady states: we need to learn about the experimental behavior of the quantities $[R]$, $[N]$, $[S]^{\theta}$, $[Q_b(\beta)]$, $[C_{\omega\omega}]$, etc., so as to be able to attempt an explanation of that behavior in terms of atoms and molecules; as I see it, the learning comes first and the explanation comes later.

Head versus Hand

It is a commonplace observation that the manner of carrying out and reporting on an experiment is influenced by the theoretical framework into which the experimenter expects to fit the results. The interlocking of theory and practice gives rise to procedures that we can characterize by considering two polar sequences: (i) *doing*, *describing*, *explaining*, and (ii) *speculating*, *testing*, *readjusting*. In sequence (i) the activity starts in the laboratory, and the acts of describing and explaining are conditioned by the laboratory procedures. The resulting language tends to be operational (couched in terms of idealized laboratory operations), and the task of theory is to build a bridge between the relations that it considers fundamental (the laws of mechanics, e.g.) and the laboratory-oriented quantities (heat, energy, and entropy, e.g.) of the descriptive language. In sequence (ii) the theoretical conception is primary, and it is the task of the experimenter to devise some way of testing the consequences of the theory and then to modify, if necessary, the theoretical conception in the light of the experimental results. The laboratory work accompanying sequence (ii) is sometimes cramped or hampered by the unoperational nature of the theoretical constructs being considered. That sequences (i) and (ii) are but the extreme poles of a continuous spectrum of investigative procedures is clear from the facts that in sequence (i) we usually have some definite reason for undertaking the experiment, some interest—often enough of a theoretical nature—extraneous to the actual laboratory manipulations, and that in sequence (ii) our starting theoretical conceptions are conditioned by our previous knowledge and experience, including our knowledge of earlier experimental results. The gist of the matter is that in sequence (i) the experimenter arranges things to suit himself, and the theoretician is constrained to operate within the framework set out by the experimenter, whereas in sequence (ii) the theoretician has complete freedom, and it is the experimenter who is constrained to try to actualize the theoretical conceptions within the confines of the laboratory.

I feel that classical thermodynamics leans more toward sequence (i) than toward sequence (ii). I also feel that the developments initiated by Onsager [11] and pursued by such men as Prigogine [12] and de Groot [13] lean more toward sequence (ii) than toward sequence (i) and result in a rather peculiar thermodynamic perspective. Considerations dealing with the regression of fluctuations in an isolated system are rather far removed from ordinary laboratory procedures. An obsessive concern with the explicit dependence of currents on affinities and other parameters of the system is rather uncharacteristic of thermodynamics: in the case of chemical equilibrium, for example, we do not need to know the exact kinetic mechanism (the precise forward and backward rate expressions) in order to find the thermodynamic conditions of equilibrium and the expression for the equilibrium constant. I feel that just as ordinary thermodynamics places its main emphasis on the conditions of equilibrium so the thermodynamics of steady states should place its *main* emphasis on the conditions of migrational equilibrium in given spatial fields rather than on problems of "matter and motion" (items that are more a part of general physics than of anything else). Furthermore, the fundamental experimental system is the container plus the contents plus the interaction of container and contents with the surroundings. The experimenter would prefer a global language that reflects the laboratory realities. Now the experimenter never *measures* directly what happens at a single point in space, and a language couched in terms of local properties and gradients makes his life that much more difficult and gives him little or no guidance in dealing with the effect of the container on the process being studied and in deciding on ways to minimize that effect.

Apologia

What it amounts to is that in a roundabout way I have said that I like thermodynamics, that I have my own personal way of looking at the subject, that I favor a laboratory-oriented language based on global concepts, that I find currently popular treatments of nonequilibrium thermodynamics more *kinetic* than *thermodynamic*, and that I have constructed a nonequilibrium thermodynamics more to my taste.

References

1. R. T. Cox, *Statistical Mechanics of Irreversible Change* (The Johns Hopkins Press, Baltimore, 1955), p. 3.
2. M. Planck, *Treatise on Thermodynamics* (Dover Publications, New York, 1945).

3. J. N. Brønsted, *Principles and Problems in Energetics* (Interscience Publishers, New York, 1955).
4. L. Tisza, *Ann. Phys.*, **13**, 1 (1961).
5. P. T. Landsberg, *Thermodynamics* (Interscience Publishers, New York, 1961).
6. G. Hatsopoulos and J. H. Keenan, *Principles of General Thermodynamics* (John Wiley and Sons, New York, 1965).
7. M. Tribus, *Thermostatics and Thermodynamics* (D. Van Nostrand Company, Princeton, 1961).
8. A. A. Noyes and W. C. Bray, *J. Am. Chem. Soc.*, **33**, 1643 (1911).
9. G. N. Lewis and M. Randall, *Thermodynamics and the Free Energy of Chemical Substances* (McGraw-Hill Book Company, New York, 1923).
10. P. Debye and E. Hückel, *Physik. Z.*, **24**, 185 (1923).
11. L. Onsager, *Phys. Rev.*, **37**, 405 (1931); **38**, 2265 (1931).
12. I. Prigogine, *Introduction to the Thermodynamics of Irreversible Processes*, second edition (John Wiley and Sons, New York, 1961).
13. S. de Groot and P. Mazur, *Non-Equilibrium Thermodynamics* (North-Holland Publishing Company, Amsterdam, 1962).

PART II. APPLICATIONS

8

Migrational Equilibrium in Polythermal Fields: Applications

Thermoösmosis ($\dot{W}_0 = 0$)

If we connect two different thermal states of a gaseous system by means of a rubber diaphragm instead of by a capillary linkage, the situation is closely analogous to the thermomolecular pressure case but we now speak of *thermoösmotic* effects. Figure 8–1 is a schematic rendering of the situation; let us assume that the gas–membrane interfaces at α and β are at the appropriate thermostat temperatures and that the temperature gradient is localized inside the rubber membrane. The standard procedure—the initiation of a steady flow of mass between terminal parts and the application of the operation $(\delta/\tilde{\delta}\dot{n}_\alpha)_{\beta,T_\alpha,\langle T\rangle}$—leads to the relation

$$\mu_\alpha^{(g)} - \mu_\beta^{(g)} + T_\alpha[S_\alpha^{(M)}] - T_\beta[S_\beta^{(M)}] - [h_M(\beta\alpha)] = 0 \tag{8.1}$$

as the condition for migrational equilibrium; the superscripts g and M refer to the gas phase and the membrane phase, respectively. Since in the state of migrational equilibrium $\mu_\omega^{(g)} = \mu_\omega^{(M)} = \mu_\omega$, it follows that we may write Eq. (8.1) as

$$[H_\alpha^{(M)}] - [H_\beta^{(M)}] = [h_M(\beta\alpha)] \tag{8.2}$$

or

$$[G_\alpha^{(M)}] - [G_\beta^{(M)}] = 0, \tag{8.3}$$

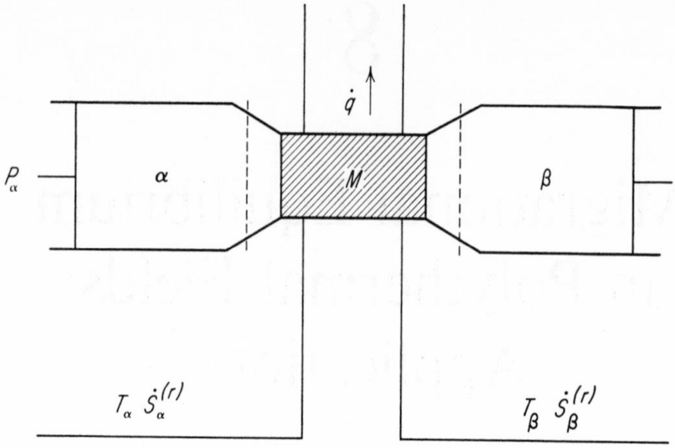

Figure 8–1. Two thermal states (α, β) of a gas connected by a rubber membrane (M); arbitrary linkage.

where

$$[H_\omega^{(M)}] \equiv \mu_\omega^{(M)} + T_\omega[S_\omega^{(M)}] \quad \text{and} \quad [G_\omega^{(M)}] \equiv [H_\omega^{(M)}] - \langle T(\alpha\beta)\rangle[S_\omega^{(M)}].$$

We can also write

$$\overline{V}_\omega^{(g)}\left(\frac{\partial P_\omega}{\partial T_\omega}\right)_\chi = \overline{S}_\omega^{(g)} - [S_\omega^{(M)}]^\partial \tag{8.4}$$

in a familiar fashion; thus the thermoösmotic effect ($P_\alpha \neq P_\beta$ for $T_\alpha \neq T_\beta$) depends on $[S_\omega^{(M)}]^\partial \equiv -(\partial\mu_\omega/\partial T_\omega)_\chi$ being different from $\overline{S}_\omega^{(g)}$.

If we treat the gas as ideal, Eqs. (8.4) and (5.29) enable us to write

$$\left(\frac{\partial \ln P_\omega}{\partial T_\omega}\right)_\chi \approx \frac{T_\omega(\overline{S}_\omega^{(g)} - [S_\omega^{(M)}]^\partial)}{RT_\omega{}^2} = \frac{[Q_\omega]^\partial}{RT_\omega{}^2}, \tag{8.5}$$

where

$$[Q_\omega]^\partial = \overline{H}_\omega^{(g)} - [H_\omega^{(M)}]^\partial = \overline{H}_\omega^{(g)} - \overline{H}_\omega^{(M)} + \overline{H}_\omega^{(M)} - [H_\omega^{(M)}]^\partial = \Delta\overline{H}_\omega + [Q_\omega^{(M)}]^\partial.$$

The quantity $[Q_\omega]^\partial$ thus contains an interphase and an intraphase effect.

By referring back to the remarks just preceding Eq. (5.31) we see that we can integrate Eq. (8.5) to obtain

$$\ln\frac{P_\beta}{P_\alpha} = -\frac{\langle[Q]^\partial\rangle}{R}\left(\frac{1}{T_\beta} - \frac{1}{T_\alpha}\right). \tag{8.6}$$

Denbigh [1], in a series of measurements involving a number of gases, a rubber membrane, and fixed temperatures T_1, T_2, found that the quantity $\langle[Q]^\partial\rangle$ was approximately constant (gave the same value, approximately, for all pairings (P_1, P_2) on the bitherm segment) for the bitherm segments that he investigated; the results obtained by Bearman [2] were similar.

Exercise 8–1. Show that Eq. (8.6) is just a disguised version of Eq. (5.38) with

$$\langle [Q]^{\partial} \rangle = T_{\omega}(\bar{S}_{\omega}^{(g)} - \langle [S]^{\partial} \rangle) - T_{\omega}\bar{C}_{P}^{(g)} + \frac{T_{\omega}T_{\chi}\bar{C}_{P}^{(g)}}{T_{\chi} - T_{\omega}} \ln \frac{T_{\chi}}{T_{\omega}}. \tag{8.7}$$

Exercise 8–2. If integration from state α to state β is to yield the same results as integration from β to α, then Eq. (8.7) must be invariant with respect to interchange of the subscripts ω and χ. Hence, show that if $\langle [Q]^{\partial} \rangle$ is independent of position on the bitherm then (i) $\bar{S}_{\omega}^{(g)} - \langle [S]^{\partial} \rangle$ must be independent of P_{ω}, and that (ii) $T_{\omega}(\bar{S}_{\omega}^{(g)} - \langle [S]^{\partial} \rangle - \bar{C}_{P}^{(g)})$ must equal $T_{\chi}(\bar{S}_{\chi}^{(g)} - \langle [S]^{\partial} \rangle - \bar{C}_{P}^{(g)})$.

Exercise 8–3. The apparatus of Denbigh and Raumann [1] consisted of a rubber membrane held in place by porous bronze discs. An arrangement of thermocouples allowed the temperature of each rubber-bronze disc junction to be determined. Temperatures and pressures characteristic of each face of the rubber membrane were measured. A sample of the data appears in the following table.

Table 8–1

Sample Collection of Data from the Thermoösmotic Measurements of Denbigh and Raumann [1]

Gas	T_1	T_2	P_1(cm Hg)	P_2(cm Hg)
	306.0	315.0	42.07	45.96
CO_2	289.8	301.9	22.09	25.07
	296.2	312.4	28.23	33.28
	299.1	315.9	66.66	68.24
N_2	298.6	316.0	66.88	68.50
	302.3	321.0	71.92	73.67
	300.4	316.8	54.82	54.23
H_2	299.7	316.5	62.51	61.74
	304.2	321.8	71.61	71.07

Use Eq. (8.6) to calculate the value of $[Q]^{\partial}$ for each set of data. Denbigh and Raumann took as appropriate values of the heat of evaporation $\Delta\bar{H}$ of the gas from the membrane the numbers (calories) -2800, $+100$, and $+800$ for the gases CO_2, N_2, and H_2, respectively. Average the $[Q]^{\partial}$ values for each gas and determine the average value of $[Q^{(M)}]^{\partial}$ for each gas from the relation $[Q]^{\partial} = \Delta\bar{H} + [Q^{(M)}]^{\partial}$.

Thermal Diffusion in Gases

I take up next the thermal diffusion of gases. The thermal diffusion effect in gases was predicted theoretically by Enskog and by Chapman [3] before it was ever measured experimentally; as a result the language used for describing the effect is slanted toward the kinetic theory derivations and uses of the effect,* rather than toward an efficient thermodynamic encoding of the experimental information. Consider a 2-component gaseous mixture in an apparatus consisting of two bulbs connected by a tube as in Figure 8–2. Let the heavier gas be referred to as component 1. Now, keep the two bulbs at different temperatures and examine the resulting state of migrational equilibrium with respect to component 1. If the mole fraction of component 1 is different in the two bulbs when the temperatures of the bulbs are different, then we say that a thermal diffusion effect exists.

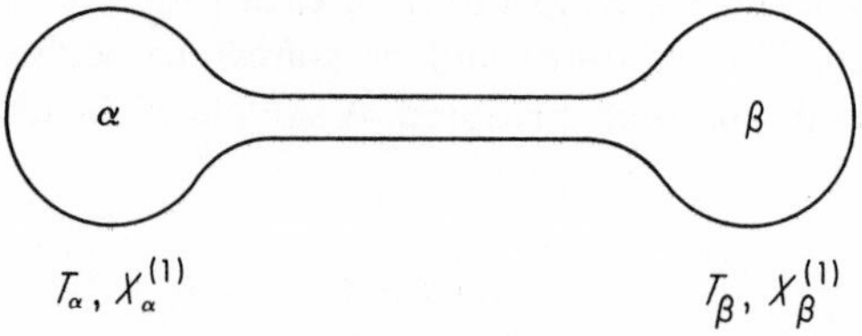

Figure 8–2. Thermal diffusion effect in gases; schematic.

We can carry out an ordinary thermodynamic analysis of the thermal diffusion phenomenon just as we did in the case of the thermomolecular pressure effect. Consider the situation shown in Figure 8–3. Establish a steady flow of component 1 between the terminal parts $\alpha(1)$ and $\beta(1)$ and determine the conditions of migrational equilibrium with respect to component 1. Do the same for component 2. The result of these operations will be equations such as

$$\mu_\alpha^{(i)} + T_\alpha[S_\alpha^{(i)}] - \mu_\beta^{(i)} - T_\beta[S_\beta^{(i)}] - [h_i(\beta\alpha)] = 0 \qquad i = 1, 2 \qquad (8.8)$$

and

$$[G_\alpha^{(i)}] = [G_\beta^{(i)}] \qquad i = 1, 2 \qquad (8.9)$$

for the state of migrational equilibrium. In dealing with a multicomponent mixture, it is sometimes convenient to specify the thermodynamic state in terms of the temperature T_ω and the chemical potentials $\mu_\omega^{(j)}$ of each of the separate components, thus I write

$$[S_\omega^{(i)}]^\partial \equiv -\left(\frac{\partial \mu_\omega^{(i)}}{\partial T_\omega}\right)_{T_\chi, \mu_\chi^{(j)}} \equiv -\left(\frac{\partial \mu_\omega^{(i)}}{\partial T_\omega}\right)_\chi . \qquad (8.10)$$

* The kinetic theory of gases uses the thermal diffusion effect as a way of learning about the law of force between molecules.

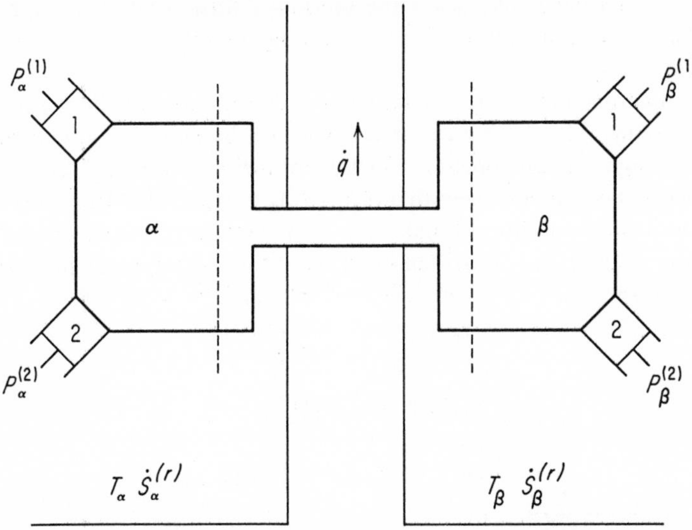

Figure 8–3. Gaseous thermal diffusion. Pure components 1 and 2 are in terminal parts in contact with the gaseous mixture through semipermeable membranes at α and β.

Now for the 2-component gaseous mixture at α, under conditions of migrational equilibrium, we have the relations

$$S_\alpha^{(m)}\,dT_\alpha - V_\alpha^{(m)}\,dP_\alpha + n_\alpha^{(1)}\,d\mu_\alpha^{(1)} + n_\alpha^{(2)}\,d\mu_\alpha^{(2)} = 0, \tag{8.11}$$

$$S_\alpha^{(m)} - V_\alpha^{(m)}\left(\frac{\partial P_\alpha}{\partial T_\alpha}\right)_\beta - n_\alpha^{(1)}[S_\alpha^{(1)}]^\partial - n_\alpha^{(2)}[S_\alpha^{(2)}]^\partial = 0, \tag{8.12}$$

$$\begin{aligned}\left(\frac{\partial \mu_\alpha^{(1)}}{\partial T_\alpha}\right)_\beta &\equiv -[S_\alpha^{(1)}]^\partial \\ &= -\bar{S}_\alpha^{(1)} + \bar{V}_\alpha^{(1)}\left(\frac{\partial P_\alpha}{\partial T_\alpha}\right)_\beta + \left(\frac{\partial \mu_\alpha^{(1)}}{\partial X_\alpha^{(1)}}\right)_{T_\alpha, P_\alpha}\left(\frac{\partial X_\alpha^{(1)}}{\partial T_\alpha}\right)_\beta,\end{aligned} \tag{8.13}$$

where the superscript m refers to properties of the gaseous mixture, P_α is the pressure of the gaseous mixture at α (i.e., $P_\alpha \approx P_\alpha^{(1)} + P_\alpha^{(2)}$), $X_\alpha^{(1)}$ is the mole fraction of component 1 in the gaseous mixture at α, and the superior bar indicates an appropriate molar, partial molar, or mean molar property.

Equation (8.11) is just the Gibbs–Duhem relation for the gaseous mixture at α; Eq. (8.12) is the result of applying the operation $(\partial/\partial T_\alpha)_\beta$ to Eq. (8.11); and Eq. (8.13) is the result of setting $\mu_\alpha^{(1)} = \mu_\alpha^{(1)}(T_\alpha, P_\alpha, X_\alpha^{(1)})$. It follows from Eq. (8.13) and the considerations of Chapter 5 that

$$\left(\frac{\partial X_\alpha^{(1)}}{\partial T_\alpha}\right)_\beta + \frac{\bar{V}_\alpha^{(1)}(\partial P_\alpha/\partial T_\alpha)_\beta}{(\partial \mu_\alpha^{(1)}/\partial X_\alpha^{(1)})_{T_\alpha, P_\alpha}} = \frac{\bar{S}_\alpha^{(1)} - [S_\alpha^{(1)}]^\partial}{(\partial \mu_\alpha^{(1)}/\partial X_\alpha^{(1)})_{T_\alpha, P_\alpha}} = f(T_\alpha, P_\alpha, X_\alpha^{(1)}) = f(\alpha); \tag{8.14}$$

and thus bithermal relations for the thermal diffusion effect are subject to the same sort of constraint as are the analogous relations for the thermomolecular pressure effect.*

The quantity $(\partial P_\alpha/\partial T_\alpha)_\beta$ is essentially a thermomolecular pressure effect for the gaseous mixture; we can make it vanish by choosing a wide enough tube or a high enough pressure. In the following relations I assume that matters have been so arranged that $(\partial P_\alpha/\partial T_\alpha)_\beta \approx 0$ and that the gases can be treated as ideal; in addition I make use of the fact that an extensive property $Z_\alpha^{(m)}$ of the mixture can be written in terms of the partial molar properties of the components; i.e., $Z_\alpha^{(m)} = n_\alpha^{(1)}\bar{Z}_\alpha^{(1)} + n_\alpha^{(2)}\bar{Z}_\alpha^{(2)}$ or $\bar{Z}_\alpha^{(m)} = X_\alpha^{(1)}\bar{Z}_\alpha^{(1)} + X_\alpha^{(2)}\bar{Z}_\alpha^{(2)}$:

$$\left(\frac{\partial \ln X_\alpha^{(1)}}{\partial \ln T_\alpha}\right)_\beta = \frac{[Q_\alpha^{(1)}]^\partial}{RT_\alpha}, \tag{8.15}$$

$$X_\alpha^{(1)}[Q_\alpha^{(1)}]^\partial + X_\alpha^{(2)}[Q_\alpha^{(2)}]^\partial = 0, \tag{8.16}$$

where

$$[Q_\alpha^{(i)}]^\partial \equiv T_\alpha(\bar{S}_\alpha^{(i)} - [S_\alpha^{(i)}]^\partial).$$

Exercise 8–4. Derive Eqs. (8.15) and (8.16) from Eqs. (8.12) and (8.13).

In discussions of thermal diffusion phenomena motivated by kinetic theory considerations [3, 4] the following quantities frequently occur (assume that $T_\alpha > T_\beta$):

the separation $\mathbf{S} \equiv X_\beta^{(1)} - X_\alpha^{(1)}$, (8.17)

the separation factor $\mathbf{q} \equiv (X_\beta^{(1)}/X_\alpha^{(1)})/(X_\beta^{(2)}/X_\alpha^{(2)})$, (8.18)

the thermal diffusion ratio $\mathbf{k}_T \equiv -(\partial X_\alpha^{(1)}/\partial \ln T_\alpha)_\beta$, (8.19)

the thermal diffusion factor $\boldsymbol{\alpha} \equiv -(1/X_\alpha^{(2)})(\partial \ln X_\alpha^{(1)}/\partial \ln T_\alpha)_\beta$. (8.20)

We see from Eqs. (8.15) and (8.16) and from the definitions (8.17) to (8.20) that the following relations hold:

$$\boldsymbol{\alpha} = \frac{\mathbf{k}_T}{X_\alpha^{(1)}X_\alpha^{(2)}}, \tag{8.21}$$

$$\begin{aligned}\langle \mathbf{k}_T\rangle &= \frac{X_\beta^{(1)} - X_\alpha^{(1)}}{\ln (T_\alpha/T_\beta)} = \frac{\mathbf{S}}{\ln (T_\alpha/T_\beta)}\\ &= -\left\langle\frac{X^{(1)}[Q^{(1)}]^\partial}{RT}\right\rangle = \left\langle\frac{X^{(2)}[Q^{(2)}]^\partial}{RT}\right\rangle,\end{aligned} \tag{8.22}$$

$$\begin{aligned}\langle \boldsymbol{\alpha}\rangle &= \frac{\ln \{(X_\beta^{(1)}/X_\beta^{(2)})/(X_\alpha^{(1)}/X_\alpha^{(2)})\}}{\ln (T_\alpha/T_\beta)} = \frac{\ln \mathbf{q}}{\ln (T_\alpha/T_\beta)}\\ &= -\left\langle\frac{[Q^{(1)}]^\partial}{X^{(2)}RT}\right\rangle = \left\langle\frac{[Q^{(2)}]^\partial}{X^{(1)}RT}\right\rangle.\end{aligned} \tag{8.23}$$

* The analog of assumption Q (see the note in Chapter 5) in this case is that

$$\left(\frac{\partial X_\alpha^{(1)}}{\partial\langle T\rangle}\right)_{\beta,T_\alpha} = 0.$$

For the case $X_\alpha^{(1)} \to 0$, we have $[Q_\alpha^{(2)}]^\partial \to 0$ and $\langle \boldsymbol{\alpha} \rangle \to -\langle [Q^{(1)}]^\partial/RT \rangle$; for the case $X_\alpha^{(2)} \to 0$, we have $[Q_\alpha^{(1)}]^\partial \to 0$ and $\langle \boldsymbol{\alpha} \rangle \to \langle [Q^{(2)}]^\partial/RT \rangle$. Note also that according to Eq. (8.15)

$$\frac{\ln (X_\beta^{(1)}/X_\alpha^{(1)})}{\ln (T_\alpha/T_\beta)} = -\left\langle \frac{[Q^{(1)}]^\partial}{RT} \right\rangle = \left\langle \frac{X^{(2)}[Q^{(2)}]^\partial}{X^{(1)}RT} \right\rangle. \tag{8.24}$$

Harrison Brown [4] suggested that average quantities such as $\langle \boldsymbol{\alpha} \rangle$ be associated with a unique reference temperature T_r given by

$$T_r \equiv \frac{T_\alpha T_\beta}{T_\alpha - T_\beta} \ln \frac{T_\alpha}{T_\beta}. \tag{8.25}$$

We can thus compute reference quantities $\langle [Q^{(i)}]^\partial \rangle_r$ from the relation

$$\langle [Q^{(i)}]^\partial \rangle_r \equiv RT_r \left\langle \frac{[Q^{(i)}]^\partial}{RT} \right\rangle; \tag{8.26}$$

and it is natural for us to assume that these reference quantities obey the relation

$$\langle X^{(1)} \rangle \langle [Q^{(1)}]^\partial \rangle_r + \langle X^{(2)} \rangle \langle [Q^{(2)}]^\partial \rangle_r = 0, \tag{8.27}$$

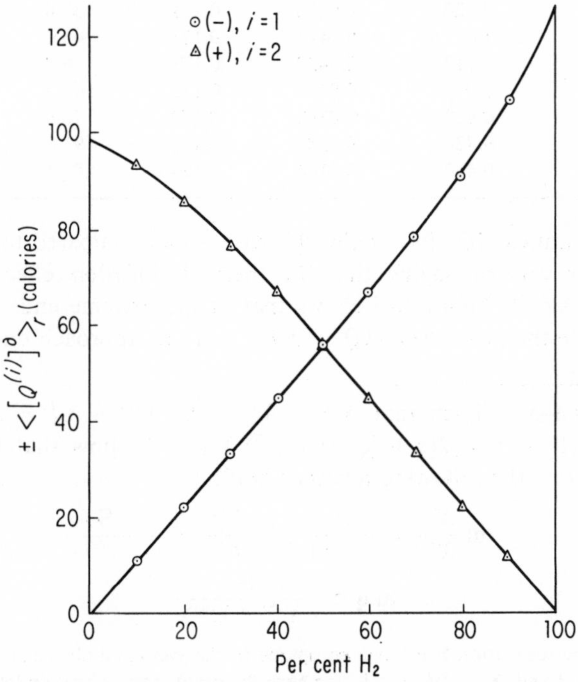

Figure 8-4. $\langle [Q^{(i)}]^\partial \rangle_r$ versus $\% H_2$ for thermal diffusion in H_2–D_2 mixtures (data of Heath, Ibbs, and Wild).

where $\langle X^{(i)} \rangle$ is defined by some such relation as

$$\langle X^{(i)} \rangle \equiv \frac{1}{T_\alpha - T_\beta} \int_{T_\beta}^{T_\alpha} X_\alpha^{(i)} \, dT_\alpha,$$

the state (β) at b being held constant. I assume that $\langle X^{(i)} \rangle$ can be approximated by the relation $\langle X^{(i)} \rangle \approx \frac{1}{2}(X_\alpha^{(i)} + X_\beta^{(i)})$.*

I have taken the thermal diffusion data of Heath, Ibbs, and Wild [5] pertaining to mixtures of hydrogen and deuterium and have made some illustrative calculations which I display in Table 8–2 and in Figures 8–4 and 8–5.

Table 8–2

Thermal Diffusion Results for H_2–D_2 Mixtures with $T_\alpha = 373°K$, $T_\beta = 288°K$, and $T_r = 326°K$

(Data of Heath, Ibbs, and Wild [5]; $RT_r = 648$ cal)

$\%H_2$ ($100\langle X^{(2)} \rangle$)	$\%Sep$ (100S)	$\langle \mathbf{k}_T \rangle$	$\langle \boldsymbol{\alpha} \rangle$	$-\langle [Q^{(1)}]^\partial \rangle_r$ (*cal*)	$\langle [Q^{(2)}]^\partial \rangle_r$ (*cal*)
10	0.374	0.0145	0.161	10.4	93.8
20	0.685	0.0265	0.165	21.5	85.6
30	0.920	0.0356	0.171	33.0	76.7
40	1.071	0.0416	0.173	45.0	67.3
50	1.112	0.0432	0.173	56.0	56.0
60	1.071	0.0416	0.173	67.3	45.0
70	0.938	0.0362	0.172	78.0	33.4
80	0.726	0.0281	0.176	91.0	22.8
90	0.420	0.0166	0.184	107.5	12.0

The quantities $\langle [Q^{(i)}]^\partial \rangle_r$ are, in this case, small compared to RT_r; this is but another way of saying that the thermal diffusion effect in H_2–D_2 mixtures is small. Figure 8–5 shows that at the extreme ends of the mole fraction scale the quantities $|\langle [Q^{(i)}]^\partial / RT \rangle|$ and $\langle \boldsymbol{\alpha} \rangle$ approach one another.

Exercise 8–5. Given that $X_\beta^{(1)} - X_\alpha^{(1)} = \mathbf{S}$, $X_\alpha^{(i)} + X_\beta^{(i)} = 2\langle X^{(i)} \rangle$, and $\ln \{(1 + z)/(1 - z)\} = 2\{z + (z^3/3) + (z^5/5) + \cdots\}$, show that for the case $(\mathbf{S}/2\langle X^{(i)} \rangle) \ll 1$ the following relations hold:

$$\ln \frac{X_\beta^{(1)}}{X_\alpha^{(1)}} \approx \frac{\mathbf{S}}{\langle X^{(1)} \rangle}, \quad \ln \frac{X_\beta^{(2)}}{X_\alpha^{(2)}} \approx -\frac{\mathbf{S}}{\langle X^{(2)} \rangle},$$

$$\ln \mathbf{q} \approx \frac{\mathbf{S}}{\langle X^{(1)} \rangle \langle X^{(2)} \rangle}.$$

* When the separation **S** is small compared to the average mole fractions—i.e., when $(\mathbf{S}/2\langle X^{(1)} \rangle) \ll 1$ and $(\mathbf{S}/2\langle X^{(2)} \rangle) \ll 1$—we have the useful approximate relation

$$\langle \boldsymbol{\alpha} \rangle \approx \frac{\langle \mathbf{k}_T \rangle}{\langle X^{(1)} \rangle \langle X^{(2)} \rangle}.$$

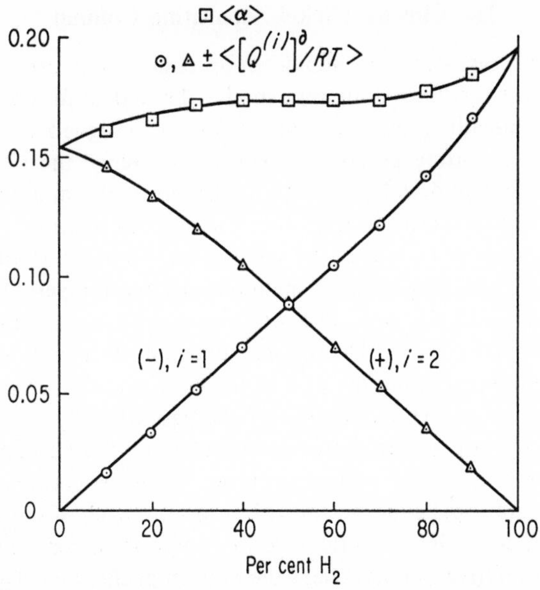

Figure 8–5. $\langle [Q^{(i)}]^{\partial}/RT\rangle$ and $\langle \alpha\rangle$ versus %H_2 for thermal diffusion in H_2–D_2 mixtures (data of Heath, Ibbs, and Wild).

Use these approximate relations to calculate the quantities $\langle \alpha\rangle$, $\langle [Q^{(1)}]^{\partial}/RT\rangle$, and $\langle [Q^{(2)}]^{\partial}/RT\rangle$ from the data in Table 8–3, listing the results of Atkins, Bastick, and Ibbs [6] for mixtures of helium and krypton; plot the results in the manner of Figure 8–5.

Table 8–3

Thermal Diffusion Results for He–Kr Mixtures with $T_\alpha = 373$°K, $T_\beta = 288$°K, and $T_r = 326$°K
(Data of Atkins, Bastick, and Ibbs [6])

%He ($100\langle X^{(2)}\rangle$)	%Sep (100S)	$\langle k_T\rangle$
30	1.75	0.0677
40	2.20	0.0852
50	2.58	0.1000
60	2.79	0.1080
70	2.76	0.1068

Exercise 8–6. Show that Eq. (8.15) can be integrated to yield

$$\ln \frac{X_\beta^{(1)}}{X_\alpha^{(1)}} = -\frac{\langle [Q^{(1)}]^{\partial}\rangle}{R}\left(\frac{1}{T_\beta} - \frac{1}{T_\alpha}\right)$$

and show that

$$\langle [Q^{(1)}]^{\partial}\rangle = \langle [Q^{(1)}]^{\partial}\rangle_r.$$

The Clusius–Dickel Separating Column

Just as the conditions of liquid–vapor equilibrium are the basis for practically useful distilling columns, so the thermal diffusion effect is the basis for a practically useful separating column designed by Clusius and Dickel [7] for separating gaseous mixtures. In essence the Clusius–Dickel column is a long cylindrical tube with a wire down the middle. We mount the tube in a vertical position, introduce the gaseous mixture, heat the wire to a high temperature (~800°C) by passing an electric current through it, cool the walls of the tube so as to maintain a large temperature difference between the wire and the wall, and wait for migrational equilibrium to be established along the column. The thermal diffusion effect tends to concentrate the heavier component along the wall of the tube, and the gravitational field induces a slow convective circulation of the gas, whereby the lighter component moves upward in the center of the tube and the heavier component moves downward along the wall of the tube. When the entire system comes to a state of migrational equilibrium with respect to each of the components, there is usually a significant difference in composition for points near the top of the tube relative to points near the bottom of the tube. The separation factor **q** for the gaseous mixture depends on the length of the column, the diameter of the tube, the difference in molecular weight for the component gases, the temperature difference between the heated wire and the wall of the tube, and on just how the motion of each component along the tube couples with the flow of heat from the wire to the wall. The Clusius–Dickel column has been used for the separation of gaseous isotopes, and kinetic theory analyses of the workings of the column have been attempted [7, 8].

For an analysis of the workings of the Clusius–Dickel column by steady-state thermodynamic methods, I arrange things in the manner indicated in Figure 8–6. I place the gaseous mixture into a region MIX in contact with two heat reservoirs a and b ($T_a > T_b$). On the b-side of the MIX region I set up two terminal parts, α and β, communicating with the MIX region via semipermeable membranes. With respect to the Clusius–Dickel column, T_a

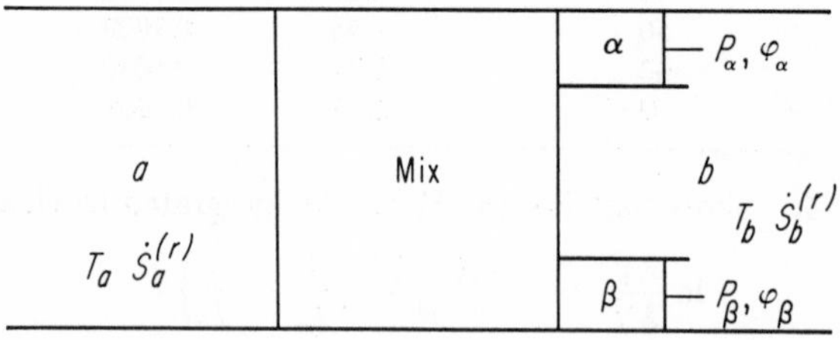

Figure 8–6. Schematic treatment of the Clusius–Dickel separating column.

corresponds to the temperature of the wire, T_b corresponds to the temperature of the wall, the distance between terminal parts α and β corresponds to the length of the column, and the distance between the reservoirs a and b corresponds to the radius of the tube. After filling the MIX region with the gaseous mixture, I introduce one of the components (component 1, say) into the terminal parts at α and β, adjusting the semipermeable membranes accordingly. I then set up a steady flow of component 1 through the MIX region from one terminal part to the other in such a way that $\dot{n}_\alpha + \dot{n}_\beta = 0$:

$$\dot{n}_\alpha\{(\overline{H}_\alpha + \varphi_\alpha) - (\overline{H}_\beta + \varphi_\beta)\} + \dot{Q}_a^{(r)} + \dot{Q}_b^{(r)} = 0, \tag{8.28}$$

$$\begin{aligned}\Theta &= \dot{n}_\alpha(\overline{S}_\alpha - \overline{S}_\beta) + \frac{\dot{Q}_a^{(r)}}{T_a} + \frac{\dot{Q}_b^{(r)}}{T_b} \\ &= \dot{n}_\alpha\left(\frac{\overline{H}_\beta + \varphi_\beta}{T_b} - \frac{\overline{H}_\alpha + \varphi_\alpha}{T_b} + \overline{S}_\alpha - \overline{S}_\beta\right) + \dot{Q}_a^{(r)}\left(\frac{1}{T_a} - \frac{1}{T_b}\right) \\ &= \dot{n}_\alpha \frac{\mu_\beta + \varphi_\beta - \mu_\alpha - \varphi_\alpha}{T_b} + \dot{Q}_a^{(r)}\left(\frac{1}{T_a} - \frac{1}{T_b}\right) \\ &= Y_1\Omega_1 + Y_2\Omega_2,\end{aligned} \tag{8.29}$$

where φ_ω is the molar gravitational energy of the material in the ω terminal part. Applying the operation $(\delta/\tilde{\delta}\dot{n}_\alpha)_{T_a,T_b}$ to Eq. (8.28) and making use of assumption IV, we get, as the condition for the migrational equilibrium of component 1,

$$0 = \frac{\mu_\beta + \varphi_\beta - \mu_\alpha - \varphi_\alpha}{T_b} + \left(\frac{\delta\dot{Q}_a^{(r)}}{\tilde{\delta}\dot{n}_\alpha}\right)_{T_a,T_b}\left(\frac{1}{T_a} - \frac{1}{T_b}\right)$$

or

$$0 = \mu_\beta + \varphi_\beta - \mu_\alpha - \varphi_\alpha + \left(\frac{\delta\dot{S}_a^{(r)}}{\tilde{\delta}\dot{n}_\alpha}\right)_{T_a,T_b}(T_b - T_a). \tag{8.30}$$

Upon explicitly introducing the fact that it is component 1 we have been dealing with, we have

$$RT_b \ln\frac{X_\beta^{(1)}}{X_\alpha^{(1)}} = M^{(1)}g(h_\alpha - h_\beta) + \left(\frac{\delta\dot{S}_a^{(r)}}{\tilde{\delta}\dot{n}_\alpha^{(1)}}\right)_{T_a,T_b}(T_a - T_b), \tag{8.31}$$

with $X_\omega^{(1)}$ being the mole fraction of component 1 in the gaseous mixture at a point adjacent to the ω terminal part, $M^{(1)}$ being the molecular weight of component 1, g being the acceleration due to gravity, and h_ω being the height of the ω terminal part above some reference plane.

If, now, we repeat the entire procedure with respect to component 2, we obtain

$$RT_b \ln\frac{X_\beta^{(2)}}{X_\alpha^{(2)}} = M^{(2)}g(h_\alpha - h_\beta) + \left(\frac{\delta\dot{S}_a^{(r)}}{\tilde{\delta}\dot{n}_\alpha^{(2)}}\right)_{T_a,T_b}(T_a - T_b) \tag{8.32}$$

and

$$RT_b \ln \frac{(X_\beta^{(1)}/X_\alpha^{(1)})}{(X_\beta^{(2)}/X_\alpha^{(2)})} = g(M^{(1)} - M^{(2)})(h_\alpha - h_\beta) + (T_a - T_b)\left\{\left(\frac{\delta \dot{S}_\alpha^{(r)}}{\tilde{\delta}\dot{n}_\alpha^{(1)}}\right)_{T_a, T_b} - \left(\frac{\delta \dot{S}_\alpha^{(r)}}{\tilde{\delta}\dot{n}_\alpha^{(2)}}\right)_{T_a, T_b}\right\}. \tag{8.33}$$

Thus

$$RT_b \ln \mathbf{q} = g\,\Delta M\,\Delta h + \Delta T\,\Delta\left(\frac{\delta \dot{S}_\alpha^{(r)}}{\tilde{\delta}\dot{n}_\alpha}\right)_{T_a, T_b}. \tag{8.34}$$

We see, then, that the separation factor $\mathbf{q}$ depends on the difference in molecular weight ΔM for the components, on the length Δh of the column, on the temperature difference ΔT between the wire and the wall, and on the quantity $\Delta(\delta \dot{S}_\alpha^{(r)}/\tilde{\delta}\dot{n}_\alpha)_{T_a, T_b}$, which is a complicated function of the dimensions of the tube and of the exact way in which the motion of the gaseous mixture along the tube couples with the flow of heat from the wire to the wall [8].

Clusius and Dickel [7] used a column 20 meters long with $\Delta T \approx 700°\text{K}$ to effect a separation of the isotopes of chlorine. They filled the column with a mixture of $H^{35}Cl$ and $H^{37}Cl$. When the state of migrational equilibrium was reached, their analysis showed that the gas at the bottom of the tube was 75.7% $H^{35}Cl$, whereas the gas at the top of the tube was 99.6% $H^{35}Cl$. They had thus achieved a separation factor of ~ 80. From Eq. (8.34) we see that in this case

$$600 \ln 80 = 980 \times 2 \times 2000(4.18 \times 10^7)^{-1} + 700\,\Delta\left(\frac{\delta \dot{S}_\alpha^{(r)}}{\tilde{\delta}\dot{n}_\alpha}\right)_{T_a, T_b}$$

$$\approx 0.1 + 700\,\Delta\left(\frac{\delta \dot{S}_\alpha^{(r)}}{\tilde{\delta}\dot{n}_\alpha}\right)_{T_a, T_b}, \tag{8.35}$$

and the simple gravitational effect is negligible compared to the thermal diffusion-based effect.

Thermal Diffusion in Solutions—Soret Effect

Consider two different thermal states of a ν-component solution connected by a narrow tube linkage (Figure 8–7). Let one of the components be designated as the solvent and be indicated by the index 1, and let the composition of the solution be expressed by the molalities* of the other $\nu - 1$ components relative to component 1 or in terms of the mole fractions $X_\omega^{(k)}$ of the same $\nu - 1$ components. If in Figure 8–7 $m_\alpha^{(k)} \neq m_\beta^{(k)}$ for $T_\alpha \neq T_\beta$, we say that the solution shows a *Soret effect* with respect to component k. (For convenience let $m_\omega^{(1)} \equiv 1000/M_1$, with M_1 being the gram-molecular weight of component 1.)

* The molality $m^{(k)}$ of component k is the number of moles of component k per kilogram of component 1.

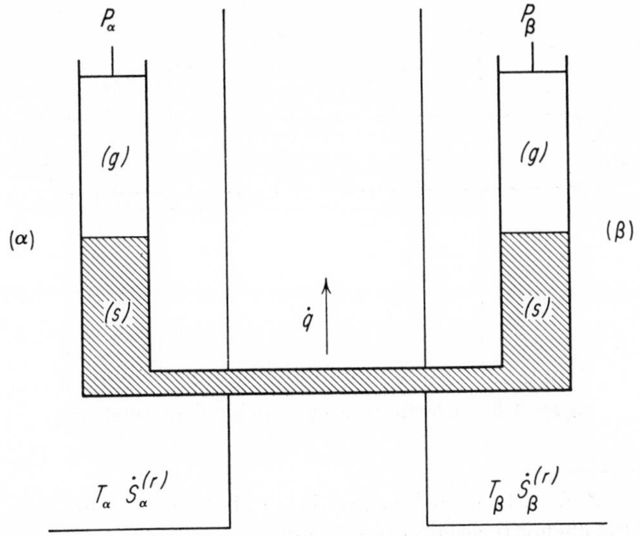

Figure 8–7. Two thermal states of a ν-component solution connected by a narrow-tube arbitrary linkage.

Now if the solvent is volatile while the other $\nu - 1$ components are not, then by letting P_ω differ from the solvent vapor pressure $P_\omega^{(1)}$ appropriate to the state of migrational equilibrium we can initiate a steady flow of component 1 between terminal parts and can converge on the state of migrational equilibrium via a sequence of steady-flow states. Equation (6.39) with $(\delta/\bar{\delta}\dot{n})_{\Omega'} = (\delta/\bar{\delta}\dot{n}_\alpha^{(1)})_{\Omega'}$ and $\dot{W}_0 = 0$—together with the relation $\mu_\omega^{(g)} = \mu_\omega^{(1)}$—yields

$$\mu_\alpha^{(1)} - \mu_\beta^{(1)} + T_\alpha[S_\alpha^{(1)}] - T_\beta[S_\beta^{(1)}] - [h_1(\beta\alpha)] = 0, \tag{8.36}$$

$$[H_\alpha^{(1)}] - [H_\beta^{(1)}] = [h_1(\beta\alpha)], \tag{8.37}$$

$$[G_\alpha^{(1)}] - [G_\beta^{(1)}] = 0. \tag{8.38}$$

For the steady flow of any single component k between terminal parts, Eq. (6.39) taken with respect to $(\delta/\bar{\delta}\dot{n}_\alpha^{(k)})_{\Omega'}$ yields

$$[H_\alpha^{(k)}] - [H_\beta^{(k)}] = [h_k(\beta\alpha)], \tag{8.39}$$

$$[G_\alpha^{(k)}] - [G_\beta^{(k)}] = 0. \tag{8.40}$$

For aqueous solutions of electrolytes the maintenance of a steady flow of an electrolyte component probably requires electrochemical adjuncts. (I discuss such systems more fully under the title *thermocells* in Chapter 9.) As long as the steady flow of a component between *terminal parts* can be maintained in *some* way, Eq. (8.40) must hold for the migrational equilibrium of that component.

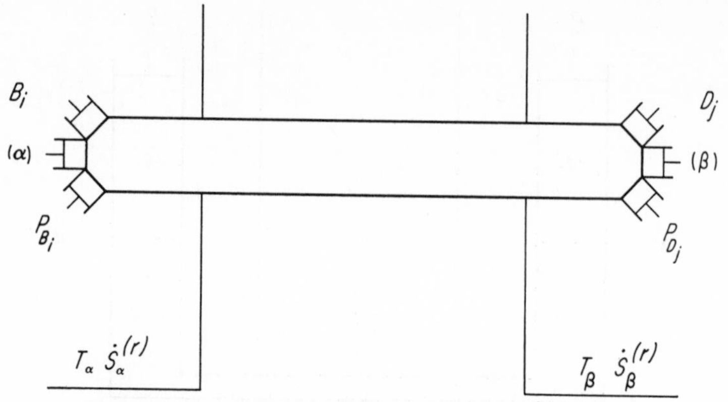

Figure 8–8. Chemical reaction in a polythermal field.

Exercise 8–7. Chemical Reaction in a Polythermal Field
Consider the chemical reaction (see Chapter 2)

$$\sum \nu_i B_i = \sum \nu_j D_j$$

and the situation indicated in Figure 8–8. Let the reactant reservoirs B_i be immersed in a thermostat of temperature T_α, and let the product reservoirs D_j be immersed in a thermostat of temperature T_β; let the reaction vessel function as a linkage between the thermostats. For the situation in which there is a steady flow of $\dot{\xi}$ reaction measures in unit time from reactants to products, show that the migrational equilibrium condition for the chemical reaction in the polythermal field is that

$$\sum \nu_j[G_\beta^{(j)}] - \sum \nu_i[G_\alpha^{(i)}] = 0. \tag{8.41}$$

From the definitions (for the case $P_\alpha = P_\beta = P(\text{atmospheric}) =$ constant)

$$[S_\omega^{(j)}]^\partial \equiv -\left(\frac{\partial \mu_\omega^{(j)}}{\partial T_\omega}\right)_\chi \qquad j = 1, 2, \ldots, \nu, \tag{8.42}$$

$$\mu_\omega^{(k)} \equiv (\mu_\omega^{(k)})^0 + RT_\omega \ln(\gamma_\omega^{(k)}\zeta_\omega^{(k)}) \quad k = 2, 3, \ldots, \nu, \quad \zeta = m \text{ or } X, \tag{8.43}$$

and the Gibbs–Duhem relation for the solution phase (s) at ω,

$$S_\omega^{(s)}\, dT_\omega - V_\omega^{(s)}\, dP_\omega + \sum_{j=1}^{\nu} n_\omega^{(j)}\, d\mu_\omega^{(j)} = 0, \tag{8.44}$$

we see that

$$\sum_{j=1}^{\nu} \zeta_\omega^{(j)}[Q_\omega^{(j)}]^\partial = T_\omega \sum_{j=1}^{\nu} \zeta_\omega^{(j)}(\bar{S}_\omega^{(j)} - [S_\omega^{(j)}]^\partial) = 0, \tag{8.45}$$

$$[Q_\omega^{(j)}]^\partial = \sum_{k=2}^{\nu}\left(\frac{\partial \mu_\omega^{(j)}}{\partial \ln \zeta_\omega^{(k)}}\right)_{T_\omega, P, \zeta_\omega}\left(\frac{\partial \ln \zeta_\omega^{(k)}}{\partial \ln T_\omega}\right)_{\chi, P}. \tag{8.46}$$

For the special case of a 2-component solution

$$[Q_{\omega}^{(2)}]^{\partial} = RT_{\omega}^{2}\left\{1 + \left(\frac{\partial \ln \gamma_{\omega}^{(2)}}{\partial \ln \zeta_{\omega}^{(2)}}\right)_{T_{\omega},P}\right\}\left(\frac{\partial \ln \zeta_{\omega}^{(2)}}{\partial T_{\omega}}\right)_{X,P} \qquad \zeta = m, X. \tag{8.47}$$

The subscript ζ_{ω} in Eq. (8.46) means that the other $\nu - 2$ concentration variables are to be kept constant during the differentiation; the $\gamma_{\omega}^{(j)}$ quantities are activity coefficients appropriate to the choice of concentration variables (m or X). The integration of Eq. (8.47) between the states α and β yields

$$\ln \frac{\zeta_{\beta}^{(2)}}{\zeta_{\alpha}^{(2)}} = -\left\langle \frac{[Q^{(2)}]^{\partial}}{R\{1 + (\partial \ln \gamma^{(2)}/\partial \ln \zeta^{(2)})_{T,P}\}} \right\rangle \left(\frac{1}{T_{\beta}} - \frac{1}{T_{\alpha}}\right). \tag{8.48}$$

It has become customary to perform Soret-type experiments in wide-diameter vertical tubes with small ($\sim 10°$) temperature differences between top and bottom and to report the results in terms of a *Soret coefficient* $\boldsymbol{\sigma} \equiv -\partial \ln m/\partial T$; from Eq. (8.47) we see that

$$\boldsymbol{\sigma} \approx -\frac{\ln (m_{\beta}^{(2)}/m_{\alpha}^{(2)})}{T_{\beta} - T_{\alpha}} = -\left\langle \frac{[Q^{(2)}]^{\partial}}{RT^{2}\{1 + (\partial \ln \gamma^{(2)}/\partial \ln m^{(2)})_{T,P}\}} \right\rangle. \tag{8.49}$$

In dealing with solutions of electrolytes, it is customary to express Eqs. (8.43) and (8.46) to (8.49) in terms of mean ionic activity coefficients $\gamma_{\pm}$ [9]. Figure 8–9 shows the results obtained by Chipman [10] for the system H_2O—HCl. The Soret coefficient defined in the preceding manner is taken to be a function of the average temperature and average concentration in the

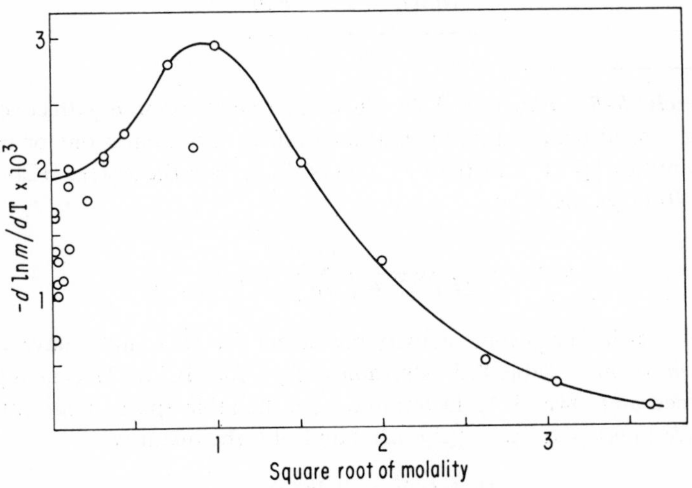

Figure 8–9. Soret effect for the system H_2O—HCl at 25°C (data of Chipman). (From the *J. Am. Chem. Soc.*, **48**, 2577 (1926), by permission.)

tube. A positive value of σ means that the substance is more concentrated at the colder end of the tube. Agar and Turner [11–13] have been especially active in this field; Table 8–4 is a compilation of some typical results obtained by Turner [13].

Table 8–4

Soret Effect for 1–1 Electrolytes at 0.01 Mole/Liter and a Mean Temperature of ~25°C
(Data of Snowdon and Turner [13])

Substance	$10^3\sigma(\text{deg}^{-1})$
LiF	2.35
LiCl	0.02
LiBr	0.08
LiI	−1.44
KF	3.81
KCl	1.41
KBr	1.44
KI	−0.08
KNO_3	0.64
KOH	13.34
$KClO_4$	0.79
KIO_4	2.47
$TlNO_3$	1.87
$AgNO_3$	3.40
HCl	9.03
$HClO_4$	8.29

Exercise 8–8. Equation (8.49) shows that variation in σ with concentration for a fixed temperature interval may reflect variation in one or both of the quantities $[Q^{(2)}]^{\partial}$ and $(\partial \ln \gamma^{(2)}/\partial \ln m^{(2)})_{T,P}$. For the system HCl—$H_2O$, Eq. (8.49) takes the form

$$\sigma \approx -\left\langle \frac{[Q^{(2)}]^{\partial}}{2RT^2\{1 + (\partial \ln \gamma_{\pm}/\partial \ln m)_{T,P}\}} \right\rangle,$$

where $\gamma_{\pm}$ is the mean ionic activity coefficient for HCl, and I have written simply m for $m^{(2)}$. Table 8–5 lists values of $\gamma_{\pm}$ for HCl at 25°C as reported by Harned and Owen [14]. Determine from the table approximate values of $(\partial \ln \gamma_{\pm}/\partial \ln m)_{T,P} \approx (m/\gamma_{\pm})(\Delta\gamma_{\pm}/\Delta m)$ and plot the quantity

$$\{1 + (\partial \ln \gamma_{\pm}/\partial \ln m)_{T,P}\}^{-1}$$

versus $m^{1/2}$. Compare the general shape of this plot with that of Chipman's plot (Figure 8–9).

Table 8–5

The Mean Ionic Activity Coefficient $\gamma_{\pm}$ for HCl(aq) at 25°C
(Compilation of Harned and Owen [14])

m	$\gamma_{\pm}$
0.001	0.9656
0.002	0.9521
0.005	0.9285
0.01	0.9048
0.02	0.8755
0.05	0.8304
0.1	0.7964
0.5	0.7571
1.0	0.8090
1.5	0.8962
2	1.0090
3	1.316

I should like to see the measurement and theoretical treatment of the Soret effect based firmly on the linkage concept developed in Chapter 5 in conjunction with the thermomolecular pressure effect. In wide-diameter tubes the possibility of convection currents is an ever present source of annoyance. Would it not be better to introduce a well-defined linkage between terminal parts, to calculate quantities appropriate to either end of the linkage (the quantities $[Q_{\omega}^{(i)}]^{\partial}$, say), to make plots such as $[Q_{\omega}^{(i)}]^{\partial}$ versus $[Q_{\chi}^{(i)}]^{\partial}$ for a given (T_{ω}, T_{χ}) bitherm, and to study a *series* of linkages of varying diameter so as to be able to extrapolate the results to an infinite-diameter limit? Such a procedure would produce a *complete* study: we would obtain apparatus-dependent results of importance for engineering applications, and we could *confidently* use the apparatus-independent, infinite-diameter limiting values in theoretical discussions.

Three-Component Soret Cell with Constraint, Full-Flux Linkage

Consider an aqueous solution containing both a sparingly soluble salt and a second quite soluble salt. Such a solution is a 3-component system; let components 1, 2, and 3 be water, sparingly soluble salt, and quite soluble salt, respectively. Figure 8–10 is a schematic rendering of the situation. The system of interest is composed of two terminal parts (α, β) at temperatures T_{α} and T_{β}; the terminal parts are connected by a gradient part that is the site of the temperature gradient in the system; the connecting link is of the full-flux

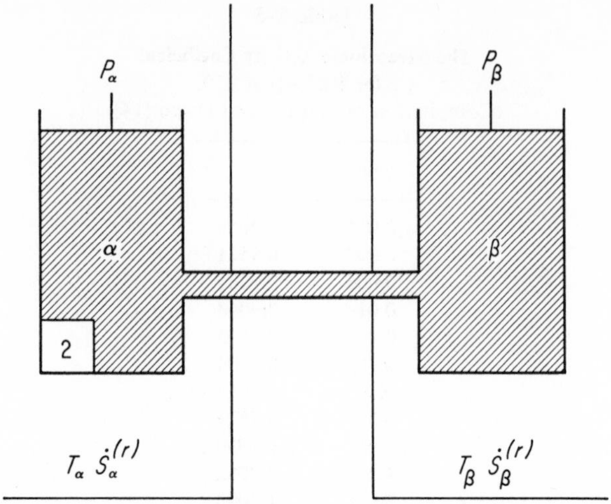

Figure 8–10. Schematic version of a 3-component Soret cell, full-flux linkage. Terminal part α contains some solid component 2.

type and $\dot{W}_0 = 0$. Fill the apparatus with the 3-component solution and saturate the terminal part at α with the sparingly soluble salt (let it contain some solid salt). The chemical potential of the second component in the α terminal part $\mu_\alpha^{(2)}$ is then fixed for a given T_α. Let $T_\alpha \neq T_\beta$; let $P_\alpha = P_\beta = P$ (atmospheric); and let the subscript $\chi(i)$ mean constant T_χ, P_χ, $\mu_\chi^{(i)}$. Thus we have prepared a polythermal field subject to a constraint; the chemical potential of component 2 in the α terminal part $\mu_\alpha^{(2)}$ is maintained constant; i.e., $\mu_\alpha^{(2)} = \mu_\alpha^{(2)}(\text{sat})$. I wonder if this constraint influences other parts of the polythermal field as well? Is $\mu_\beta^{(2)}$ equal to $\mu_\beta^{(2)}(\text{sat})$ under conditions of migrational equilibrium? Is $\mu_\beta^{(2)}$ independent of the molality of the third component at constant T_α, T_β? In order to explore the situation, we need to investigate operations such as $(\partial/\partial T_\beta)_{\alpha(2),m_\alpha^{(3)}}$ and $(\partial/\partial m_\alpha^{(3)})_{\alpha(2),T_\beta}$, where $m_\alpha^{(3)}$ is the molality of component 3 in the α terminal part. I lay down the following definitions:

$$\left(\frac{\partial \mu_\beta^{(2)}}{\partial T_\beta}\right)_{\alpha(2),m_\alpha^{(3)}} \equiv -[S_\beta^{(22)}]^\partial, \tag{8.50}$$

$$\left(\frac{\partial \mu_\beta^{(2)}}{\partial m_\alpha^{(3)}}\right)_{\alpha(2),T_\beta} \equiv RT_\beta[M_\beta^{(23)}]^\partial, \tag{8.51}$$

$$\mu_\beta^{(2)} \equiv \mu_\beta^{(2)}(\text{sat}) + RT_\beta \ln \theta_\beta^{(2)}, \tag{8.52}$$

$$\mu_\beta^{(2)}(m_\alpha^{(3)}) \equiv \mu_\beta^{(2)}(0) + RT_\beta m_\alpha^{(3)}[M_\beta^{(23)}] \quad \text{const. } \mu_\alpha^{(2)}, P, T_\alpha, T_\beta, \tag{8.53}$$

where $\mu_\beta^{(2)}(\text{sat})$ represents the value of the given chemical potential in a solution saturated with component 2 at temperature T_β and pressure P. We also have available a number of standard relationships:

$$\mu_\beta^{(2)} - \mu_\alpha^{(2)} = -\int_{T_\alpha}^{T_\beta} [S_b^{(22)}]^\partial \, dT_b, \tag{8.54}$$

$$\left(\frac{\partial \mu_\beta^{(2)}}{\partial T_\beta}\right)_{\alpha(2), m_\alpha^{(3)}} = -\left(\frac{\partial \mu_\beta^{(2)}}{\partial m_\alpha^{(3)}}\right)_{\alpha(2), T_\beta} \left(\frac{\partial m_\alpha^{(3)}}{\partial T_\beta}\right)_{\alpha(2), \mu_\beta^{(2)}}, \tag{8.55}$$

$$\mu_\beta^{(2)} = (\mu_\beta^{(2)})^0 + RT_\beta \ln a_\beta^{(2)} = (\mu_\beta^{(2)})^0 + RT_\beta \ln (\gamma_\beta^{(2)} m_\beta^{(2)}), \tag{8.56}$$

where $a_\beta^{(2)}$ is the activity of component 2 in terminal part β. We need two composition variables such as $(X^{(2)}, X^{(3)})$ or $(m^{(2)}, m^{(3)})$ to help fix the thermodynamic state of each terminal part.

Equations (8.50) to (8.56) lead to the following theorems:

$$[M_\beta^{(23)}]^\partial = \left(\frac{\partial \ln \theta_\beta^{(2)}}{\partial m_\alpha^{(3)}}\right)_{\alpha(2), T_\beta}, \tag{8.57}$$

$$\begin{aligned}\left(\frac{\partial \ln \theta_\beta^{(2)}}{\partial T_\beta}\right)_{\alpha(2), m_\alpha^{(3)}} &= \frac{\bar{H}_\beta^{(2)}(\text{sat}) - \bar{H}_\beta^{(2)} + \bar{H}_\beta^{(2)} - [H_\beta^{(22)}]^\partial}{RT_\beta^2} \\ &= \frac{\Delta \bar{H}_\beta^{(2)} + [Q_\beta^{(22)}]^\partial}{RT_\beta{}^2},\end{aligned} \tag{8.58}$$

$$[M_\beta^{(23)}] = \frac{1}{m_\alpha^{(3)}} \int_0^{m_\alpha^{(3)}} [M_\beta^{(23)}]^\partial \, dm_\alpha^{(3)}, \tag{8.59}$$

$$\left(\frac{\partial [M_\beta^{(23)}]}{\partial T_\beta}\right)_{\alpha(2), m_\alpha^{(3)}} = \frac{[H_\beta^{(22)}]^\partial - [H_\beta^{(22)}(0)]^\partial}{m_\alpha^{(3)} RT_\beta{}^2}, \tag{8.60}$$

$$-[M_\beta^{(23)}]^\partial = \frac{1}{RT_\beta} \int_{T_\alpha}^{T_\beta} \left(\frac{\partial [S_b^{(22)}]^\partial}{\partial m_\alpha^{(3)}}\right)_{\alpha(2), T_b} dT_b, \tag{8.61}$$

$$[S_\beta^{(22)}]^\partial = RT_\beta [M_\beta^{(23)}]^\partial \left(\frac{\partial m_\alpha^{(3)}}{\partial T_\beta}\right)_{\alpha(2), \mu_\beta^{(2)}}, \tag{8.62}$$

$$[M_\beta^{(23)}]^\partial = \left(\frac{\partial \ln a_\beta^{(2)}}{\partial m_\beta^{(3)}}\right)_{\alpha(2), T_\beta} \left(\frac{\partial m_\beta^{(3)}}{\partial m_\alpha^{(3)}}\right)_{\alpha(2), T_\beta}, \tag{8.63}$$

$$\begin{aligned}\left(\frac{\partial \ln m_\beta^{(2)}}{\partial T_\beta}\right)_{\alpha(2), m_\alpha^{(3)}} &= \frac{\bar{S}_\beta^{(2)} - [S_\beta^{(22)}]^\partial}{RT_\beta} + \left(\frac{\partial \ln \gamma_\beta^{(2)}}{\partial T_\beta}\right)_{m_\beta^{(2)}, m_\beta^{(3)}} - \left(\frac{\partial \ln \gamma_\beta^{(2)}}{\partial T_\beta}\right)_{\alpha(2), m_\alpha^{(3)}} \\ &= \frac{[Q_\beta^{(22)}]^\partial}{RT_\beta{}^2} + \Delta\left(\frac{\partial \ln \gamma_\beta^{(2)}}{\partial T_\beta}\right),\end{aligned} \tag{8.64}$$

where $[H]^\partial \equiv \mu + T[S]^\partial$ and $[Q]^\partial \equiv \bar{H} - [H]^\partial$.

We can often evaluate the quantities in the preceding equations by inserting suitable electrodes into the solution in the β terminal part and making emf measurements. By way of example let the sparingly soluble salt be $PbCl_2$; let the quite soluble salt be KNO_3; and let Pb(s) and Ag(s), AgCl(s) electrodes be inserted into the solution at β. We then have at β the cell Pb(s)|solution|AgCl(s), Ag(s) with overall reaction

$$Pb(s) + 2AgCl(s) = 2Ag(s) + PbCl_2(solution)$$

for every 2 Faradays of electricity passing through the cell. For the given cell we have the relations

$$-2FE_\beta = \mu_\beta^{(PbCl_2)} + 2\mu_\beta^{(Ag)} - 2\mu_\beta^{(AgCl)} - \mu_\beta^{(Pb)}, \tag{8.65}$$

$$-2F\left(\frac{\partial E_\beta}{\partial m_\alpha^{(3)}}\right)_{\alpha(2),T_\beta} = RT_\beta[M_\beta^{(23)}]^\partial, \tag{8.66}$$

$$-2F\left(\frac{\partial E_\beta}{\partial T_\beta}\right)_{\alpha(2),m_\alpha^{(3)}} = -[S_\beta^{(22)}]^\partial - 2\bar{S}_\beta^{(Ag)} + 2\bar{S}_\beta^{(AgCl)} + \bar{S}_\beta^{(Pb)}, \tag{8.67}$$

$$-2F\{E_\beta - E_\beta(\mathrm{sat})\} = RT_\beta \ln \theta_\beta^{(2)}, \tag{8.68}$$

$$-2F\{E_\beta - E_\beta(0)\} = RT_\beta m_\alpha^{(3)}[M_\beta^{(23)}], \tag{8.69}$$

where E_β is the emf of the cell at β and F is the Faraday.

The most direct experimental procedure is to keep T_α and T_β fixed, keep the terminal part at α saturated with $PbCl_2$, and measure the emf at β as $m_\alpha^{(3)}$ is varied. Repeat this procedure for the same T_α but a new T_β. From a family of E_β versus $m_\alpha^{(3)}$ plots, analyses of the solutions at α and β for the various $m_\omega^{(i)}$ quantities, and studies of the temperature dependence of E_β(sat), we can evaluate the various defined quantities appearing in the preceding equations. In terms of the various quantities introduced, we see that $[Q_\beta^{(22)}]^\partial \neq 0$ implies that there is a Soret effect; $\theta_\beta^{(2)} \neq 1$ implies that the Soret effect is not due merely to the temperature coefficient of solubility; and $[M_\beta^{(23)}]^\partial \neq 0$ implies that the distribution of the given component in the polythermal field depends on the chemical environment as well as the thermal environment.

We have here an example of another language function of thermodynamics: in addition to its efficient encoding and processing of experimental information, the language of thermodynamics (here and in the last section of Chapter 2, e.g.), sometimes suggests interesting new experiments.

References

1. K. Denbigh and G. Raumann, *Proc. Roy. Soc.* (London), **A210**, 518 (1952).
2. R. J. Bearman, *J. Phys. Chem.*, **61**, 708 (1957).
3. S. Chapman and T. Cowling, *The Mathematical Theory of Non-Uniform Gases*, second edition (Cambridge University Press, Cambridge, 1952).
4. K. E. Grew and T. L. Ibbs, *Thermal Diffusion in Gases* (Cambridge University Press, Cambridge, 1952), Chapters 3 and 4.

5. H. R. Heath, T. L. Ibbs, and N. E. Wild, *Proc. Roy. Soc.* (London), **A178**, 380 (1941).
6. B. E. Atkins, R. E. Bastick, and T. L. Ibbs, *Proc. Roy. Soc.* (London), **A172**, 142 (1939).
7. K. Clusius and G. Dickel, *Z. Phys. Chem.*, **B44**, 397, 451 (1939).
8. M. N. Saha and B. N. Srivastava, *A Treatise on Heat*, fourth edition (The Indian Press Private Ltd., Allahabad, 1958), p. 918.
9. H. J. V. Tyrrell, *Diffusion and Heat Flow in Liquids* (Butterworths, London, 1961), Chapter 4.
10. J. Chipman, *J. Am. Chem. Soc.*, **48**, 2577 (1926).
11. J. Agar, *Trans. Faraday Soc.*, **56**, 776 (1960).
12. J. Agar and J. Turner, *Proc. Roy. Soc.* (London), **A255**, 307 (1960).
13. P. Snowdon and J. Turner, *Trans. Faraday Soc.*, **56**, 1409 (1960).
14. H. S. Harned and B. B. Owen, *The Physical Chemistry of Electrolytic Solutions*, second edition (Reinhold Publishing Company, New York, 1950), p. 340

9

Thermocouples and Thermocells

One of the more interesting and practical of the polythermal field effects is the Seebeck effect: the state of migrational equilibrium with respect to the charge carriers in a thermocouple is accompanied by an electrical potential difference (the Seebeck potential difference) that depends only on the temperatures of the bi-material junctions. The situation to be analyzed is indicated schematically in Figure 9–1; the electric engine e at γ is a device for converting electric current to mechanical work (a d-c motor used to raise a weight, say).

Thermocouples

In Figure 9–1 let I be the negative electric current flowing through the system, let the electric engine e be such that the heat effects at γ are purely dissipative heat effects—i.e., $(\delta \dot{Q}_\gamma^{(r)}/\tilde{\delta} I)_T = 0$—and let a sign convention for the direction of the electric current flow be established. Now when a steady current I flows through the system, the entire system is stationary and

$$\dot{U}(\text{system}) = -\dot{Q}_\alpha^{(r)} - \dot{Q}_\beta^{(r)} - \dot{Q}_\gamma^{(r)} - \sum_{i=1}^{6} \dot{Q}_i^{(r)} - \sum \dot{q}(ij) + \dot{W}_0 = 0, \qquad (9.1)$$

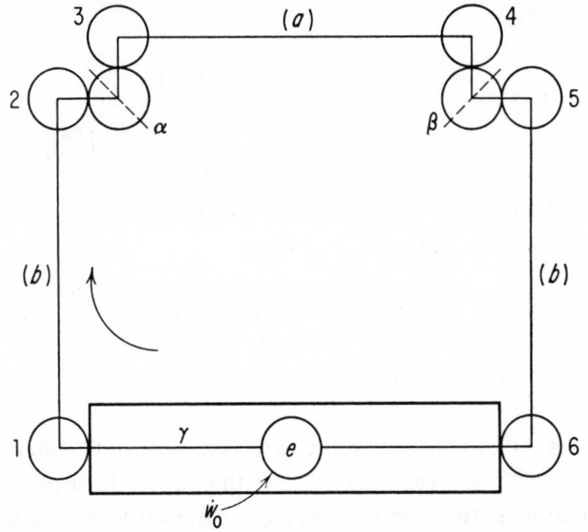

Figure 9–1. Schematic version of a thermocouple: *e*—electric engine at temperature T; 1, γ, 6—heat reservoirs at temperature T; 2, α, 3—heat reservoirs at temperature T_α; 4, β, 5—heat reservoirs at temperature T_β; wire segments e–1–2–α and β–5–6–e of material (*b*); wire segment α–3–4–β of material (*a*); junctions between materials (*a*) and (*b*) occur in reservoirs α and β; $\dot{W}_0$—rate at which work is supplied to the electric engine *e* in order to make negative current I flow in the direction indicated. For convenience let all current-carrying elements of the engine *e* be made of material (*b*).

$$\begin{aligned}\Theta &= \frac{\dot{Q}_\alpha^{(r)}}{T_\alpha} + \frac{\dot{Q}_\beta^{(r)}}{T_\beta} + \frac{\dot{Q}_\gamma^{(r)}}{T} + \sum_{i=1}^{6} \frac{\dot{Q}_i^{(r)}}{T_i} + \sum \frac{\dot{q}(ij)}{\langle T(ij)\rangle} \\
&= \frac{\dot{W}_0}{T} + \dot{Q}_\alpha^{(r)}\left(\frac{1}{T_\alpha} - \frac{1}{T}\right) + \dot{Q}_\beta^{(r)}\left(\frac{1}{T_\beta} - \frac{1}{T}\right) + \sum_{i=2}^{5} \dot{Q}_i^{(r)}\left(\frac{1}{T_i} - \frac{1}{T}\right) \\
&\qquad + \sum \dot{q}(ij)\left(\frac{1}{\langle T(ij)\rangle} - \frac{1}{T}\right) \\
&= I\left(\frac{\dot{W}_0}{IT}\right) + \dot{Q}_\alpha^{(r)}\left(\frac{1}{T_\alpha} - \frac{1}{T}\right) + \dot{Q}_\beta^{(r)}\left(\frac{1}{T_\beta} - \frac{1}{T}\right) + \sum_{i=2}^{5} \dot{Q}_i^{(r)}\left(\frac{1}{T_i} - \frac{1}{T}\right) \\
&\qquad + \sum \dot{q}(ij)\left(\frac{1}{\langle T(ij)\rangle} - \frac{1}{T}\right) \\
&= \sum Y_k \Omega_k, \end{aligned} \tag{9.2}$$

where the quantities $\dot{q}(ij)$ are the rates of lateral heat leakage from the links 12, 34, 56 to the surroundings. We can write Eq. (9.1) as

$$-\dot{W}_0 = -\dot{Q}_\alpha^{(r)} - \dot{Q}_\beta^{(r)} - \dot{Q}_\gamma^{(r)} - \sum \dot{Q}_i^{(r)} - \sum \dot{q}(ij), \tag{9.3}$$

and it follows that

$$\left(\frac{\delta(-\dot{W}_0)}{\delta I}\right)_{T_\alpha, T_\beta, T, \langle T(ij)\rangle} = -\left(\frac{\delta\dot{Q}_\alpha^{(r)}}{\delta I}\right)_{T_\alpha,\ldots} - \left(\frac{\delta\dot{Q}_\beta^{(r)}}{\delta I}\right)_{T_\alpha,\ldots} - \sum\left(\frac{\delta\dot{Q}_i^{(r)}}{\delta I}\right)_{T_\alpha,\ldots} - \sum\left(\frac{\delta\dot{q}(ij)}{\delta I}\right)_{T_\alpha,\ldots}. \tag{9.4}$$

From Eqs. (6.38) and (9.2) we see that the operation $(\delta/\tilde{\delta}I)_{T_\alpha,\ldots}$ is of the form $(\delta/\tilde{\delta}\, Y_{0x})_{\Omega'}$. We can also express Eq. (9.4) as

$$\begin{aligned} \Delta\psi &= \int_T^{T_\alpha}[c^{(b)}]\,dT + \pi_\alpha^{(ba)} + \int_{T_\alpha}^{T_\beta}[c^{(a)}]\,dT + \pi_\beta^{(ab)} + \int_{T_\beta}^{T}[c^{(b)}]\,dT \\ &= \int_{T_\alpha}^{T_\beta}\{[c^{(a)}] - [c^{(b)}]\}\,dT + \pi_\alpha^{(ba)} + \pi_\beta^{(ab)}, \end{aligned} \tag{9.5}$$

where $\Delta\psi \equiv (\delta(-\dot{W}_0)/\tilde{\delta}I)_{T_\alpha,\ldots}$ is the Seebeck potential difference of the thermocouple,* $\pi_\omega^{(ba)} \equiv -(\delta\dot{Q}_\omega^{(r)}/\tilde{\delta}I)_{T_\alpha,\ldots}$ is the Peltier heat absorbed at the bimetallic junction as the current goes from material b to material a,† and I have made use of the assumed properties of the engine e $[(\delta\dot{Q}_\gamma^{(r)}/\tilde{\delta}I)_T = 0]$ and of the definition, e.g.,‡

$$\left(\frac{\delta(\dot{Q}_1^{(r)} + \dot{Q}_2^{(r)} + \dot{q}(12))}{\tilde{\delta}I}\right)_{T_1, T_2, \langle T(12)\rangle} \equiv -\int_{T_1}^{T_2}[c^{(b)}]\,dT \tag{9.6}$$

for the Thomson coefficient $[c]$ (defined in terms of the flow of negative electricity).

We see from Eq. (9.5) that

$$\begin{aligned} \left(\frac{\partial\,\Delta\psi}{\partial T_\beta}\right)_{T_\alpha} &= [c_\beta^{(a)}] - [c_\beta^{(b)}] + \left(\frac{\partial \pi_\beta^{(ab)}}{\partial T_\beta}\right)_{T_\alpha} \\ &= [c_\beta^{(a)}] - [c_\beta^{(b)}] + \frac{\pi_\beta^{(ab)}}{T_\beta} + T_\beta\frac{d(\pi_\beta^{(ab)}/T_\beta)}{dT_\beta}, \end{aligned} \tag{9.7}$$

where for convenience I have written $\pi_\beta^{(ab)} = \pi_\beta^{(ab)}(T_\beta, a, b)$ as $T_\beta(\pi_\beta^{(ab)}/T_\beta)$. The application of assumption IV to the present situation leads to

$$-\left(\frac{\delta\Theta}{\tilde{\delta}I}\right)_{T_\alpha,\ldots} = \int_{T_\alpha}^{T_\beta}\frac{[c^{(a)}] - [c^{(b)}]}{T}\,dT + \frac{\pi_\alpha^{(ba)}}{T_\alpha} + \frac{\pi_\beta^{(ab)}}{T_\beta} = 0 \tag{9.8}$$

and, by the application of the operation $(\partial/\partial T_\beta)_{T_\alpha}$ to Eq. (9.8), to

$$\frac{[c_\beta^{(a)}] - [c_\beta^{(b)}]}{T_\beta} + \frac{d(\pi_\beta^{(ab)}/T_\beta)}{dT_\beta} = 0. \tag{9.9}$$

* Depending on the sign convention for the direction of electric current flow, we have $\Delta\psi = \pm(\psi' - \psi'')$ with ψ' and ψ'' being the electrical potentials of the binding posts of the electric engine e. See the note in Chapter 4.

† The Peltier heat has the property that $\pi_\omega^{(ba)} = -\pi_\omega^{(ab)}$.

‡ See Eq. (6.17).

Equations (9.7) and (9.9) lead to the Thomson relations [1] for the thermocouple:

$$\left(\frac{\partial\,\Delta\psi}{\partial T_\beta}\right)_{T_\alpha} = \frac{\pi_\beta^{(ab)}}{T_\beta}, \tag{9.10}$$

$$T_\beta\left(\frac{\partial^2\,\Delta\psi}{\partial {T_\beta}^2}\right)_{T_\alpha} = [c_\beta^{(b)}] - [c_\beta^{(a)}], \tag{9.11}$$

$$\left(\frac{\partial\,\Delta\psi}{\partial T}\right)_{T_\alpha, T_\beta} = 0. \tag{9.12}$$

Thus the Thomson relations (Eqs. 9.10 and 9.11) depend only on the applicability of assumption IV; if IV is satisfied, the Thomson relations must hold whether we deal with metallic conductors or with semiconductors. Indeed, the wide applicability [2] of the Thomson relations is evidence for the general acceptance of assumption IV.* The treatment here is essentially that of Thomson [1] cast into a physically more reasonable (assumption IV) form.†

Inasmuch as the form of Eq. (9.8) is not immediately obvious, I here give a derivation. Consider a loop of a single, homogeneous piece of wire arranged as in Figure 9–2. Let the 12 link be of the partial-flux type, and let the 34 link be of the zero-flux type; i.e., an infinite number of auxiliary thermal reservoirs are stationed along the 34 link and exchange heat with the link in such a way as to maintain the temperature distribution in the 34 link in the $I = 0$ configuration even when $I \neq 0$. The total heat exchanged between the auxiliary reservoirs and the 34 link per unit current in the limit of vanishing current is just $(\delta\dot{q}(34)/\bar{\delta}I)_{T_\gamma, T_\delta} = -\int_{T_\delta}^{T_\gamma} [c]\, dT$. The application of assumption IV to this situation leads to

$$\left(\frac{\delta\,\Theta}{\bar{\delta}I}\right)_{T_1,\ldots} = \left(\frac{\delta(\dot{S}_1^{(r)} + \dot{S}_2^{(r)} + \dot{s}(12))}{\bar{\delta}I}\right)_{T_1,\ldots} - \int_{T_\delta}^{T_\gamma} \frac{[c]}{T}\, dT = 0, \tag{9.13}$$

* Lancia and McGervey [3] have questioned the validity of the Thomson relations for inhomogeneous materials. They measured Peltier heats in a Bunsen-type ice calorimeter and made Seebeck measurements by using resistance heating of the thermocouple junctions; they used currents of several tenths of an ampere in these measurements. For thermocouples made from bismuth–tellurium alloys and copper wire, they found that the percentage difference, $\{(\partial\,\Delta\psi/\partial T - \pi/T)/\partial\,\Delta\psi/\partial T\} \times 100$, ranged from 5–17% for their Bi–Te alloys. The alloys showed a 5–10% variation in resistivity over a 30-cm length, and Lancia and McGervey attribute the apparent breakdown of the Thomson relations to the inhomogeneity of the samples.

I feel that the significance of the results of Lancia and McGervey would have been greater had they made measurements at various current levels and had they systematically extrapolated the results to zero current. As it is, the rather large currents used in the inhomogeneous medium somewhat cloud the issue: we cannot be sure that the deviations from the Thomson relations do not vanish in the limit of zero current.

† Remember that assumption IV is a necessary and sufficient condition for the existence of Onsager reciprocal relations in the linear current-affinity region; see Chapter 3.

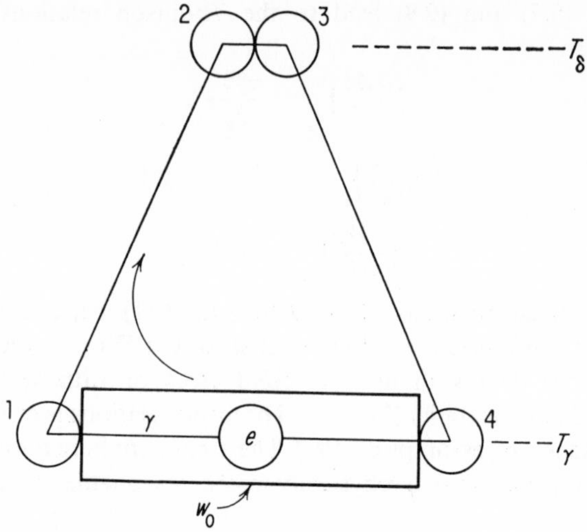

Figure 9–2. A single, homogeneous loop of wire attached to an electric engine e: 1, γ, 4—heat reservoirs at temperature T_γ; 2,3—heat reservoirs at temperature T_δ; $\dot{W}_0$—rate at which work is supplied to the electric engine so as to make negative current I flow in the direction indicated. Let all current-carrying elements of the engine e be made of the same wire as the loop.

where $\dot{s}(12)$ is the rate of gain of entropy in the surroundings of the 12 link associated with the heat quantity $\dot{q}(12)$, and the integral represents the entropy gain of the auxiliary (Thomson) reservoirs per unit current in the limit of vanishing current. Equation (9.13) shows that for any arbitrary ij link (current flowing from i to j) we have*

$$-\left(\frac{\delta(\dot{S}_i^{(r)} + \dot{S}_j^{(r)} + \dot{s}(ij))}{\delta I}\right)_{T_i,\dots} = \int_{T_i}^{T_j} \frac{[c]}{T}\, dT \tag{9.14}$$

regardless of the nature (full, partial, or zero flux) of the linkage. For the case analyzed in Figure 9–1 we have

$$-\Theta = -\frac{\dot{Q}_\alpha^{(r)}}{T_\alpha} - \frac{\dot{Q}_\beta^{(r)}}{T_\beta} - \frac{\dot{Q}_\gamma^{(r)}}{T} - \sum \dot{S}_i^{(r)} - \sum \dot{s}(ij); \tag{9.15}$$

if we apply the operation $(\delta/\delta I)_{T_\alpha,\dots}$ to Eq. (9.15), and if we make use of assumption IV, of the definition of $\pi_\omega^{(ab)}$, and of Eq. (9.14), we arrive at Eq. (9.8).

* Note the *order*, with respect to the direction of current flow, of the limits of integration in Eqs. (9.13) and (9.14).

Electrons in Homogeneous Isotropic Metallic Wires

If we turn to thermocouples composed of homogeneous isotropic metallic wires and if we assume that electrons are the only charge carriers, we can then carry out an analysis of the situation in terms of the electrochemical potential $\bar{\mu}$ of the electron and can arrive at some surprising results. Let $\bar{Z}$ represent a thermodynamic property associated with 1 mole of electrons in a given medium and let $\mathscr{Z} \equiv \bar{Z} - F\psi$, where F is the Faraday and ψ is the electric potential for electrons in the given medium; then

$$\mathscr{G} \equiv \bar{\mu} \equiv \mu - F\psi \; (\mu \equiv \bar{G} = \bar{U} + P\bar{V} - T\bar{S}).$$

In Figure 9–1 let materials (a) and (b) be homogeneous isotropic metallic wires and set

$$\Delta\psi = \psi_1 - \psi_6; \tag{9.16}$$

then

$$F\Delta\psi = \bar{\mu}_6 - \bar{\mu}_1 = \sum_{i=1}^{6} (-1)^i \bar{\mu}_i, \tag{9.17}$$

since [4] $\bar{\mu}_2 = \bar{\mu}_3$ and $\bar{\mu}_4 = \bar{\mu}_5$. We can now write Eq. (9.5) as

$$\sum_{i=1}^{6} (-1)^i \bar{\mu}_i = F\Delta\psi = F\left\{\int_T^{T_\alpha} [c^{(b)}]\, dT + \int_{T_\alpha}^{T_\beta} [c^{(a)}]\, dT + \int_{T_\beta}^{T} [c^{(b)}]\, dT \right.$$
$$\left. + T_\alpha\left(\frac{\pi_\alpha^{(ba)}}{T_\alpha}\right) + T_\beta\left(\frac{\pi_\beta^{(ab)}}{T_\beta}\right)\right\}. \tag{9.18}$$

At this point a digression is necessary in order to show that $F\pi_\omega^{(ab)}/T_\omega = \bar{S}_\omega^{(b)} - \bar{S}_\omega^{(a)}$. Consider the situation indicated in Figure 9–3. If the entropy change associated with the chemical reaction in the cell per Faraday of charge transferred around the loop is written as ΔS(reaction), then the total entropy change associated with the cell ΔS(cell) is [5]

$$\Delta S(\text{cell}) = \Delta S(\text{reaction}) + \bar{S}^{(-)} - \bar{S}^{(+)}. \tag{9.19}$$

For the reversible transfer of charge around the loop (limit of a sequence of steady currents), we have

$$\Delta S(\text{system}) + \Delta S(\text{surroundings}) = 0, \tag{9.20}$$

with

$$\Delta S(\text{system}) = \Delta S(\text{reaction}) \tag{9.21}$$

and

$$\Delta S(\text{surroundings}) = -\Delta S(\text{cell}) - \frac{F}{T}(\pi^{(-,b)} + \pi^{(b,a)} + \pi^{(a,+)}). \tag{9.22}$$

Therefore,

$$\bar{S}^{(+)} - \bar{S}^{(-)} = \frac{F}{T}(\pi^{(-,b)} + \pi^{(b,a)} + \pi^{(a,+)}). \tag{9.23}$$

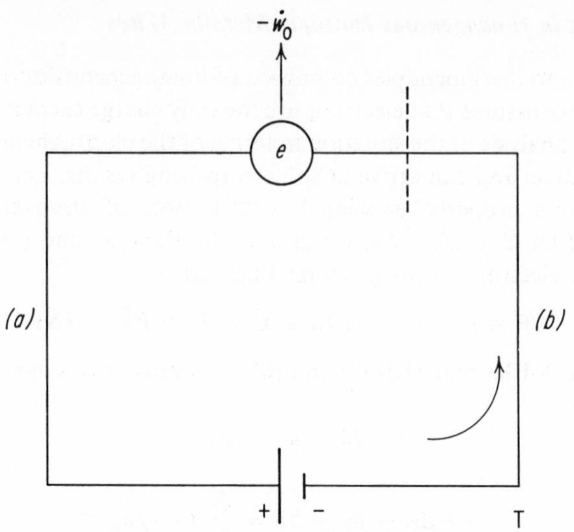

Figure 9–3. Galvanic cell plus bimetal loop in a thermostat. The anode $(-)$ adjoins to metal (b); the cathode $(+)$ adjoins to metal (a); the junction of metals (a) and (b) occurs at the point marked by the dotted line; there is an electric engine at e—for convenience let all current-carrying elements of the engine e be of material (a). When negative current flows in the direction indicated by the arrow, the engine at e delivers work at the rate $-\dot{W}_0$ to the surroundings.

A sufficient condition for the validity of Eq. (9.23) is that

$$\frac{F\pi^{(x,y)}}{T} = \bar{S}^{(y)} - \bar{S}^{(x)}. \tag{9.24}$$

Suppose instead that

$$\frac{F\pi^{(x,y)}}{T} = \bar{S}^{(y)} + f(y, T) - \{\bar{S}^{(x)} + f(x, T)\}; \tag{9.25}$$

then

$$\frac{F}{T}(\pi^{(-,b)} + \pi^{(b,a)} + \pi^{(a,+)}) = \bar{S}^{(+)} - \bar{S}^{(-)} + f(+, T) - f(-, T). \tag{9.26}$$

For Eq. (9.26) to be in accord with Eq. (9.23) it is necessary that

$$f(+, T) = f(-, T). \tag{9.27}$$

Inasmuch as Eq. (9.27) must hold regardless of the nature of the anode and cathode materials, it seems to be required that in general

$$f(z, T) = f(T). \tag{9.28}$$

But if $f(z, T) = f(T)$ only, then Eq. (9.25) reduces to Eq. (9.24).

Thus it seems that the normal situation for isotropic metals requires that $F\pi/T = \Delta\bar{S}$. Some doubt has been expressed concerning this result because the Peltier effect in experiments using anisotropic single metal crystals was found to depend on the orientation of the crystal relative to the second metal [6]. Bridgman [7] has shown that an internal heat effect is to be expected in anisotropic metal crystals whenever the electric current changes direction with respect to a principal axis of the crystal. These observations merely show that a very careful analysis is needed to establish just what is meant by a partial molar property $\bar{Z}$ in an anisotropic medium (operational definition) and just how current flow in a given direction is related to $\bar{Z}$; such an analysis has yet to be carried out.

The digression now being over, consider once again Eq. (9.18). Since $\bar{\mu} \equiv \mathscr{H} - T\bar{S}$, we can rewrite Eq. (9.18) (making use of Eq. 9.24 and of the fact that $\bar{S}_1 = \bar{S}_6$) as

$$\sum_{i=1}^{6} (-1)^i \mathscr{H}_i = F\left\{\int_T^{T_\alpha} [c^{(b)}]\, dT + \int_{T_\alpha}^{T_\beta} [c^{(a)}]\, dT + \int_{T_\beta}^{T} [c^{(b)}]\, dT\right\}. \quad (9.29)$$

Now for the ij link

$$\mathscr{H}_j - \mathscr{H}_i = \int_{T_i}^{T_j} \frac{d\mathscr{H}}{dT}\, dT; \quad (9.30)$$

so it follows that

$$\frac{d\mathscr{H}}{dT} = F[c]. \quad (9.31)$$

ZERO-FLUX LINKAGE

If we take each of the ij links in Figure 9–1 to be of the zero-flux type, i.e., $(\delta\dot{q}(ij)/\delta I)_{T_i,\ldots} = -\int_{T_i}^{T_j} [c]\, dT$, then our application of assumption IV to this case yields

$$-\left(\frac{\delta\Theta}{\delta\dot{n}}\right)_{T,\ldots} = F\left\{\frac{\pi_\alpha^{(ba)}}{T_\alpha} + \frac{\pi_\beta^{(ab)}}{T_\beta} + \int_T^{T_\alpha} [c^{(b)}]\, d\ln T + \int_{T_\alpha}^{T_\beta} [c^{(a)}]\, d\ln T + \int_{T_\beta}^{T} [c^{(b)}]\, d\ln T\right\} = 0, \quad (9.32)$$

where $\dot{n}$ is the number of Faradays traversing the thermocouple in unit time. Since $F\pi/T = \Delta\bar{S}$, $\bar{S}_1 = \bar{S}_6$, and, e.g., $\bar{S}_2 = \bar{S}_\alpha^{(b)}$, we can also write Eq. (9.32) as

$$\left\{\bar{S}_1 - \bar{S}_2 + F\int_T^{T_\alpha} [c^{(b)}]\, d\ln T\right\} + \left\{\bar{S}_3 - \bar{S}_4 + F\int_{T_\alpha}^{T_\beta} [c^{(a)}]\, d\ln T\right\} + \left\{\bar{S}_5 - \bar{S}_6 + F\int_{T_\beta}^{T} [c^{(b)}]\, d\ln T\right\} = 0, \quad (9.33)$$

each bracketed set of terms applying to a single link. The separate ij links being independent of one another, Eq. (9.33) requires that for each ij link

$$\bar{S}_i - \bar{S}_j + F\int_{T_i}^{T_j} [c]\, d\ln T = 0. \tag{9.34}$$

Now for electrons in wires it is customary to assume that the entropy is independent of the electrical potential; i.e., $\bar{S} \neq \bar{S}(\psi)$. Thus

$$\bar{S}_i - \bar{S}_j = \int_{T_j}^{T_i} \bar{C}_P\, d\ln T, \tag{9.35}$$

where $\bar{C}_P \equiv d\bar{H}/dT$ is the ordinary heat capacity associated with 1 mole of electrons in the given medium. Equations (9.31), (9.34), (9.35), and the definition $\mathscr{H} \equiv \bar{H} - F\psi$ lead to the relation

$$-\int_{T_i}^{T_j} \bar{C}_P\, d\ln T + \int_{T_i}^{T_j} \left(\bar{C}_P - F\frac{d\psi}{dT}\right) d\ln T = 0, \tag{9.36}$$

and hence to

$$\int_{T_i}^{T_j} \frac{d\psi}{dT}\, d\ln T = 0. \tag{9.37}$$

Thus assumption IV applied to zero-flux linkages leads to the conclusion that a *homogeneous* thermoelectric effect does not exist for electrons in wires; i.e., $d\psi/dT = 0$ and $\psi_j = \psi_i$ even though $T_j \neq T_i$. This conclusion immediately leads to the relations

$$F\Delta\psi = \mu_2 - \mu_3 + \mu_4 - \mu_5 = \mu_\alpha^{(b)} - \mu_\alpha^{(a)} + \mu_\beta^{(a)} - \mu_\beta^{(b)}, \tag{9.38}$$

$$F\left(\frac{\partial\,\Delta\psi}{\partial T_\beta}\right)_{T_\alpha} = \bar{S}_\beta^{(b)} - \bar{S}_\beta^{(a)} = \frac{F\pi_\beta^{(ab)}}{T_\beta}, \tag{9.39}$$

$$F[c] = \bar{C}_P, \tag{9.40}$$

$$FT_\beta\left(\frac{\partial^2\,\Delta\psi}{\partial {T_\beta}^2}\right)_{T_\alpha} = \bar{C}_P^{(b)}(\beta) - \bar{C}_P^{(a)}(\beta) = F\{[c_\beta^{(b)}] - [c_\beta^{(a)}]\}. \tag{9.41}$$

The very same relations—Eqs. (9.38) to (9.41)—appear if we take the linkages to be of the full-flux type.

FULL-FLUX LINKAGES

Equation (6.39) when applied to the situation indicated in Figure 9–1 with full-flux linkages yields the relation

$$-F\Delta\psi = -\sum_{i=1}^{6}(-1)^i\bar{\mu}_i = T\{[S_6] - [S_1]\} + T_\alpha\{[S_2] - [S_3]\} + T_\beta\{[S_4] - [S_5]\}. \tag{9.42}$$

We can rearrange Eq. (9.42) to give

$$\sum_{i=1}^{6}(-1)^i[\mathscr{H}_i] = 0, \tag{9.43}$$

with $[\mathscr{H}_i] \equiv \bar{\mu}_i + T_i[S_i]$. Equation (9.43) together with the independence of the links with respect to one another leads to

$$[\mathscr{H}_i] - [\mathscr{H}_j] = 0 \tag{9.44}$$

for each full-flux link in the system. Assumption IV implies that

$$[S_i] = [S_j] \tag{9.45}$$

for each full-flux link. Now the definition (for the *ij* full-flux link)

$$[S_i]^\partial \equiv -\left(\frac{\partial \bar{\mu}_i}{\partial T_i}\right)_j, \tag{9.46}$$

where the subscript j means that the thermodynamic state at j is to be kept constant (i.e., constant T_j, ψ_j, etc.), leads to

$$F\left(\frac{\partial \psi_i}{\partial T_i}\right)_j = [S_i]^\partial - \bar{S}_i \quad \text{(const. } P\text{)}. \tag{9.47}$$

Equation (9.47) shows clearly that if $[S_i]^\partial - \bar{S}_i = 0$ for a full-flux link then again there is no homogeneous thermoelectric effect; i.e., $(\partial\psi_i/\partial T_i)_j = 0$ and $\psi_i = \psi_j$. We see from Chapter 6 that Eq. (9.45) implies that

$$[S_i]^\partial = [S_i(i)]; \tag{9.48}$$

so if it turns out that $[S_i(i)] = \bar{S}_i$ for a full-flux link, then the nonexistence of the homogeneous thermoelectric effect will be established.

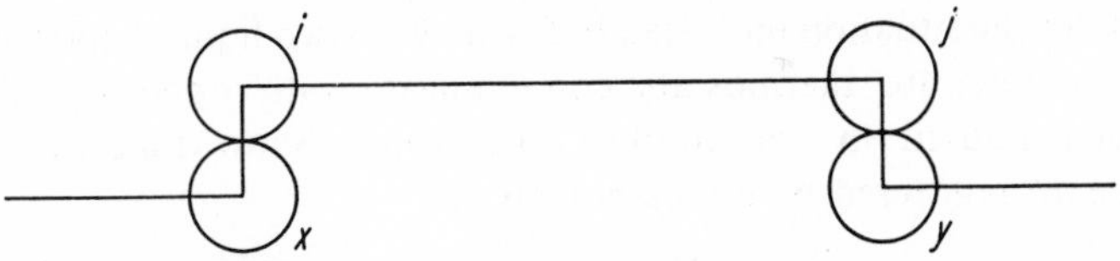

Figure 9–4. Full-flux linkage under equithermal conditions. The thermostats at i, j, x, y are all at the same temperature T; one single, homogeneous piece of metallic wire.

Consider the situation indicated in Figure 9–4. When a steady current of $\dot{n}$ Faradays per second flows through the *ij* link, the heat developed per second in the link is given by $R_{ij}(\dot{n}F)^2$, where R_{ij} is the resistance of the *ij* segment of wire (the part outside the thermostats). Since the endpoints of the *ij* segment are at the same temperature, the Thomson effects in the segment are self-canceling (the Thomson effect, however, introduces a certain asymmetry in the distribution of temperatures with respect to the midpoint of the segment; this asymmetry has been used by Keesom et al. [8] as a way of measuring Thomson coefficients). A certain fraction ϑ_i of the heat developed in the ij segment will find its way into the ith thermostat; thus

$$\dot{S}_i^{(r)} = \frac{1}{T}(R_i + \vartheta_i R_{ij})(\dot{n}F)^2, \tag{9.49}$$

where R_i is the resistance of the wire in the ith thermostat and $0 < \vartheta_i < 1$, and

$$\left(\frac{\delta \dot{S}_i^{(r)}}{\delta \dot{n}}\right)_T \equiv \{\bar{S}_i - [S_i(i)]\} = 0. \tag{9.50}$$

Equations (9.47), (9.48), and (9.50) show that a homogeneous thermoelectric effect does not exist across a full-flux linkage if assumption IV holds; Eqs. (9.38) to (9.41) follow in this case just as in the zero-flux case.

General Remarks

The relations derived for the thermocouple in this chapter hinge on the applicability of assumption IV; if IV is valid, then the Thomson relations (Eqs. 9.10 and 9.11) are generally true. For electrons in isotropic metallic wires there is no homogeneous thermoelectric effect, the Seebeck potential difference being due entirely to the temperature coefficient of the interfacial equilibrium condition $\psi_\omega^{(a)} - \psi_\omega^{(b)} = (\mu_\omega^{(a)} - \mu_\omega^{(b)})/F$; i.e., $\bar{\mu}_\omega^{(a)} = \bar{\mu}_\omega^{(b)}$—Eqs. (9.38) to (9.41) following at once.

Exercise 9–1. Liquid–Vapor Analog of the Thermocouple

Consider the situation indicated in Figure 9–5: two liquid-vapor interfaces situated in separate thermostats communicate with opposite sides of a manometer housed in yet another thermsotat. Show that the pressure difference ΔP registered by the manometer at γ is

$$\Delta P = P_0(\alpha) + \int_{T_\alpha}^{T} \frac{\bar{S}^{(g)} - [S^{(g)}]^\partial}{\bar{V}^{(g)}}\, dT - P_0(\beta) - \int_{T_\beta}^{T} \frac{\bar{S}^{(g)} - [S^{(g)}]^\partial}{\bar{V}^{(g)}}\, dT,$$

where $P_0(\omega)$ is the saturated vapor pressure of the liquid at temperature T_ω and the integrals are over the appropriate communicating tubes. Also show that the condition $(\partial \Delta P/\partial T)_{T_\alpha, T_\beta} = 0$ implies that $\bar{S}^{(g)} - [S^{(g)}]^\partial = 0$, and hence that

$$\Delta P = P_0(\alpha) - P_0(\beta),$$

$$\left(\frac{\partial \Delta P}{\partial T_\alpha}\right)_{T_\beta} = \frac{\Delta \bar{S}(\alpha)}{\Delta \bar{V}(\alpha)}.$$

Exercise 9–2. Simplify the situation shown in Figure 9–1 in the following ways: connect thermostats 2, α, 3 together to form a single thermostat

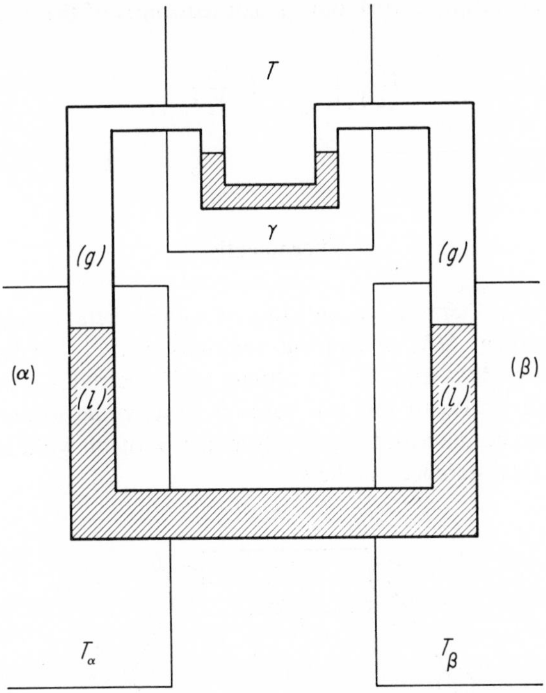

Figure 9–5. Liquid–vapor analog of the thermocouple; arbitrary linkage.

A ($\dot{Q}_A^{(r)} = \dot{Q}_2^{(r)} + \dot{Q}_\alpha^{(r)} + \dot{Q}_3^{(r)}$) and do a similar thing for thermostats-4, β, 5 ($\dot{Q}_B^{(r)} = \dot{Q}_4^{(r)} + \dot{Q}_\beta^{(r)} + \dot{Q}_5^{(r)}$); let $\langle T(ij)\rangle = T = T_R$ with T_R being room temperature, and take state R as a reference thermostatic state.

(i) Show that Eq. (9.2) then simplifies to

$$\Theta = I\left(\frac{\dot{W}_0}{IT_R}\right) + \dot{Q}_A^{(r)}\left(\frac{1}{T_A} - \frac{1}{T_R}\right) + \dot{Q}_B^{(r)}\left(\frac{1}{T_B} - \frac{1}{T_R}\right).$$

(ii) Show that the relations $(\partial\Omega_i/\partial Y_i)_{\Omega',R} > 0$ imply that

$$\left(\frac{\partial I}{\partial(\dot{W}_0/I)}\right)_{T_R,T_B,T_A} > 0, \qquad \left(\frac{\partial \dot{Q}_A^{(r)}}{\partial T_A}\right)_{T_R,T_B,\dot{W}_0/I} < 0, \qquad \text{etc.}$$

(iii) Show that the relations $(\partial Y_i/\partial\Omega_k)_{\Omega',R} = (\partial Y_k/\partial\Omega_i)_{\Omega',R}$ imply that

$$-T_A{}^2\left(\frac{\partial I}{\partial T_A}\right)_{T_R,T_B,\dot{W}_0/I} = T_R\left(\frac{\partial \dot{Q}_A^{(r)}}{\partial(\dot{W}_0/I)}\right)_{T_R,T_B,T_A},$$

$$T_B{}^2\left(\frac{\partial \dot{Q}_A^{(r)}}{\partial T_B}\right)_{T_R,T_A,\dot{W}_0/I} = T_A{}^2\left(\frac{\partial \dot{Q}_B^{(r)}}{\partial T_A}\right)_{T_R,T_B,\dot{W}_0/I}, \qquad \text{etc.}$$

(iv) In a similar fashion, work out the consequences of the assumption that

$$\left(\frac{\partial \Omega_i}{\partial Y_k}\right)_{Y',R} = \left(\frac{\partial \Omega_k}{\partial Y_i}\right)_{Y',R}.$$

Thermocells

I consider next thermocells consisting of molten metal halides or nitrates of the general form MX_ν or aqueous solutions of such halides or nitrates (yielding the ions $M^{\nu+}$ and X^-) in contact with electrodes of metal M; the formalism appropriate to the two cases is exactly the same. I find that thermocells can be described rigorously either with or without the use of current ratios (transference numbers).

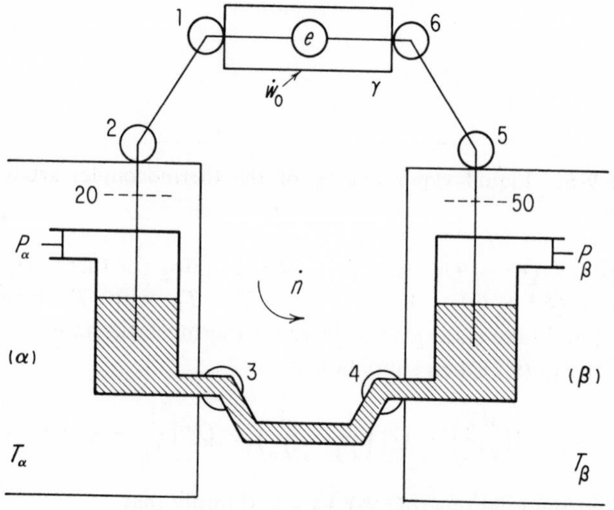

Figure 9–6. Schematic version of a thermocell. $1, \gamma, 6$—heat reservoirs at temperature T; $2, \alpha, 3$—heat reservoirs at temperature T_α; $4, \beta, 5$—heat reservoirs at temperature T_β. Wire of metal M dips into the molten salt or solution at α and β and is joined to copper wires at the points 20 and 50; the copper wires attach to an electric engine e at temperature T; all current-carrying elements of the engine e are to be of copper. When work is supplied to the engine e at the rate $\dot{W}_0$, a current of $\dot{n}$ Faradays/sec flows in the direction indicated. The pressures P_ω are solvent partial pressures for the aqueous case and atmospheric pressure for the molten salt case.

Consider the case shown schematically in Figure 9–6. The equation setting out the migrational equilibrium condition for this situation is Eq. (6.39); I rewrite it here for convenience:

$$\sum_j \sum_\rho \sum_i \mathscr{G}_\rho^{(i)} \left(\frac{\delta \dot{n}_\rho^{(i)}}{\tilde{\delta} \dot{n}} \right)_{\Omega'} + \sum_k T_k \left\{ \left(\frac{\delta \dot{S}_k(\text{in})}{\tilde{\delta} \dot{n}} \right)_{\Omega'} - \left(\frac{\delta \dot{S}_k(\text{out})}{\tilde{\delta} \dot{n}} \right)_{\Omega'} \right\} + \sum \left(\frac{\delta \dot{q}(kh)}{\tilde{\delta} \dot{n}} \right)_{\Omega'} = \left(\frac{\delta \dot{W}_0}{\tilde{\delta} \dot{n}} \right)_{\Omega'} = -F \Delta\psi, \quad (9.51)$$

where $\Delta\psi \equiv -(\delta \dot{W}_0/\tilde{\delta}\dot{n})_{\Omega'}/F$ is the potential difference of the thermocell. Let the superscripts *el*, $+$, and $-$ refer to electrons in the copper wires, to the cation $M^{\nu+}$, and to the anion X^-, respectively. Upon introducing the current ratios τ_+, and τ_-,

$$\tau_+ \equiv \left| \frac{\nu \dot{n}_\omega^{(+)}(\text{in})}{\dot{n}} \right|, \qquad \tau_- \equiv \left| \frac{\dot{n}_\omega^{(-)}(\text{in})}{\dot{n}} \right|, \qquad \tau_+ + \tau_- = 1, \quad (9.52)$$

we can write Eq. (9.51) in the form

$$\begin{aligned} -F\Delta\psi = {} & \Delta G_\alpha + \Delta G_\beta + T\{[S_6^{(el)}] - [S_1^{(el)}]\} \\ & + T_\alpha \left\{ [S_2^{(el)}] + \left(\frac{\delta \dot{n}_\alpha^{(L)}}{\tilde{\delta} \dot{n}} \right)_{\Omega'} [S_\alpha^{(1)}] + \frac{\tau_+}{\nu} [S_\alpha^{(+)}] - \tau_- [S_\alpha^{(-)}] \right\} \\ & + T_\beta \left\{ \tau_- [S_\beta^{(-)}] - \frac{\tau_+}{\nu} [S_\beta^{(+)}] + \left(\frac{\delta \dot{n}_\beta^{(L)}}{\tilde{\delta} \dot{n}} \right)_{\Omega'} [S_\beta^{(1)}] - [S_5^{(el)}] \right\} \\ & + [h(12)] + [h(34)] + [h(56)], \end{aligned} \quad (9.53)$$

where $\Delta G_\omega \equiv \{\delta(\dot{n}_\omega^{(g)} \mu_\omega^{(g)} + \dot{n}_\omega^{(M)} \mu_\omega^{(M)} + \dot{n}_\omega^{(1)} \mu_\omega^{(1)} + \dot{n}_\omega^{(MX_\nu)} \mu_\omega^{(MX_\nu)})/\tilde{\delta}\dot{n}\}_{\Omega'}$ — the superscripts referring to the gas phase, the metal phase, the solvent component in the 2-component case, and the metal halide or nitrate component, respectively*— and $\dot{n}_\omega^{(L)} \equiv \dot{n}_\omega^{(1)} + \dot{n}_\omega^{(g)}$. In the sequence of steady-flow states implicit in Eq. (9.51), it must be true that

$$\dot{n}_\alpha^{(MX_\nu)} + \dot{n}_\beta^{(MX_\nu)} = 0, \quad \dot{n}_\alpha^{(g)} + \dot{n}_\alpha^{(1)} + \dot{n}_\beta^{(g)} + \dot{n}_\beta^{(1)} \equiv \dot{n}_\alpha^{(L)} + \dot{n}_\beta^{(L)} = 0, \quad (9.54)$$

and at α, e.g., that

$$\dot{n}_\alpha^{(MX_\nu)} = \dot{n}_\alpha^{(+)}(\text{in}) - \frac{\dot{n}}{\nu} = -\frac{\dot{n}_\alpha^{(-)}(\text{out})}{\nu}. \quad (9.55)$$

Our study of the thermocouple showed that we can let

$$T_i[S_i^{(el)}] - T_j[S_j^{(el)}] + [h(ij)] = \bar{\mu}_j^{(el)} - \bar{\mu}_i^{(el)}$$

* In the molten salt case there will be no $\dot{n}_\omega^{(g)}$ or $\dot{n}_\omega^{(1)}$.

for an ij link. Thus we can cast Eq. (9.53) into the form

$$\begin{aligned}
-F\Delta\psi = {} & \left(\frac{\delta\dot{n}_\alpha^{(g)}}{\tilde{\delta}\dot{n}}\right)_{\Omega'} (\mu_\alpha^{(g)} - \mu_\alpha^{(1)}) + \left(\frac{\delta\dot{n}_\alpha^{(L)}}{\tilde{\delta}\dot{n}}\right)_{\Omega'} (\mu_\alpha^{(1)} + T_\alpha[S_\alpha^{(1)}]) \\
& + \frac{1}{\nu}\mu_\alpha^{(M)} - \frac{\tau_-}{\nu}\mu_\alpha^{(MX_\nu)} + T_\alpha[S_\alpha^{(\pm)}] \\
& + \left(\frac{\delta\dot{n}_\beta^{(g)}}{\tilde{\delta}\dot{n}}\right)_{\Omega'} (\mu_\beta^{(g)} - \mu_\beta^{(1)}) - \frac{1}{\nu}\mu_\beta^{(M)} \\
& + \left(\frac{\delta\dot{n}_\beta^{(L)}}{\tilde{\delta}\dot{n}}\right)_{\Omega'} (\mu_\beta^{(1)} + T_\beta[S_\beta^{(1)}]) + \frac{\tau_-}{\nu}\mu_\beta^{(MX_\nu)} - T_\beta[S_\beta^{(\pm)}] \\
& + \bar{\mu}_1^{(el)} - \bar{\mu}_2^{(el)} + \bar{\mu}_5^{(el)} - \bar{\mu}_6^{(el)} + [h(34)], \qquad (9.56)
\end{aligned}$$

where $[S_\omega^{(\pm)}] \equiv (\tau_+/\nu)[S_\omega^{(+)}] - \tau_-[S_\omega^{(-)}] \equiv (1/\nu)[S_\omega^{(+)}] - (\tau_-/\nu)[S_\omega^{(MX_\nu)}]$. We can also write Eq. (9.56) as

$$\begin{aligned}
-F\Delta\psi = {} & \left(\frac{\delta\dot{n}_\alpha^{(g)}}{\tilde{\delta}\dot{n}}\right)_{\Omega'} (\mu_\alpha^{(g)} - \mu_\alpha^{(1)}) + \left(\frac{\delta\dot{n}_\beta^{(g)}}{\tilde{\delta}\dot{n}}\right)_{\Omega'} (\mu_\beta^{(g)} - \mu_\beta^{(1)}) \\
& + \left(\frac{\delta\dot{n}_\alpha^{(L)}}{\tilde{\delta}\dot{n}}\right)_{\Omega'} \{[G_\alpha^{(1)}] - [G_\beta^{(1)}]\} - \frac{\tau_-}{\nu}\{[G_\alpha^{(MX_\nu)}] - [G_\beta^{(MX_\nu)}]\} \\
& + \frac{1}{\nu}\{\mu_\alpha^{(M)} + T_\alpha[S_\alpha^{(+)}] - \langle T(34)\rangle[S_\alpha^{(+)}]\} \\
& - \frac{1}{\nu}\{\mu_\beta^{(M)} + T_\beta[S_\beta^{(+)}] - \langle T(34)\rangle[S_\beta^{(+)}]\} + \bar{\mu}_1^{(el)} - \bar{\mu}_2^{(el)} \\
& + \bar{\mu}_5^{(el)} - \bar{\mu}_6^{(el)}, \qquad (9.57)
\end{aligned}$$

where $[G_\omega^{(i)}] \equiv \mu_\omega^{(i)} + T_\omega[S_\omega^{(i)}] - \langle T(34)\rangle[S_\omega^{(i)}]$, $[h(34)] = \langle T(34)\rangle[s(34)]$, and

$$\begin{aligned}
[s(34)] + \left(\frac{\delta\dot{n}_\alpha^{(L)}}{\tilde{\delta}\dot{n}}\right)_{\Omega'} [S_\alpha^{(1)}] + \left(\frac{\tau_+}{\nu}\right)[S_\alpha^{(+)}] - \tau_-[S_\alpha^{(-)}] + \tau_-[S_\beta^{(-)}] - \left(\frac{\tau_+}{\nu}\right) \\
\times [S_\beta^{(+)}] + \left(\frac{\delta\dot{n}_\beta^{(L)}}{\tilde{\delta}\dot{n}}\right)_{\Omega'} [S_\beta^{(1)}] = 0.
\end{aligned}$$

Now in the state of migrational equilibrium $\mu_\omega^{(g)} = \mu_\omega^{(1)}$ and $[G_\alpha^{(i)}] = [G_\beta^{(i)}]$, so Eq. (9.57) reduces to

$$\begin{aligned}
-F\Delta\psi = {} & \bar{\mu}_1^{(el)} - \bar{\mu}_2^{(el)} + \bar{\mu}_5^{(el)} - \bar{\mu}_6^{(el)} \\
& + \frac{1}{\nu}\{(\mu_\alpha^{(M)} + T_\alpha[S_\alpha^{(+)}] - \langle T(34)\rangle[S_\alpha^{(+)}]) \\
& - (\mu_\beta^{(M)} + T_\beta[S_\beta^{(+)}] - \langle T(34)\rangle[S_\beta^{(+)}])\}. \qquad (9.58)
\end{aligned}$$

If, however, we formally choose to leave in the current ratio τ_- [going back to Eq. (9.56)], then

$$\begin{aligned}
-F\Delta\psi = {} & \bar{\mu}_1^{(el)} - \bar{\mu}_2^{(el)} + \bar{\mu}_5^{(el)} - \bar{\mu}_6^{(el)} + \\
& \frac{1}{\nu}\{(\mu_\alpha^{(M)} - \tau_-\mu_\alpha^{(MX_\nu)} + \nu T_\alpha[S_\alpha^{(\pm)}] - \nu\langle T(34)\rangle[S_\alpha^{(\pm)}]) \\
& - (\mu_\beta^{(M)} - \tau_-\mu_\beta^{(MX_\nu)} + \nu T_\beta[S_\beta^{(\pm)}] - \nu\langle T(34)\rangle[S_\beta^{(\pm)}])\}. \qquad (9.59)
\end{aligned}$$

The current ratios τ are well-defined experimental quantities when measured *in situ*; they may or may not have any *direct* relationship to transference numbers determined in isothermal experiments. The fact that in the state of migrational equilibrium the potential difference of thermocells of the type being investigated does not depend on current ratios is well known [9, 10]. From Eq. (9.58) it follows that

$$\nu F\left(\frac{\partial\,\Delta\psi}{\partial T_\alpha}\right)_{T_\beta,T,\langle T\rangle} = \nu[S_\alpha^{(el)}]^\partial + \bar{S}_\alpha^{(M)} - [S_\alpha^{(+)}]^\partial, \tag{9.60}$$

$$\nu F\left(\frac{\partial\,\Delta\psi}{\partial T_\beta}\right)_{T_\alpha,T,\langle T\rangle} = [S_\beta^{(+)}]^\partial - \bar{S}_\beta^{(M)} - \nu[S_\beta^{(el)}]^\partial, \tag{9.61}$$

$$\begin{aligned}\nu F\left(\frac{\partial\,\Delta\psi}{\partial T}\right)_{T_\alpha,T_\beta,\langle T\rangle} &= \nu\{[S_6^{(el)}]^\partial - [S_1^{(el)}]^\partial\}\\ &= \nu(\bar{S}_6^{(el)} - \bar{S}_1^{(el)}) = 0,\end{aligned} \tag{9.62}$$

with, e.g., $[S_\alpha^{(+)}]^\partial \equiv \{\partial(T_\alpha[S_\alpha^{(+)}] - T_\beta[S_\beta^{(+)}] + \langle T\rangle([S_\beta^{(+)}] - [S_\alpha^{(+)}]))/\partial T_\alpha\}_{\beta,\langle T\rangle}$, $\langle T\rangle \equiv \langle T(34)\rangle$, and $[S_\alpha^{(el)}]^\partial \equiv -(\partial\bar{\mu}_2^{(el)}/\partial T_2)_1$. I have assumed that $(\partial\,\Delta\psi/\partial\langle T\rangle)_{T_\alpha,T_\beta} = 0$.*

I showed earlier in connection with the discussion of the thermocouple that for electrons in wires $[S^{(el)}]^\partial = \bar{S}^{(el)}$. As the entropy associated with the electron in copper wires is quite small [11], Eqs. (9.60) and (9.61) enable us to evaluate the $[S^{(+)}]^\partial$ quantity for the cation from thermocell potential difference measurements and third-law calculations of $\bar{S}^{(M)}$; thus, e.g.,

$$[S_\alpha^{(+)}]^\partial \approx \bar{S}_\alpha^{(M)} - \nu F\left(\frac{\partial\,\Delta\psi}{\partial T_\alpha}\right)_{T_\beta}. \tag{9.63}$$

Pitzer [10] has compiled a table of values of $[S_\omega^{(+)}]^\partial$ for the cation in a number of molten salt electrolytes; Table 9–1 shows a few typical entries from that table.

Table 9–1

Thermocells with Fused Salt Electrolyte (Units: cal/deg-mole)
(Compilation of Pitzer [10])

Electrolyte	T°K	$\bar{S}^{(M)}$	$-\nu Fd\,\Delta\psi/dT$	$[S^{(+)}]^\partial$
$AgNO_3$	500	13.37	7.6	21.0
AgCl	800	16.43	9.3	26
AgBr	750	16.00	11	27
AgI	850	16.84	10	27
$ZnCl_2$	~600	14.41	−6	8
$SnCl_2$	~600	20.59	+1	22

* This is the analog of assumption *Q*, Chapter 5.

For formal completeness I point out that Eq. (9.59) leads to

$$\nu F\left(\frac{\partial \Delta\psi}{\partial T_\alpha}\right)_{T_\beta,T,\langle T\rangle} = \nu[S_\alpha^{(el)}]^\partial + \bar{S}_\alpha^{(M)} - \tau_-[S_\alpha^{(MX_\nu)}]^\partial - \nu[S_\alpha^{(\pm)}]^\partial + \{\mu_\alpha^{(MX_\nu)} - \mu_\beta^{(MX_\nu)}\}\left(\frac{\partial \tau_-}{\partial T_\alpha}\right)_{T_\beta,T,\langle T\rangle}, \quad (9.64)$$

with, e.g., $[S_\alpha^{(\pm)}]^\partial \equiv \{\partial(T_\alpha[S_\alpha^{(\pm)}] - T_\beta[S_\beta^{(\pm)}] + \langle T\rangle([S_\beta^{(\pm)}] - [S_\alpha^{(\pm)}]))/\partial T_\alpha\}_{\beta,\langle T\rangle}$. The relation

$$[S_\alpha^{(+)}]^\partial = \tau_-[S_\alpha^{(MX_\nu)}]^\partial + \nu[S_\alpha^{(\pm)}]^\partial - (\Delta\mu^{(MX_\nu)})\left(\frac{\partial \tau_-}{\partial T_\alpha}\right)_{T_\beta,T,\langle T\rangle} \quad (9.65)$$

must then hold between the various quantities. For a molten salt, since there can be no Soret effect in a 1-component system, $[S_\omega^{(MX_\nu)}]^\partial = \bar{S}_\omega^{(MX_\nu)}$.

For 1-component molten salt thermocells there is nothing further to say; for 2-component aqueous solutions it is customary to measure an initial potential difference $(\Delta\psi)_0$ for the thermocell when there is an essentially steady flow of heat through the system and *before* the Soret effect has brought about any appreciable change in the compositions of the solutions at α and β. Such $(\Delta\psi)_0$ values are *not* steady-state values (the potential difference characteristic of the final state of complete migrational equilibrium is $\Delta\psi$); however, we can approximately reach the envisaged state of the system by allowing the solvent to flow at a steady rate from one terminal part to the other so as approximately to counteract by its dragging tendency the Soret motion of the solute. The situation to be analyzed, then, is one in which we place a solution of average composition $n^{(MX_\nu)}/n^{(1)} \equiv r$ into the apparatus indicated in Figure 9–6; we then set the pressures P_ω equal to the solvent partial pressures appropriate to solutions of composition r and temperature T_ω at thermostatic equilibrium. As in the case of the concentration cell (Chapter 13) it is necessary to agitate gently the solutions at α and β so as to keep them nearly uniform in composition. There will ultimately be a steady flow of solvent from one terminal part to the other; i.e., $\dot{n}_\alpha^{(g)} + \dot{n}_\beta^{(g)} = 0$. If now we superimpose a flow of electric current on the solvent flow and if we carry out the operation $\delta/\delta\dot{n}$ at constant $T_\alpha, T_\beta, \langle T(ij)\rangle, P_\alpha, P_\beta$,* then the $\Delta\psi$ value of the limiting state should be approximately equal to $(\Delta\psi)_0$.

The appropriate equations are Eqs. (9.54) to (9.56); so

$$-F(\Delta\psi)_0 \approx \left(\frac{\delta\dot{n}_\alpha^{(L)}}{\tilde{\delta}\dot{n}}\right)_{\Omega'}\{[G_\alpha^{(1)}] - [G_\beta^{(1)}]\} - \frac{\tau_-}{\nu}\{[G_\alpha^{(MX_\nu)}] - [G_\beta^{(MX_\nu)}]\} + \frac{1}{\nu}\{\mu_\alpha^{(M)} + T_\alpha[S_\alpha^{(+)}] - \langle T(34)\rangle[S_\alpha^{(+)}]\} - \frac{1}{\nu}\{\mu_\beta^{(M)} + T_\beta[S_\beta^{(+)}] - \langle T(34)\rangle[S_\beta^{(+)}]\} + \bar{\mu}_1^{(el)} - \bar{\mu}_2^{(el)} + \bar{\mu}_5^{(el)} - \bar{\mu}_6^{(el)}, \quad (9.66)$$

* If we neglect kinetic energy terms, the indicated operation is of the form $(\delta/\tilde{\delta}\dot{n})_{\Omega'}$.

where I have made use of the "gentle agitation" condition $\mu_{\omega}^{(g)} = \mu_{\omega}^{(1)}$. The Hittorf assumption is that $(\delta\dot{n}_{\alpha}^{(L)}/\delta\bar{\dot{n}})_{\Omega'} = 0$ (no coupling between the flow of the electric current and the flow of the solvent).* If we accept the Hittorf assumption, then the temperature coefficient of $(\Delta\psi)_0$ is

$$\nu F\left(\frac{\partial(\Delta\psi)_0}{\partial T_\alpha}\right)_{\beta,r,T,\langle T\rangle} \approx \bar{S}_{\alpha}^{(M)} - [S_{\alpha}^{(+)}]^{\partial} - \nu[S_{\alpha}^{(el)}]^{\partial} + \tau_-\left(\frac{\partial\Delta[G^{(MX_\nu)}]}{\partial T_\alpha}\right)_{\beta,r,T,\langle T\rangle} + \left(\frac{\partial\tau_-}{\partial T_\alpha}\right)_{\beta,r,T,\langle T\rangle}\{[G_{\alpha}^{(MX_\nu)}] - [G_{\beta}^{(MX_\nu)}]\}. \tag{9.67}$$

We can put Eq. (9.67) into the form of Eq. (9.64) (but not into the form of Eq. (9.60) as $[G_{\alpha}^{(i)}] - [G_{\beta}^{(i)}] \neq 0$). Further simplifications are possible if we assume that $(\partial\tau_-/\partial T_\alpha)_{\beta,r,T,\langle T\rangle} \approx 0$ and that $[S_{\omega}^{(el)}]^{\partial} \approx 0$:

$$\nu F\left(\frac{\partial(\Delta\psi)_0}{\partial T_\alpha}\right)_{\beta,r,T,\langle T\rangle} \approx \bar{S}_{\alpha}^{(M)} - [S_{\alpha}^{(+)}]^{\partial} + \tau_-\left(\frac{\partial\Delta[G^{(MX_\nu)}]}{\partial T_\alpha}\right)_{\beta,r,T,\langle T\rangle}. \tag{9.68}$$

References

1. W. Thomson, *Mathematical and Physical Papers*, Vol. I (Cambridge University Press, Cambridge, 1882), pp. 232–291.
2. D. G. Miller, *Chem. Revs.*, **60**, 15 (1960).
3. F. N. Lancia and J. D. McGervey, *Rev. Sci. Instruments*, **35**, 1302 (1964).
4. E. A. Guggenheim, *Thermodynamics* (North Holland Publishing Company, Amsterdam, 1950), Chapter 10.
5. C. Reid, *Principles of Chemical Thermodynamics* (Reinhold Publishing Corporation, New York, 1960), Chapter 9.
6. J. Agar, *Revs. Pure Appl. Chem.*, **8**, 19 (1958).
7. P. Bridgman, *The Thermodynamics of Electric Phenomena in Metals* (The Macmillan Company, New York, 1934), Chapter 6.
8. G. Borelius, W. Keesom, and C. Johanson, *Comm. Leiden*, 196a.
9. J. deBethune, *J. Electrochem. Soc.*, **107**, 829 (1960).
10. K. Pitzer, *J. Phys. Chem.*, **65**, 147 (1961).
11. M. Tempkin and A. Khoroshin, *Zhur. Fiz. Khim.*, **26**, 500, 773 (1952).

* See the discussion relative to concentration cells in Chapter 13.

10

Thermal Converters and Polythermal Processes

Thermal Converters

We can use some of the polythermal field effects considered in the previous chapters as the basis for devices of the heat-to-work type, devices that I hereafter call *thermal converters.* These devices are sites of heat currents due to maintained temperature differences; the heat currents give rise to currents of electricity, mass, or chemical reaction measures that are agents for the supply of work to the surroundings.

Figure 10–1 is a schematic rendering of one type of thermal converter, a *closed-loop* converter with full-flux linkages (heat is exchanged only with the heat reservoirs at α and β). The heat flows $\dot{Q}_{\omega}^{(r)}$ drive a current $\dot{n}$ around the loop with the result that work is delivered at the rate $-\dot{W}$ to the surroundings. Let T_{α} be greater than T_{β}, and let the direction of spontaneous current flow for a small temperature difference $T_{\alpha} - T_{\beta}$ be taken as the positive direction of current flow. For a closed-loop converter we have, then (in the steady state),

$$\dot{U}(\text{system}) = -\dot{Q}_{\alpha}^{(r)} - \dot{Q}_{\beta}^{(r)} + \dot{W} = 0, \tag{10.1}$$

$$\dot{U}(0) = -\dot{Q}_{\alpha}^{(r)}(0) - \dot{Q}_{\beta}^{(r)}(0) = 0, \tag{10.2}$$

or

$$-\dot{W} = -\dot{Q}_{\alpha}^{(r)} - \dot{Q}_{\beta}^{(r)} = -\Delta\dot{Q}_{\alpha}^{(r)} - \Delta\dot{Q}_{\beta}^{(r)}, \tag{10.3}$$

where $\dot{Z}(0)$ represents the rate of change of the Z quantity for the case $\dot{n} = 0$, $\Delta\dot{Z} \equiv \dot{Z}(\dot{n}) - \dot{Z}(0)$, and $\dot{Q}_{\omega}^{(r)}$ is the rate of influx of heat into the ω heat

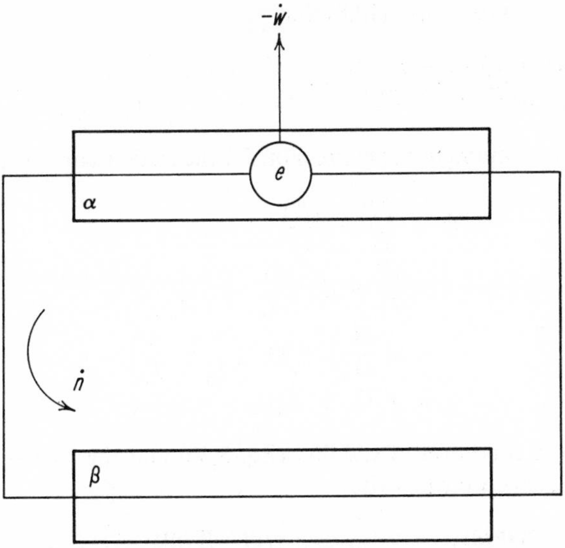

Figure 10–1. Closed-loop thermal converter with full-flux linkages; schematic. α—heat reservoir at temperature T_α; β—heat reservoir at temperature T_β; $\dot{n}$—appropriate current; e—appropriate engine, activated by the current $\dot{n}$, for delivering work at the rate $-\dot{W}$ to the surroundings; $T_\alpha > T_\beta$.

reservoir. We can express the efficiency of the thermal conversion process in two ways: in terms of the *total* heat flow $\dot{Q}_\omega^{(r)}$ or in terms of the *participating* heat flow $\Delta\dot{Q}_\omega^{(r)}$; i.e.,

$$\eta \equiv \frac{-\dot{W}}{-\dot{Q}_\alpha^{(r)}} \tag{10.4}$$

and

$$[\eta] \equiv \frac{-\dot{W}}{-\Delta\dot{Q}_\alpha^{(r)}}. \tag{10.5}$$

We can relate these efficiencies to the rate of entropy production associated with the process:

$$\eta = \frac{T_\alpha - T_\beta}{T_\alpha}\left(\frac{-\dot{W}}{-\dot{W} + T_\beta\Theta}\right), \tag{10.6}$$

$$[\eta] = \frac{T_\alpha - T_\beta}{T_\alpha}\left(\frac{-\dot{W}}{-\dot{W} + T_\beta\Delta\Theta}\right). \tag{10.7}$$

For the case of the thermocouple used as a source of work it has become customary to introduce a figure of merit ζ into discussions about efficiency [1]; the figure of merit is related to the maximum value of η for a given T_α, T_β by

$$\eta_{\max} = \frac{T_\alpha - T_\beta}{T_\alpha}\,\frac{\{1 + [\zeta(T_\alpha + T_\beta)/2]\}^{1/2} - 1}{\{1 + [\zeta(T_\alpha + T_\beta)/2]\}^{1/2} + (T_\beta/T_\alpha)}. \tag{10.8}$$

We see from Eqs. (10.6) and (10.8) that

$$\frac{\{1 + [\zeta(T_\alpha + T_\beta)/2]\}^{1/2} - 1}{\{1 + [\zeta(T_\alpha + T_\beta)/2]\}^{1/2} + (T_\beta/T_\alpha)} = \left(\frac{-\dot{W}}{-\dot{W} + T_\beta \Theta}\right)_{\max}. \tag{10.9}$$

Consider for a moment the expression for the rate of entropy production:

$$\begin{aligned}\Theta &= \frac{\dot{Q}_\alpha^{(r)}}{T_\alpha} + \frac{\dot{Q}_\beta^{(r)}}{T_\beta} \\ &= \frac{\dot{W}}{T_\beta} + \dot{Q}_\alpha^{(r)}\left(\frac{1}{T_\alpha} - \frac{1}{T_\beta}\right) \\ &= \dot{n}\left(\frac{\dot{W}}{\dot{n}T_\beta}\right) + \dot{Q}_\alpha^{(r)}\left(\frac{1}{T_\alpha} - \frac{1}{T_\beta}\right) \\ &= Y_1\Omega_1 + Y_2\Omega_2.\end{aligned} \tag{10.10}$$

If we invoke the condition of stability (Eq. 3.30) and the *haste-makes-waste* principle (Eq. 3.29), we can write

$$\left(\frac{\partial(\dot{W}/\dot{n})}{\partial \dot{n}}\right)_{T_\alpha, T_\beta} > 0 \quad \text{or} \quad \left(\frac{\partial(-\dot{W}/\dot{n})}{\partial \dot{n}}\right)_{T_\alpha, T_\beta} < 0 \tag{10.11}$$

and, since we are taking $\dot{n}$ to be a positive quantity,*

$$\left(\frac{\partial \Theta}{\partial \dot{n}}\right)_{T_\alpha, T_\beta} \geqslant 0. \tag{10.12}$$

Now the expected behavior of $-\dot{W}$ is that indicated in Figure 10–2 for a given converter and fixed values of T_α, T_β: we see that $-\dot{W}$ reaches a maximum for some value of $\dot{n}$ and then decreases, ultimately becoming zero at a value of $\dot{n}$ equal to $\dot{n}_{\max}$; in order to force a current of magnitude greater than $\dot{n}_{\max}$ around the converter loop it is necessary for $-\dot{W}$ to be negative—i.e., it is necessary to *supply* work to the system. The shape of the η versus $\dot{n}$ curve is similar to that of the $-\dot{W}$ versus $\dot{n}$ curve, η being zero at those points where $-\dot{W}$ is zero. However, the current-value $\dot{n}(\eta_{\max})$ that makes η a maximum is, in general, not the same as the value $\dot{n}(-\dot{W}_{\max})$ that makes $-\dot{W}$ a maximum: when $-\dot{W} = -\dot{W}_{\max}$, it follows that

$$\left(\frac{\partial \eta}{\partial \dot{n}}\right)_{T_\alpha, T_\beta} = \frac{\dot{W}T_\beta(T_\alpha - T_\beta)}{T_\alpha(-\dot{W} + T_\beta\Theta)^2}\left(\frac{\partial \Theta}{\partial \dot{n}}\right)_{T_\alpha, T_\beta} < 0.$$

The negative value of $(\partial\eta/\partial\dot{n})_{T_\alpha, T_\beta}$ at the point where $-\dot{W} = -\dot{W}_{\max}$ indicates that $\dot{n}(\eta_{\max}) < \dot{n}(-\dot{W}_{\max})$.

The shape of the curve in Figure 10–2 is consistent with the condition of stability (Eq. 10.11). Let $\{\partial(-\dot{W}/\dot{n})/\partial\dot{n}\}_{T_\alpha, T_\beta} \equiv -RT_\alpha[N]$, and for

* See Eq. (3.32).

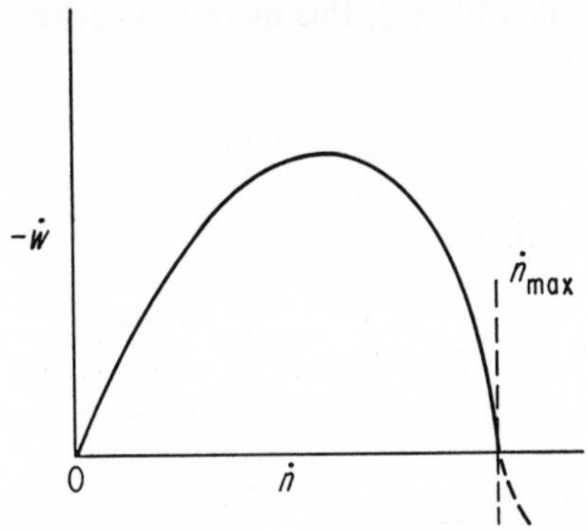

Figure 10–2. Schematic plot of $-\dot{W}$ versus $\dot{n}$ for a typical thermal converter; fixed T_α, T_β.

convenience take $[N]$ to be independent of $\dot{n}$ (this is equivalent to using a set of linear current-affinity relations); then

$$-\dot{W} = \dot{n}\{-\Delta\mathscr{G}_\alpha(0) - \dot{n}RT_\alpha[N]\}, \tag{10.13}$$

$$\dot{n}_{\max} = \frac{-\Delta\mathscr{G}_\alpha(0)}{RT_\alpha[N]}, \tag{10.14}$$

$$-\dot{W}_{\max} = \frac{(-\Delta\mathscr{G}_\alpha(0)/2)^2}{RT_\alpha[N]} = -\dot{W}(\dot{n}_{\max}/2)$$

$$= \frac{\dot{n}_{\max}}{4}\{-\Delta\mathscr{G}_\alpha(0)\}, \tag{10.15}$$

where $-\Delta\mathscr{G}_\alpha(0)$ is the Gibbs free energy difference (per unit of "charge") across the poles of the engine e in the limit of vanishing current; i.e., $-\Delta\mathscr{G}_\alpha(0) = \lim(-\dot{W}/\dot{n})$ as $\dot{n} \to 0$ (for the thermocouple: if the current is measured in Faradays, then $-\Delta\mathscr{G}_\alpha(0) = F\Delta\psi$ with $\Delta\psi$ being the no-current Seebeck potential difference). The quantity $\dot{n}_{\max}$ is a *short-circuit* current: the converter loop is merely closed with no work being exchanged between system and surroundings. Within the assumptions made in deriving Eq. (10.15) we see that the maximum rate of delivery of work to the surroundings is just one-fourth of the product of the short-circuit current and the open-circuit "potential difference"—i.e., for the thermocouple

$$-\dot{W}_{\max} = \tfrac{1}{4}I_{\max}\Delta\psi(0) = \tfrac{1}{4}\dot{n}_{\max}F\Delta\psi.$$

Exercise 10–1. From Eqs. (10.10), (3.17), and (3.18)—taking state β as the thermostatic reference state—find the relationship between the quantity $[N]$ and the quantities L_{ij} or the quantities K_{ij}.

Consider now the quantity $[\eta]$; this quantity reaches its maximum in the limit of vanishing current:

$$[\eta]_{\max} = \lim_{\dot{n}\to 0} [\eta]. \tag{10.16}$$

We see from Eq. (10.7) that

$$[\eta] = \frac{T_\alpha - T_\beta}{T_\alpha}\left\{\frac{(-\dot{W}/\dot{n})}{(-\dot{W}/\dot{n}) + T_\beta(\Delta\Theta/\dot{n})}\right\} \tag{10.17}$$

and that

$$[\eta]_{\max} = \frac{T_\alpha - T_\beta}{T_\alpha}\left\{\frac{(\delta(-\dot{W})/\bar{\delta}\dot{n})_{T_\alpha,T_\beta}}{(\delta(-\dot{W})/\bar{\delta}\dot{n})_{T_\alpha,T_\beta} + T_\beta(\delta\Theta/\bar{\delta}\dot{n})_{T_\alpha,T_\beta}}\right\}. \tag{10.18}$$

Now $\{\delta(-\dot{W})/\bar{\delta}\dot{n}\}_{T_\alpha,T_\beta} = -\Delta\mathscr{G}_\alpha(0)$, and by assumption IV $(\delta\Theta/\bar{\delta}\dot{n})_{T_\alpha,T_\beta} = 0$, so

$$[\eta]_{\max} = \frac{T_\alpha - T_\beta}{T_\alpha}. \tag{10.19}$$

Thus if we compute the efficiency on the basis of the participating heat flow, then the Carnot efficiency (Eq. 10.19) is the ideal limit. The efficiency computed on the basis of the total heat flow is much less than the Carnot efficiency since much of the heat merely passes by conduction from the higher temperature to the lower.

The engineering aspects of the thermocouple functioning as a thermal converter are receiving a good deal of attention;* in principle other sorts of thermal converters are potentially of engineering value. In Figure 10–1 if the engine e is a gas turbine and the apparatus contains a circulating gas, the links $\alpha\beta$ and $\beta\alpha$ being tubes of different diameter, then the difference in the thermomolecular pressure effect across the two links will maintain a pressure difference across the turbine and work can be delivered to the surroundings at a steady rate—a Brønsted thermal converter [3, 4].

In a similar fashion if two liquid–vapor interfaces at different temperatures (parts of a closed loop) communicate with a turbine, then the difference in vapor pressure for the two temperatures will establish the necessary pressure difference across the turbine. Consider the situation indicated schematically in Figure 10–3: two liquid–vapor interfaces maintained at different temperatures communicate with opposite sides of a turbine engine in a full-flux linkage. For a steady state with $\dot{n}$ moles of fluid circulating per second around the loop we have

$$-\dot{W} = -\dot{Q}_\alpha^{(r)} - \dot{Q}_\beta^{(r)} = -T_\alpha\dot{S}_\alpha^{(r)} - T_\beta\dot{S}_\beta^{(r)} \tag{10.20}$$

* See the many papers in the book cited in reference [1], and see also the book by Angrist [2].

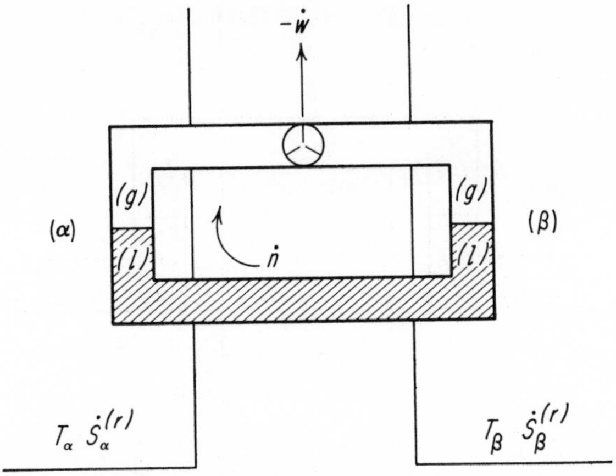

Figure 10–3. A closed-loop thermal converter of the vapor pressure–turbine type; linkages are of the full-flux type; $T_\alpha > T_\beta$.

and

$$\begin{aligned}\Theta = \dot{S}_\alpha^{(r)} + \dot{S}_\beta^{(r)} &= \dot{n}\left(\frac{\dot{W}}{\dot{n}T_\beta}\right) + \dot{Q}_\alpha^{(r)}\left(\frac{1}{T_\alpha} - \frac{1}{T_\beta}\right) \\ &= Y_1\Omega_1 + Y_2\Omega_2. \end{aligned} \tag{10.21}$$

In the limiting state ($\dot{n} \to 0$) we have

$$\left(\frac{\delta(-\dot{W})}{\tilde{\delta}\dot{n}}\right)_{T_\alpha, T_\beta} = -T_\alpha\left(\frac{\delta\dot{S}_\alpha^{(r)}}{\tilde{\delta}\dot{n}}\right)_{T_\alpha, T_\beta} - T_\beta\left(\frac{\delta\dot{S}_\beta^{(r)}}{\tilde{\delta}\dot{n}}\right)_{T_\alpha, T_\beta}, \tag{10.22}$$

$$\left(\frac{\delta\Theta}{\tilde{\delta}\dot{n}}\right)_{T_\alpha, T_\beta} = \left(\frac{\delta\dot{S}_\alpha^{(r)}}{\tilde{\delta}\dot{n}}\right)_{T_\alpha, T_\beta} + \left(\frac{\delta\dot{S}_\beta^{(r)}}{\tilde{\delta}\dot{n}}\right)_{T_\alpha, T_\beta}, \tag{10.23}$$

$$\mu_\omega^{(\text{liq})} = \mu_\omega^{(g)}. \tag{10.24}$$

In accordance with the discussion in Chapter 6, we can write $(\delta\dot{S}_\omega^{(r)}/\tilde{\delta}\dot{n})_{\Omega'} = [S_\omega(\text{in})] - [S_\omega(\text{out})]$; hence we have (assumption IV)

$$[S_\alpha^{(\text{liq})}] - [S_\alpha^{(g)}] + [S_\beta^{(g)}] - [S_\beta^{(\text{liq})}] = 0, \tag{10.25}$$

$$\begin{aligned}\left(\frac{\delta(-\dot{W})}{\tilde{\delta}\dot{n}}\right)_{T_\alpha, T_\beta} &= -T_\alpha\{[S_\alpha^{(\text{liq})}] - [S_\alpha^{(g)}]\} - T_\beta\{[S_\beta^{(g)}] - [S_\beta^{(\text{liq})}]\} \\ &= (T_\alpha - T_\beta)\{[S_\beta^{(g)}] - [S_\beta^{(\text{liq})}]\}. \end{aligned} \tag{10.26}$$

Alternatively, if we write for convenience $\mu_\alpha^{(g)} - \mu_\alpha^{(\text{liq})} + \mu_\beta^{(\text{liq})} - \mu_\beta^{(g)} = 0$ and add this expression to Eq. (10.26), we obtain

$$\left(\frac{\delta(-\dot{W})}{\tilde{\delta}\dot{n}}\right)_{T_\alpha, T_\beta} = [H_\alpha^{(g)}] - [H_\alpha^{(\text{liq})}] + [H_\beta^{(\text{liq})}] - [H_\beta^{(g)}]. \tag{10.27}$$

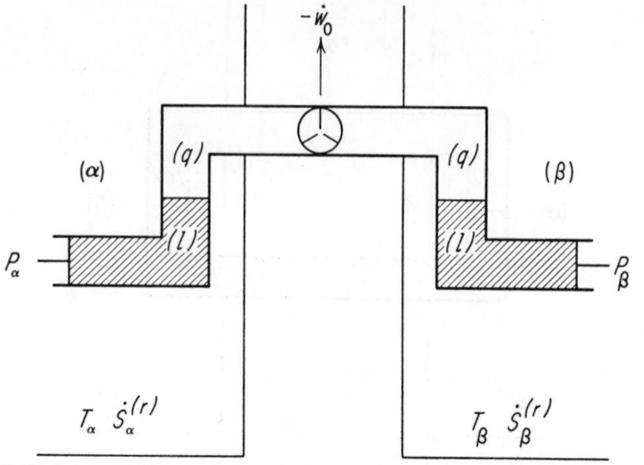

Figure 10–4. A source-sink thermal converter of the vapor pressure–turbine type; full-flux linkage; $T_\alpha > T_\beta$.

Now, there being no hindrance to the migration of liquid through the lower link, it should be true that $[H_\alpha^{(\mathrm{liq})}] - [H_\beta^{(\mathrm{liq})}] = 0$; hence Eq. (10.27) should reduce to

$$\left(\frac{\delta(-\dot{W})}{\delta\dot{n}}\right)_{T_\alpha, T_\beta} = [H_\alpha^{(g)}] - [H_\beta^{(g)}]. \tag{10.28}$$

Equation (10.28) shows that in a certain sense the maximum work (per unit "charge" transferred) obtainable out of a full-flux linkage is governed by the magnitude of the $\Delta[H]$ quantity across the linkage.

Exercise 10–2. Analyze the slightly different situation indicated in Figure 10–4 (make use of Eq. 6.39) and show that

$$\left(\frac{\delta(-\dot{W}_0)}{\delta\dot{n}}\right)_{T_\alpha, T_\beta} = [H_\alpha^{(g)}] - [H_\beta^{(g)}].$$

Steady Bithermal Mass Flow with Full-Flux Linkage

Consider the case indicated in Figure 10–5: the situation is the same as that analyzed in establishing the migrational equilibrium condition for the thermomolecular pressure effect; I now investigate the relations governing the simultaneous flow of heat and mass. Assume for a given gas and (full-flux) linkage that $\dot{n}_\alpha = \dot{n}_\alpha(T_\alpha, T_\beta, P_\alpha, P_\beta)$; it follows then

$$\left(\frac{\partial\dot{n}_\alpha}{\partial T_\alpha}\right)_{\beta, P_\alpha} = -\left(\frac{\partial\dot{n}_\alpha}{\partial P_\alpha}\right)_{\beta, T_\alpha}\left(\frac{\partial P_\alpha}{\partial T_\alpha}\right)_{\beta, \dot{n}_\alpha}. \tag{10.29}$$

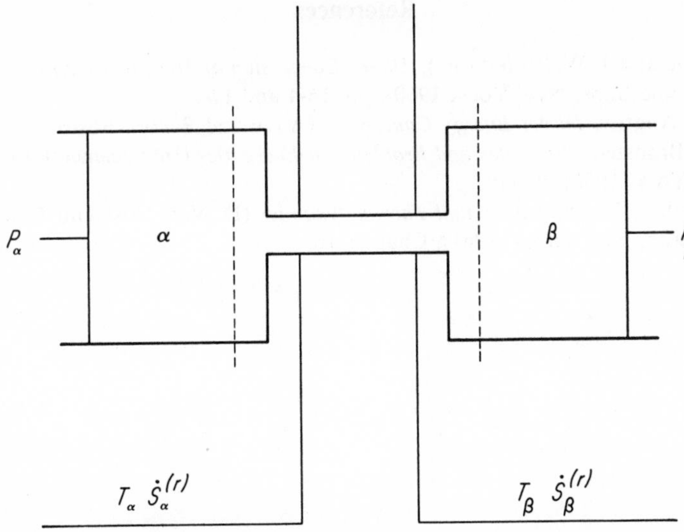

Figure 10–5. Steady bithermal flow of a gas across a capillary, full-flux linkage.

Equation (10.29) has an interesting consequence. Since $(\partial \dot{n}_\alpha/\partial P_\alpha)_{\beta,T_\alpha}$ is necessarily negative, it follows from Eq. (10.29) that $(\partial \dot{n}_\alpha/\partial T_\alpha)_{\beta,P_\alpha}$ and $(\partial P_\alpha/\partial T_\alpha)_{\beta,\dot{n}_\alpha}$ have the same sign. The thermomolecular pressure type of experiment at moderate values of $\dot{n}_\alpha$ yields positive values for $(\partial P_\alpha/\partial T_\alpha)_{\beta,\dot{n}_\alpha}$ [since $(\partial P_\alpha/\partial T_\alpha)_{\beta,\dot{n}_\alpha=0}$ is positive]; the implication, then, is that the change in state $\{T_\alpha(*),\ P_\alpha(*),\ T_\beta(*),\ P_\beta(*)\} \to \{T_\alpha(*) + \Delta T_\alpha,\ P_\alpha(*),\ T_\beta(*),\ P_\beta(*)\}$—the first state being one of migrational equilibrium—results in a mass flow *into* the α terminal part if ΔT_α is positive.

Exercise 10–3. The preceding considerations suggest that relations such as

$$-\left(\frac{\partial \dot{Q}_\alpha^{(r)}}{\partial \dot{n}_\alpha}\right)_{\beta,T_\alpha} = T_\alpha \bar{V}_\alpha \left(\frac{\partial P_\alpha}{\partial T_\alpha}\right)_{\beta,\dot{n}_\alpha} \qquad (10.30)$$

may hold for the case considered with $\dot{Q}_\alpha^{(r)} = \dot{Q}_\alpha^{(r)}(T_\alpha, P_\alpha, T_\beta, P_\beta)$ for a given gas and linkage. Investigate the applicability of Eq. (10.30) in the limit $\dot{n}_\alpha \to 0$, showing the consequences of its assumed truth. On the basis of the findings for the $\dot{n}_\alpha \to 0$ case, decide on the reasonableness of the equation for the case $\dot{n}_\alpha \neq 0$.

References

1. J. Kaye and J. Walsh (editors), *Direct Conversion of Heat to Electricity* (John Wiley and Sons, New York, 1960), pp. 16-4 and 17-3.
2. S. W. Angrist, *Direct Energy Conversion* (Allyn and Bacon, Boston, 1965).
3. J. N. Brønsted, *Principles and Problems in Energetics* (Interscience Publishers, New York, 1955), p. 110.
4. M. Tribus, *Thermostatics and Thermodynamics* (D. Van Nostrand Company, Princeton, New Jersey, 1961), Chapter 16.

11

Heat Conduction

One-Dimensional Heat Conduction

Consider the situation indicated schematically in Figure 11–1. The system of interest, taken to be in the shape of a bar for convenience, forms a full-flux linkage between two thermostats α and β; the cross-sectional area of the bar *at the point where it enters the* ω *thermostat* is B_ω; and the length of the bar outside the thermostat is Λ. We determine the coefficient of thermal conductivity κ for the system from the relations

$$-\left(\frac{\partial \dot{Q}_\alpha^{(r)}}{\partial T_\alpha}\right)_\beta \equiv \frac{\kappa_\alpha B_\alpha}{\Lambda}, \tag{11.1}$$

$$\begin{aligned} -\dot{Q}_\alpha^{(r)} &= \int_{T_\beta}^{T_\alpha} \left(\frac{\kappa_a B_a}{\Lambda}\right)_\beta dT_a \\ &= \left\langle \frac{\kappa B}{\Lambda} \right\rangle (T_\alpha - T_\beta), \end{aligned} \tag{11.2}$$

where $\dot{Q}_\omega^{(r)} = T_\omega \dot{S}_\omega^{(r)}$ is the rate of influx of heat into the ω heat reservoir via the link Λ. Since we are taking the link to be a full-flux one, it follows that $\dot{Q}_\alpha^{(r)} + \dot{Q}_\beta^{(r)} = 0$, and, in general, that

$$\kappa_\omega = -\frac{\Lambda}{B_\omega}\left(\frac{\partial \dot{Q}_\omega^{(r)}}{\partial T_\omega}\right)_\chi = \frac{\Lambda}{B_\omega}\left(\frac{\partial \dot{Q}_\chi^{(r)}}{\partial T_\omega}\right)_\chi. \tag{11.3}$$

Now in the state of steady heat conduction

$$\dot{U}(\text{system}) = -\dot{Q}_\alpha^{(r)} - \dot{Q}_\beta^{(r)} = 0, \tag{11.4}$$

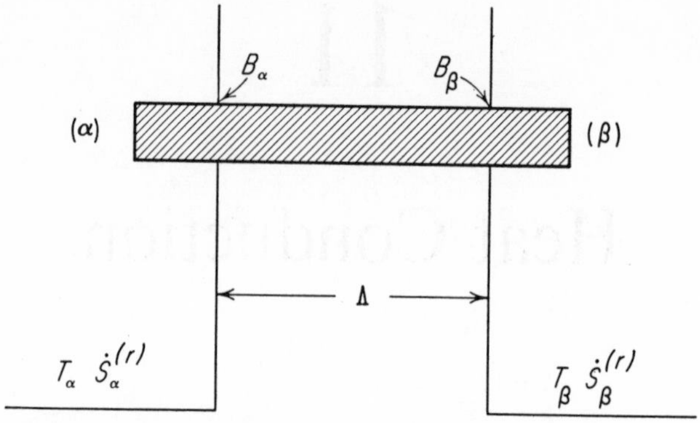

Figure 11–1. System in the form of a bar serving as a full-flux link between two thermostats α and β.

$$\Theta = \frac{\dot{Q}_\alpha^{(r)}}{T_\alpha} + \frac{\dot{Q}_\beta^{(r)}}{T_\beta} = \dot{Q}_\alpha^{(r)}\left(\frac{1}{T_\alpha} - \frac{1}{T_\beta}\right)$$
$$= Y_1\Omega_1. \tag{11.5}$$

If we take state β as our reference thermostatic state,* we can write

$$Y_1 = L_{11}(\beta)\Omega_1 \tag{11.6}$$

or

$$\dot{Q}_\alpha^{(r)} = L_{11}(\beta)\left(\frac{1}{T_\alpha} - \frac{1}{T_\beta}\right) = -\frac{L_{11}(T_\alpha - T_\beta)}{T_\alpha T_\beta}. \tag{11.7}$$

It follows from Eqs. (11.2) and (11.7) that

$$\langle\kappa\rangle = \left(\frac{L_{11}(\beta)}{T_\alpha T_\beta}\right)\frac{\Lambda}{B};\tag{11.8}$$

hence for fixed T_β, if L_{11} does not depend on T_α, then $\langle\kappa\rangle$ does, and vice versa. In addition, from the relation $L_{11} = (\partial Y_1/\partial\Omega_1)_\beta = \{\partial\dot{Q}_\alpha^{(r)}/\partial(1/T_\alpha)\}_{T_\beta}$ and Eq. (11.1), we see that

$$\frac{L_{11}}{T_\alpha^{\ 2}} = \frac{\kappa_\alpha B_\alpha}{\Lambda}. \tag{11.9}$$

Although the thermal conductivity κ for a solid material does depend on temperature [1], we have no grounds for believing that κT^2 should be a more slowly varying function of temperature than κ itself.

Multiple Heat Currents

Consider now the case outlined in Figure 11–2: a branched, full-flux linkage (a solid, heat-conducting material) connecting four separate

* See Chapter 3.

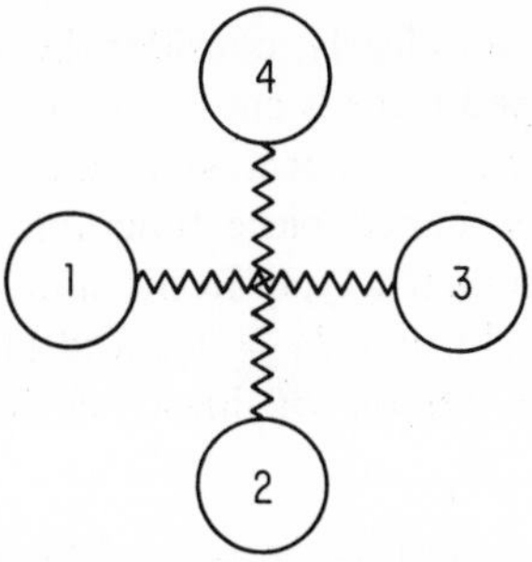

Figure 11–2. A branched, full-flux linkage (a solid, heat-conducting material) connecting four separate heat reservoirs (thermostats) 1, 2, 3, 4.

thermostats. Let terminal part 1 be in state I, part 2 in state II, and so on. The state of steady heat exchange is characterized by

$$\dot{U}(\text{system}) = -\sum_{i=1}^{4} \dot{Q}_i^{(r)} = 0 \tag{11.10}$$

and

$$\begin{aligned}\Theta &= \sum_{i=1}^{4} \frac{\dot{Q}_i^{(r)}}{T_i} \\ &= \dot{Q}_1^{(r)}\left(\frac{1}{T_1} - \frac{1}{T_4}\right) + \dot{Q}_2^{(r)}\left(\frac{1}{T_2} - \frac{1}{T_4}\right) + \dot{Q}_3^{(r)}\left(\frac{1}{T_3} - \frac{1}{T_4}\right) \\ &= Y_1\Omega_1 + Y_2\Omega_2 + Y_3\Omega_3. \end{aligned} \tag{11.11}$$

Apparently, then, the situation is a 3-current situation. Now, can some constraint be applied to the system such that Eq. (11.10) can be resolved into the separate equations $\dot{Q}_1^{(r)} + \dot{Q}_3^{(r)} = 0$ and $\dot{Q}_2^{(r)} + \dot{Q}_4^{(r)} = 0$? That is, can we set up two independent *heat currents* in the linkage?

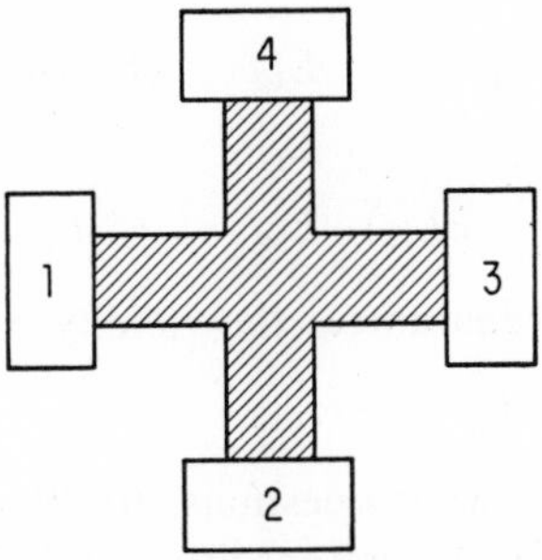

Figure 11–3. A symmetric cross-shaped piece of heat-conducting material functioning as a branched, full-flux linkage between the four heat reservoirs (thermostats) 1, 2, 3, 4.

In order to see the matter clearly, consider the situation in Figure 11–3: a homogeneous, cross-shaped piece is cut from a metal plate; the ends of the arms of the cross butt up against thermostats and exchange heat with those thermostats; i.e., the cross-shaped piece functions as a branched, full-flux linkage of an especially symmetric type. In the state of steady heat exchange, Eqs. (11.10) and (11.11) hold. Let $T_4 = T_{\mathrm{IV}}$ and take state IV as reference thermostatic state. In the region of linear current-affinity relations we have, then,

$$\dot{Q}_i^{(r)} = \sum_{j=1}^{3} L_{ij}(\mathrm{IV})\left(\frac{1}{T_j} - \frac{1}{T_4}\right) \qquad i = 1, 2, 3, 4, \tag{11.12}$$

$$L_{4j} = -\sum_{i=1}^{3} L_{ij} \qquad j = 1, 2, 3. \tag{11.13}$$

Exercise 11–1. Due to the symmetry of the cross-shaped linkage, of the nine basic coefficients in the **L** matrix, only two are independent. Consider an "old" state $\{T_1 = T_{\mathrm{I}},\ T_2 = T_{\mathrm{II}},\ T_3 = T_{\mathrm{III}},\ T_4 = T_{\mathrm{IV}}\}$ and a "new$_1$" state $\{T_1 = T_{\mathrm{I}},\ T_2 = T_{\mathrm{IV}},\ T_3 = T_{\mathrm{III}},\ T_4 = T_{\mathrm{II}}\}$; then the symmetry of the linkage requires that $\dot{Q}_1^{(r)}(\text{old}) = \dot{Q}_1^{(r)}(\text{new}_1)$, and $\dot{Q}_3^{(r)}(\text{old}) = \dot{Q}_3^{(r)}(\text{new}_1)$. Similarly, for the "new$_2$" state $\{T_1 = T_{\mathrm{III}},\ T_2 = T_{\mathrm{II}},\ T_3 = T_{\mathrm{I}},\ T_4 = T_{\mathrm{IV}}\}$ the relations $\dot{Q}_2^{(r)}(\text{old}) = \dot{Q}_2^{(r)}(\text{new}_2)$ and $\dot{Q}_4^{(r)}(\text{old}) = \dot{Q}_4^{(r)}(\text{new}_2)$ hold. Also, for the "new$_3$" state $\{T_1 = T_{\mathrm{II}},\ T_2 = T_{\mathrm{III}},\ T_3 = T_{\mathrm{IV}},\ T_4 = T_{\mathrm{I}}\}$, the relations $\dot{Q}_i^{(r)}(\text{new}_3) = \dot{Q}_{i+1}^{(r)}(\text{old})$ $i = 1, 2, 3, 4$ are valid (with the convention that $5 \equiv 1$). Show that the preceding relations constrain the matrix

$$\begin{bmatrix} L_{11} & L_{12} & L_{13} \\ L_{21} & L_{22} & L_{23} \\ L_{31} & L_{32} & L_{33} \end{bmatrix}$$

to have the form

$$\begin{bmatrix} L_{11} & L_{12} & -(L_{11} + 2L_{12}) \\ L_{12} & L_{11} & L_{12} \\ -(L_{11} + 2L_{12}) & L_{12} & L_{11} \end{bmatrix}. \tag{11.14}$$

(Note that the symmetry guarantees the validity of the Onsager relations.)

Consider now the following questions. (i) What do the conditions of stability (Eq. 3.30) imply for the present situation? The conditions of stability take the form, e.g., $\{\partial \dot{Q}_1^{(r)}/\partial(1/T_1)\}_{T_2,T_3,T_4} > 0$, or, alternatively,

$$(\partial \dot{Q}_1^{(r)}/\partial T_1)_{T_2,T_3,T_4} < 0$$

—a relation that is certainly true regardless of the nature (linear or nonlinear) of the current-affinity relations. (ii) For the case $T_1 = T_{\rm I}$, $T_2 = T_{\rm II}$, $T_4 = T_{\rm IV}$, what must be the temperature T_3 so that $\dot{Q}_3^{(r)} = 0$? The question refers to an ordinary state of "migrational equilibrium":

$$\Omega_1\left(\frac{\delta Y_1}{\bar{\delta} Y_3}\right)_{\Omega'} + \Omega_2\left(\frac{\delta Y_2}{\bar{\delta} Y_3}\right)_{\Omega'} + \Omega_3 = 0. \tag{11.15}$$

In the region of linear current-affinity relations $(\delta Y_i/\bar{\delta} Y_k)_{\Omega'} = L_{ik}/L_{kk}$, so

$$L_{13}\Omega_1 + L_{23}\Omega_2 + L_{33}\Omega_3 = 0, \tag{11.16}$$

or, if we make use of the matrix elements in relation (11.14),

$$-(L_{11} + 2L_{12})\left(\frac{1}{T_{\rm I}} - \frac{1}{T_{\rm IV}}\right) + L_{12}\left(\frac{1}{T_{\rm II}} - \frac{1}{T_{\rm IV}}\right) + L_{11}\left(\frac{1}{T_3} - \frac{1}{T_{\rm IV}}\right) = 0; \tag{11.17}$$

and the problem is solved if we know the coefficients L_{11} and L_{12}. (iii) Under what conditions is it possible to have $\dot{Q}_1^{(r)} + \dot{Q}_3^{(r)} = 0$? The relation $\dot{Q}_1^{(r)} + \dot{Q}_3^{(r)} = 0$ implies (in the linear current-affinity region) that

$$(L_{11} + L_{31})\Omega_1 + (L_{12} + L_{32})\Omega_2 + (L_{13} + L_{33})\Omega_3 = 0, \tag{11.18}$$

or, if we use relation (11.14), that

$$-\frac{1}{T_1} + \frac{1}{T_2} - \frac{1}{T_3} + \frac{1}{T_4} = 0. \tag{11.19}$$

Exercise 11–2. Consider a special case of Eq. (11.19): $T_1 = T_2 = T_{\rm II}$ (say) and $T_3 = T_4 = T_{\rm IV}$ (say). Equation (11.11) then reduces to

$$\Theta = \dot{Q}_1^{(r)}\left(\frac{1}{T_1} - \frac{1}{T_4}\right) + \dot{Q}_2^{(r)}\left(\frac{1}{T_2} - \frac{1}{T_4}\right). \tag{11.20}$$

Although Eq. (11.20) seems to indicate a 2-current situation, show that the situation is in fact only a 1-current situation.

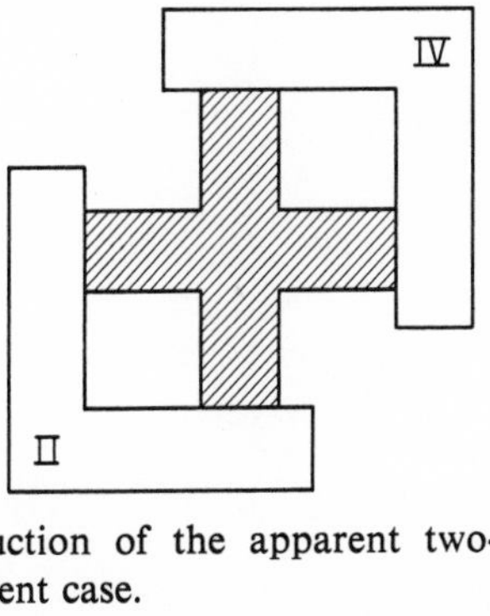

Figure 11–4. Reduction of the apparent two-current case to an equivalent one-current case.

Hint: Show that $\dot{Q}_1^{(r)}$ and $\dot{Q}_2^{(r)}$ are not independent for the special case considered—see Figure 11–4.

Exercise 11–3. Consider Figure 11–3 once again. Let the center point of the cross have the temperature T_0, and let the distance from the midpoint of the cross to each of the thermostats be Λ. Now let

$$-\dot{Q}_i^{(r)} = \frac{\kappa B}{\Lambda}(T_i - T_0) \qquad i = 1, 2, 3, 4, \tag{11.21}$$

where κ is the coefficient of thermal conductivity and B is the cross-sectional area of each arm of the cross. Show that for the condition $\dot{Q}_1^{(r)} + \dot{Q}_3^{(r)} = 0$ to hold Eq. (11.21) requires that

$$T_1 - T_2 + T_3 - T_4 = 0. \tag{11.22}$$

Show that if $|(T_i - T_4)/T_4| \ll 1$ for $i = 1, 2, 3, 4$, then Eqs. (11.19) and (11.22) are approximately equivalent.

An interesting problem in the heat-conduction field is the mapping of the three-dimensional flow of heat in an anisotropic crystal. For a discussion of the bearing of the Onsager reciprocal relations on this problem, see the treatments of Miller [2] and de Groot and Mazur [3].

References

1. R. C. L. Bosworth, *Heat Transfer Phenomena* (John Wiley and Sons, New York, 1952), Chapter 4.
2. D. G. Miller, *Chem. Revs.*, **60**, 15 (1960).
3. S. de Groot and P. Mazur, *Non-Equilibrium Thermodynamics* (North Holland Publishing Company, Amsterdam, 1962), Chapter 11.

12

Heat Radiation

General Remarks

The (equilibrium) thermodynamic treatment of thermal radiation fields (heat radiation) is given in full in the classic text of Planck [1]; in this chapter I treat a few topics pertaining to heat radiation by the steady-state methods developed in Part I. First I find it necessary to lay down a few conventions. The source of the thermal radiation being studied is always to be a heat reservoir (thermostat) of specified temperature; the reservoir is to be insulated against (other) radiative heat losses and is to be in communication with a cylinder-and-piston arrangement. The inside walls and piston face of the cylinder-and-piston arrangement are to be perfectly reflecting so that the radiation field can be considered to be localized inside the apparatus. A schematic version of the basic apparatus showing the communicating wall of the thermostat and the cylinder-and-piston arrangement appears in Figure 12–1. The system to be studied is the radiation trapped inside the cylinder-and-piston arrangement, the radiation interacting thermodynamically with the heat reservoir. It is convenient to use thermodynamic density functions in the course of the analysis; I indicate these density functions by lower case letters; thus let $z \equiv Z/V$, e.g.

Consider the situation indicated schematically in Figure 12–1, and let the volume of the radiation field be increased at a steady rate $\dot{V}$; then it follows that

$$\dot{U}(\text{system}) = -T\dot{S}^{(r)} - P\dot{V}, \tag{12.1}$$

and

$$\dot{H}(\text{system}) + T\dot{S}^{(r)} = 0, \tag{12.2}$$

where $\dot{S}^{(r)}$ represents the rate of accumulation of entropy in the heat reservoir. If we can associate well-defined thermodynamic density functions with the radiation field, so that $\dot{H}(\text{system}) = h\dot{V}$, e.g., we then arrive at the relations

$$h\dot{V} + T\dot{S}^{(r)} = 0 \tag{12.3}$$

and

$$\begin{aligned}\Theta &= \dot{S}^{(r)} + s\dot{V} = \dot{V}\left(s - \frac{h}{T}\right) = \dot{V}\left(\frac{-g}{T}\right)\\ &= Y_1\Omega_1,\end{aligned} \tag{12.4}$$

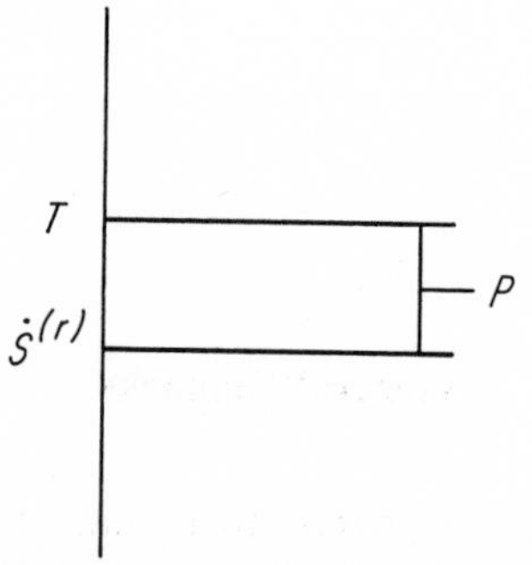

Figure 12–1. Thermostat plus cylinder-and-piston arrangement for studying heat radiation.

where $g \equiv h - Ts$. We find the properties of the equilibrium radiation field (complete radiation, blackbody radiation) by applying the operation $(\delta/\delta\dot{V})_T$ to Eq. (12.4) and by making use of assumption IV:

$$g \equiv h - Ts = 0. \tag{12.5}$$

Thus for equilibrium radiation the Gibbs free energy density of the radiation field has the value zero. Since in general $g = g(T, P)$, the relation $g(T, P) = 0$ implies that the equilibrium radiation field is a univariant system (in the phase rule sense [2]), and the properties of the radiation field are completely determined by specifying any *one* intensive property of the (equilibrium) field. Thus we have relations such as $P = P(T)$, $T = T(P)$, and $z = z(T)$; it is usually most convenient to take the temperature T as the independent variable. (Note that for equilibrium radiation $T = h/s$.)

We can spectrally decompose the equilibrium radiation field into monochromatic radiation "intervals" [1] having monochromatic density functions z_λ associated with them, and we can show that the Gibbs free energy density g_λ associated with *any* wavelength interval has the value zero for equilibrium radiation.

Consider the situation indicated schematically in Figure 12–2. Partition an equilibrium radiation field by a movable filter (permeable only to radiation of wavelength between λ and $\lambda + d\lambda$) into a region containing radiation of wavelength λ (to the right of the filter) and another region (to the left of the filter) containing complete radiation. Let the filter be moved by external forces. In the following analysis I indicate the properties of the complete radiation by unsubscripted symbols and those of the monochromatic radiation by symbols with subscript λ.

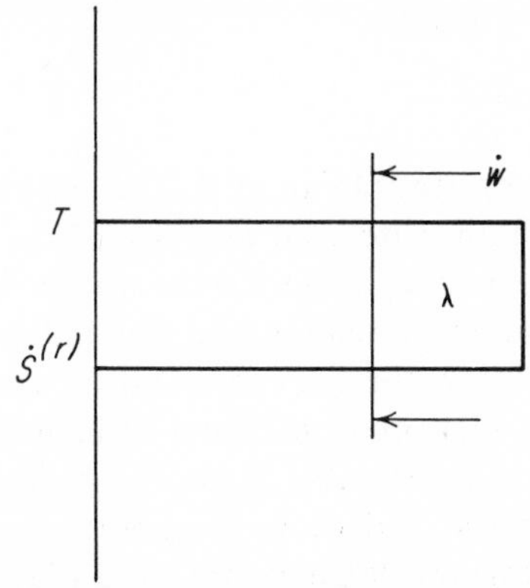

Figure 12–2. An equilibrium radiation field partitioned by a movable filter permeable only to radiation of wavelength between λ and $\lambda + d\lambda$; the filter is moved by external forces.

Let us move the filter at a steady rate so that $\dot{V} + \dot{V}_\lambda = 0$; the standard steady-state analysis then yields the relations

$$u\dot{V} + u_\lambda \dot{V}_\lambda = -T\dot{S}^{(r)} + \dot{W} \tag{12.6}$$

and

$$\Theta = \dot{S}^{(r)} + s\dot{V} + s_\lambda \dot{V}_\lambda = \dot{V}_\lambda\left(\frac{a}{T} - \frac{a_\lambda}{T} + \frac{\dot{W}}{T\dot{V}_\lambda}\right), \tag{12.7}$$

where $a \equiv u - Ts$. The application of the operation $(\delta/\delta\dot{V}_\lambda)_T$ to Eq. (12.7) and the use of assumption IV lead to the relation

$$a - a_\lambda + \left(\frac{\delta\dot{W}}{\delta\dot{V}_\lambda}\right)_T = 0, \tag{12.8}$$

where I have made use of the definition $\lim (\dot{W}/\dot{V}_\lambda)$ as $\dot{V}_\lambda \to 0 \equiv (\delta\dot{W}/\delta\dot{V}_\lambda)$. Now, if the pressure of the radiation to the left of the filter is P and that to the right of the filter is P_λ, then

$$\left(\frac{\delta\dot{W}}{\delta\dot{V}_\lambda}\right)_T = P - P_\lambda \tag{12.9}$$

and

$$g - g_\lambda = 0. \tag{12.10}$$

Exercise 12–1. For equilibrium radiation it can be shown [1, 3] that $P = u/3$ and that $(\partial U/\partial V)_T = u$; hence show that the thermodynamic relation $(\partial U/\partial V)_T = T(\partial P/\partial T)_V - P$ leads directly to the Stefan–Boltzmann relation

$$u = \Gamma T^4,$$

where Γ is a constant.

Show the explicit dependence on T of the density functions h, a, s; and verify the relation $s = -da/dT$.

The classical theory of heat radiation [1, 3] concerns itself primarily with two relations derived from a detailed analysis of the electromagnetic field and with the thermodynamic consequences of those two relations: the relations so singled out for attention are the radiation–pressure relation $P = u/3$ and the Planck law for the spectral decomposition of the radiant energy density. For describing nonequilibrium radiation, we usually introduce a number of coefficients (emissivity, absorptivity, etc.) so as to relate the properties of the observed radiation to those of complete (blackbody) radiation. In determining the temperature of a radiating body we match some property of the radiating body with the corresponding property of a blackbody and then determine a *blackbody matching temperature* (of which there are several: color temperature, brightness temperature, effective temperature, and so on [4]). In order to see some of the problems that arise in treating nonequilibrium radiation consider the case of steady forced radiation. Refer again to Figure 12–1, and consider the case where the radiation field is expanding at a steady rate $\dot{V}$. We can put Eq. (12.4) into the form

$$-(h - Ts) = \frac{T\Theta}{\dot{V}} > 0. \tag{12.11}$$

Relation (12.11) shows that for the nonequilibrium radiation field $(h/s) < T$. Now, what is the "temperature" of the radiation undergoing the forced radiation process? Is it the thermostat temperature T? Is it a blackbody temperature T_1* associated with the pressure P—i.e., $T_1* = T_1*(P)$? Is it a temperature T_2* defined by $T_2* \equiv h/s$? Or is it something else? Is it meaningful to ascribe a temperature to the radiation itself? Does $T_1* = T_2*$? We can easily ask many questions for which we have no ready answers. It seems fairly evident that any blackbody matching temperature such as T_i* will be smaller than the thermostat temperature T (in order that the forced radiation process proceed, it is necessary that the pressure P be less than the equilibrium pressure $P*(T)$, and so on). Perhaps we could consider the radiation field to

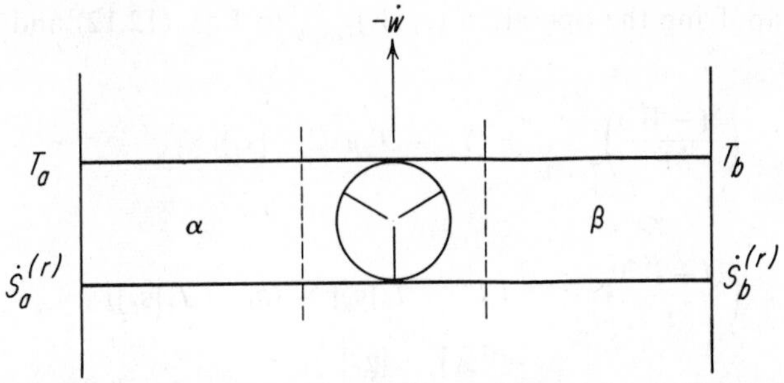

Figure 12–3. A turbine with perfectly reflecting blades placed in a radiation field; the difference in radiation pressure across the turbine results in the delivery of work at the rate $-\dot{W}$ to the surroundings; $T_a > T_b$.

be interacting thermodynamically with the surface (instead of with the bulk) of the thermostat, the radiating surface being at a lower temperature than the interior—just as in the forced vaporization process [5, 6] the region in the vicinity of the liquid–vapor interface is at a lower temperature than that of the encompassing thermostat. The various blackbody matching temperatures might then be reasonable estimates of the temperature of the radiating *surface.*

Radiation Turbine

Consider now the situation shown in Figure 12–3. A radiation turbine with perfectly reflecting blades is placed in communication with two sources of radiation ($T_a > T_b$); the difference in radiation pressure drives the turbine so as to deliver work at the rate $-\dot{W}$ to the surroundings. When the system is in a steady state, we have

$$-\dot{W} = -T_a\dot{S}_a^{(r)} - T_b\dot{S}_b^{(r)} \tag{12.12}$$

and

$$\begin{aligned}\Theta &= \dot{S}_a^{(r)} + \dot{S}_b^{(r)} = \frac{\dot{Q}_a^{(r)}}{T_a} + \frac{\dot{Q}_b^{(r)}}{T_b} \\ &= \dot{V}\left(\frac{\dot{W}}{\dot{V}T_b}\right) + \dot{Q}_a^{(r)}\left(\frac{1}{T_a} - \frac{1}{T_b}\right) \\ &= Y_1\Omega_1 + Y_2\Omega_2,\end{aligned} \tag{12.13}$$

where $\dot{V}$ is the volume swept out per unit time by the turbine blades. Now, e.g., let $z_a(T_a)$ represent a property of the equilibrium radiation appropriate to temperature T_a, and introduce the definition, e.g.,

$$\left(\frac{\delta\dot{S}_a^{(r)}}{\delta\dot{V}}\right)_{T_a,T_b} \equiv [\mathbf{s}_\alpha] - s_a. \tag{12.14}$$

Then, on applying the operation $(\delta/\delta\dot{V})_{T_a,T_b}$ to Eqs. (12.12) and (12.13), we obtain*

$$\left(\frac{\delta(-\dot{W})}{\delta\dot{V}}\right)_{T_a,T_b} = (T_a - T_b)(s_b - [\mathbf{s}_\beta]) \tag{12.15}$$

and

$$\left(\frac{\delta(-\dot{W})}{\delta\dot{V}}\right)_{T_a,T_b} = h_a - T_a[\mathbf{s}_\alpha] - (h_b - T_b[\mathbf{s}_\beta])$$
$$= [\mathbf{g}_\alpha] - [\mathbf{g}_\beta], \tag{12.16}$$

where $[\mathbf{g}] \equiv h - T[\mathbf{s}]$. The role of the nonequilibrium functions $[\mathbf{z}]$ in determining maximum-work or migrational equilibrium conditions is strikingly similar to the role of the analogous equilibrium functions z. Assumption IV implies that $[\mathbf{s}_\alpha] - s_a + s_b - [\mathbf{s}_\beta] = 0$.

The radiation turbine is another example of a thermal converter (see the general discussion of thermal converters in Chapter 10).

Inhomogeneous Radiation Field

As a final example of the application of steady-state methods to the study of radiation fields, I investigate the internal structure of an inhomogeneous radiation field. Consider the case indicated schematically in Figure 12–4. For the case $T_a \neq T_b$ there is a net flow of radiation through the reflecting cylinder from one thermostat to the other, and the properties of the radiation field vary in the direction marked x in the figure. In order to sample the radiation at an arbitrary point x in the field, I adjoin a probe cylinder-and-piston arrangement to the field at the point of interest. I indicate the properties of the radiation in the test probe by the subscript x, and I indicate reference properties of equilibrium radiation at temperature T_a or T_b by a subscript a or b, respectively.

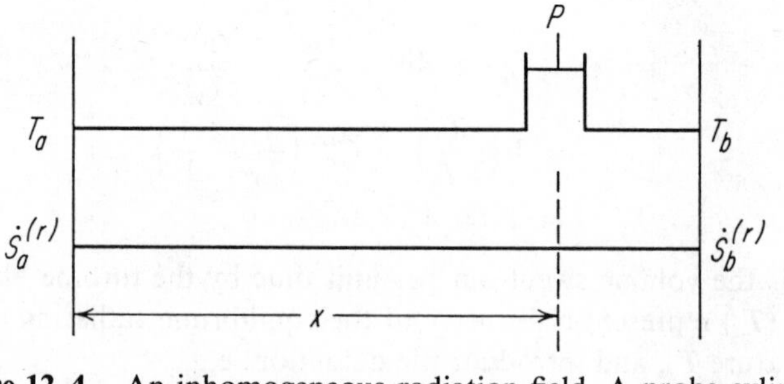

Figure 12–4. An inhomogeneous radiation field. A probe cylinder-and-piston arrangement is located at position x in the field; $T_a \neq T_b$.

* Since, e.g., $T_a s_a = h_a$.

The following relations hold for the steady-state situation:

$$h_x \dot{V}_x + T_a \dot{S}_a^{(r)} + T_b \dot{S}_b^{(r)} = 0, \tag{12.17}$$

$$\begin{aligned}\Theta &= \dot{S}_a^{(r)} + \dot{S}_b^{(r)} + s_x \dot{V}_x \\ &= \dot{V}_x\left(s_x - \frac{h_x}{T_b}\right) + \dot{Q}_a^{(r)}\left(\frac{1}{T_a} - \frac{1}{T_b}\right) \\ &= Y_1 \Omega_1 + Y_2 \Omega_2.\end{aligned} \tag{12.18}$$

To determine the properties of the *stationary* field between the two radiation sources, we apply the operation $(\delta/\tilde{\delta}\dot{V}_x)_{T_a,T_b}$ to Eqs. (12.17) and (12.18):

$$h_x + T_a\left(\frac{\delta \dot{S}_a^{(r)}}{\tilde{\delta}\dot{V}_x}\right)_{T_a,T_b} + T_b\left(\frac{\delta \dot{S}_b^{(r)}}{\tilde{\delta}\dot{V}_x}\right)_{T_a,T_b} = 0. \tag{12.19}$$

$$\left(\frac{\delta \Theta}{\tilde{\delta}\dot{V}_x}\right)_{T_a,T_b} = \left(\frac{\delta \dot{S}_a^{(r)}}{\tilde{\delta}\dot{V}_x}\right)_{T_a,T_b} + \left(\frac{\delta \dot{S}_b^{(r)}}{\tilde{\delta}\dot{V}_x}\right)_{T_a,T_b} + s_x = 0. \tag{12.20}$$

Now let

$$\text{grad} \equiv \left(\frac{\partial}{\partial x}\right)_{T_a,T_b} \tag{12.21}$$

and, e.g.,

$$\left(\frac{\delta \dot{S}_a^{(r)}}{\tilde{\delta}\dot{V}_x}\right)_{T_a,T_b} \equiv -\vartheta_x^{(a)} s_a, \tag{12.22}$$

where s_a is the blackbody value for temperature T_a; then, since, e.g., $h_a = T_a s_a$, we have (at any point x in the stationary field)

$$h_x = \vartheta_x^{(a)} h_a + \vartheta_x^{(b)} h_b, \tag{12.23}$$

$$s_x = \vartheta_x^{(a)} s_a + \vartheta_x^{(b)} s_b, \tag{12.24}$$

$$\lim_{T_a \to T_b} (\vartheta_x^{(a)} + \vartheta_x^{(b)}) = 1, \tag{12.25}$$

$$\text{grad}\, h_x - T_b \,\text{grad}\, s_x + s_a(T_b - T_a)\,\text{grad}\, \vartheta_x^{(a)} = 0, \tag{12.26}$$

$$\begin{aligned}\left(\frac{\partial h_x}{\partial T_b}\right)_{T_a} &= s_x + T_b\left(\frac{\partial s_x}{\partial T_b}\right)_{T_a} + (T_b - T_a)s_a\left(\frac{\partial \vartheta_x^{(a)}}{\partial T_b}\right)_{T_a} - \vartheta_x^{(a)} s_a \\ &= \vartheta_x^{(b)} s_b + T_b\left(\frac{\partial s_x}{\partial T_b}\right)_{T_a} + (T_b - T_a)s_a\left(\frac{\partial \vartheta_x^{(a)}}{\partial T_b}\right)_{T_a}.\end{aligned} \tag{12.27}$$

Once again we are in a position to ask a number of intriguing questions to which there are no obvious answers. Can we unambiguously define a temperature T_x for the radiation in the test probe (i.e., at any point x of the stationary radiation field) and if so, what is the relation of T_x to the quantities $\vartheta_x^{(a)} T_a + \vartheta_x^{(b)} T_b$, grad h_x/grad s_x, h_x/s_x, grad(h_x/s_x)? Is $g_x = 0$? Is the relation $\vartheta_x^{(a)} + \vartheta_x^{(b)} = 1$ true other than in the limit $T_a \to T_b$?

Conclusion

We have obtained by steady-state thermodynamic methods the following results for the radiation field: (i) A simple, direct derivation of the condition on the Gibbs free energy density of complete radiation—without making use of photon statistics or the detailed laws of electromagnetic radiation. (ii) The derivation of the maximum-work condition for a radiation turbine. (iii) A purely *thermodynamic* treatment of a stationary inhomogeneous radiation field. In addition to the results just mentioned, the steady-state formalism has shown that many interesting questions can be couched in its terms; we see exemplified here again one of the language functions (that of giving a lead to experiment) of a good thermodynamic formalism. We see then that the thermodynamics of heat radiation can still be a lively topic of conversation and a fruitful field for research.

References

1. M. Planck, *The Theory of Heat Radiation* (Dover Publications, New York, 1959).
2. J. Zernike, *Chemical Phase Theory* (Kluwer's Publishing Co., Ltd., Deventer, The Netherlands, 1958), p. 18.
3. M. Saha and B. Srivastava, *A Treatise on Heat*, fourth edition (The Indian Press Private, Ltd., Allahabad, 1958), Chapter 15.
4. C. Payne-Gaposchkin, *Temperature, Its Measurement and Control in Science and Industry*, Vol. 2 (edited by H. Wolfe) (Reinhold Publishing Corporation, New York, 1955), Chapter 4.
5. R. J. Tykodi and T. A. Erikson, *J. Chem. Phys.*, **31**, 1521 (1959); **33**, 46 (1960).
6. T. A. Erikson, *J. Phys. Chem.*, **64**, 820 (1960).

13

Migrational Equilibrium in Monothermal Fields: Applications

ν-Component Concentration Field

I considered 2-component concentration fields in Chapter 4; consider now a monothermal concentration field of ν ($\nu \geqslant 2$) components. Let the concentration field be established by the flow of component k through the ν-component MIX region (see Figure 4–1). Let the terminal parts containing the other components be arranged around the MIX region in such a way that for any stationary component (the ith component, say) $[r_{\alpha\beta}^{(ki)}] \approx [r_{\lambda}^{(ki)}]$, where $[r_{\lambda}^{(ki)}] \equiv \text{grad}\, \mu_{\lambda}^{(i)}/(\Delta\mathscr{G}_k/\Lambda_k)$, and Λ_k is the distance (measured through the MIX region) between the terminal parts containing the kth (flowing) component. By considering each component in turn and by establishing a steady flow of the chosen component (as well as of component k) between terminal parts, we can find the conditions for the migrational equilibrium of the chosen component in the concentration field in the usual way. The analysis provides us with a set of coupling coefficients from which I single out only the $[r_{\lambda}^{(ki)}]$ coefficients for discussion. For notational convenience I define one additional coefficient $[r_{\lambda}^{(kk)}]$ so that

$$[r_{\lambda}^{(kk)}] \equiv \frac{\text{grad}\, \mu_{\lambda}^{(k)}}{\Delta\mathscr{G}_k/\Lambda_k}. \tag{13.1}$$

Since the monothermal concentration field is completely described by the parameters T, $\Delta\mathcal{G}_k/\Lambda_k$, and $\nu - 1$ of the average mole fractions $\langle X^{(i)}\rangle$, the functional dependence of the $[r_\lambda^{(ki)}]$ coefficient is given (mainly) by

$$[r_\lambda^{(ki)}] = [r_\lambda^{(ki)}](T, \ldots, \langle X^{(i)}\rangle, \ldots, \Delta\mathcal{G}_k/\Lambda_k), \tag{13.2}$$

where I normally take as composition variables the average mole fractions of the stationary components. I prefer average composition variables to local ones because the average composition variables can be readily determined experimentally and are properties of the whole field.

We can determine the average composition of the field quite simply by stopping the flow of the field-inducing component and analyzing a sample drawn from the MIX region after that region has come to equilibrium. In addition, we often know from the way in which we prepared the solution in the MIX region exactly what its average composition is. Should we find, however, that the values of the $[r_\lambda^{(ki)}]$ coefficients vary from point to point in the concentration field, then it will become necessary in Eq. (13.2) to show explicit dependence on the quantities grad $X_\lambda^{(i)}$.

Consider now the case where the roles of the jth and the kth components are reversed: the jth component is now to be the flowing component, flowing over the same path that the kth component flowed over in the previous case; and the kth component is to be one of the stationary components. In the concentration field induced by the flow of the jth component, the coupling coefficients are of the form $[r_\lambda^{(ji)}]$. Now, what is the relation of the new coefficient $[r_\lambda^{(jk)}]$ to the old coefficient $[r_\lambda^{(kj)}]$? I conjecture that

$$[r_\lambda^{(jk)}][r_\lambda^{(kj)}] \approx 1 \tag{13.3}$$

for the same conditions of temperature, $\Delta\mathcal{G}/\Lambda$, and average composition. I base this conjecture on the following physical argument. The $[r_\lambda]$ coefficients seem to have the physical significance of coefficients measuring the drag effect of the flowing component on the stationary components. Such a drag effect depends on the ratio of the effective cross-sectional area of the stationary species to the similar quantity for the flowing species. According to such an interpretation, the exchange of roles between the two species leads to the type of relation suggested in Eq. (13.3).

The Gibbs–Duhem relation applied to the ν-component MIX region yields

$$\bar{S}_\lambda \operatorname{grad} T_\lambda - \bar{V}_\lambda \operatorname{grad} P_\lambda + \sum_{i=1}^{\nu} X_\lambda^{(i)} \operatorname{grad} \mu_\lambda^{(i)} = 0. \tag{13.4}$$

If we divide Eq. (13.4) through by $\Delta\mathcal{G}_k/\Lambda_k$, we get

$$\bar{S}_\lambda\left(\frac{\operatorname{grad} T_\lambda}{\Delta\mathcal{G}_k/\Lambda_k}\right) - \bar{V}_\lambda\left(\frac{\operatorname{grad} P_\lambda}{\Delta\mathcal{G}_k/\Lambda_k}\right) + \sum_{i=1}^{\nu} X_\lambda^{(i)}\,[r_\lambda^{(ki)}] = 0, \tag{13.5}$$

$$[r_\lambda^{(kk)}]\left\{\bar{S}_\lambda\left(\frac{\operatorname{grad} T_\lambda}{\operatorname{grad} \mu_\lambda^{(k)}}\right) - \bar{V}_\lambda\left(\frac{\operatorname{grad} P_\lambda}{\operatorname{grad} \mu_\lambda^{(k)}}\right) + X_\lambda^{(k)}\right\} + \sum_{i\neq k} X_\lambda^{(i)}\,[r_\lambda^{(ki)}] = 0; \tag{13.6}$$

and I conjecture that the relation

$$\sum_{i=1}^{\nu} \langle X^{(i)} \rangle [r_\lambda^{(ki)}] = 0 \tag{13.7}$$

comes pretty close to the truth.

If we limit ourselves to one-dimensional concentration fields, there is not much more to say. We can generate complicated three-dimensional concentration fields by having several components flow simultaneously through the MIX region at steady rates; the analysis of such situations, however, requires the use of vector and tensor quantities.

Chemical Reaction in a Concentration Field

Consider the reversible chemical reaction

$$\sum \nu_i B_i = \sum \nu_j D_j \tag{13.8}$$

(the reactants B_i being transformed to products D_j with stoichiometric coefficients ν_i and ν_j, respectively) taking place in a reactor of constant volume in a thermostat of temperature T. Let the reactants be individually supplied to and the products individually removed from the reaction vessel

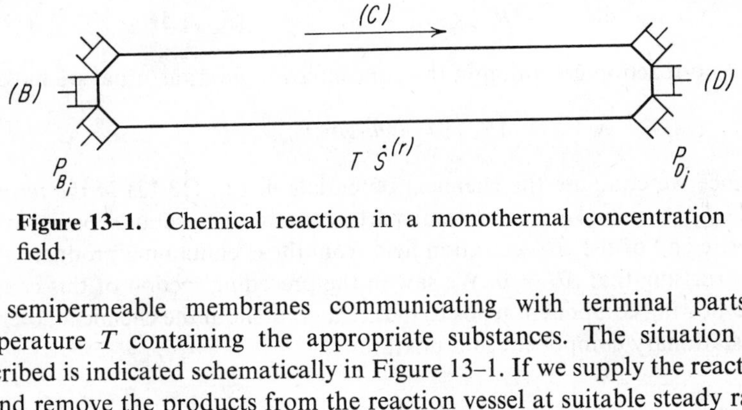

Figure 13–1. Chemical reaction in a monothermal concentration field.

via semipermeable membranes communicating with terminal parts at temperature T containing the appropriate substances. The situation just described is indicated schematically in Figure 13–1. If we supply the reactants to and remove the products from the reaction vessel at suitable steady rates, then the number of measures reacting in unit time $\dot{\xi}$ is just

$$\dot{\xi} = -\frac{\dot{n}_i}{\nu_i} = \cdots = \frac{\dot{n}_j}{\nu_j} = \cdots, \tag{13.9}$$

where $\dot{n}_k$, e.g., is the rate of influx of matter into the kth terminal part containing the product species D_k. The condition for no net reaction (equilibrium) in the reactor is, of course, that

$$\Delta G \equiv \sum \nu_j \mu_j - \sum \nu_i \mu_i = 0, \tag{13.10}$$

where μ_k, e.g., is the chemical potential of the D_k species computed for the state of affairs existing in the kth terminal part of the system.

Consider now the condition for no net reaction when the reactor is traversed by the steady flow of a nonreactive or reaction-neutral component C. In Figure 13–1 let there be included among the terminal parts at i a part C_i containing the nonreactive component C at temperature T and pressure P_{C_i}; similarly, let there be at j a terminal part C_j containing C at temperature T and pressure P_{C_j}; finally let there be a steady flow of component C through the reactor such that $\dot{n}_{C_i} + \dot{n}_{C_j} = 0$. When there is a steady flow of component C through the reactor and a steady chemical reaction ($\dot{\xi} \neq 0$) inside the reactor, we have

$$\begin{aligned} \Theta &= -\frac{\dot{G}(\text{system})}{T} = -\frac{1}{T}\{\dot{n}_{C+}(\mathscr{G}_{C+} - \mathscr{G}_{C-}) + \dot{\xi}\,\Delta G\} \\ &= Y_1\Omega_1 + Y_2\Omega_2, \end{aligned} \tag{13.11}$$

where $\mathscr{G}_C = \mu_C + \mathscr{K}_C$. I have used subscripts + and − to identify the flow source and flow sink with respect to component C, and I have neglected kinetic energy terms associated with the reactive components.

If we apply the operation $(\delta/\delta\dot{\xi})_{T,\Delta\mathscr{G}_C}$ to Eq. (13.11) and if we make use of assumption IV, we obtain

$$\Delta G = -[R_{C+}](\mathscr{G}_{C+} - \mathscr{G}_{C-}) = -[R_{C+}]\,\Delta\mathscr{G}_C \tag{13.12}$$

as the no-reaction condition in the concentration field; as usual we have

$$[R_{C+}] \equiv (\delta\dot{n}_{C+}/\delta\dot{\xi})_{T,\Delta\mathscr{G}_C}.$$

Since we compute the chemical potentials in Eq. (13.12) *in the terminal parts of the system*—the terminal parts containing reactants being at the opposite end of the concentration field from those containing products—it is not surprising that $\Delta G \neq 0$. We saw in the preceding section of this chapter that a flowing component tends to induce a gradient in the chemical potential of a stationary component in a mixture.

Exercise 13–1. Show that if we assume local equilibrium with respect to the chemical reaction in the concentration field, i.e., if we assume that at each point λ of the concentration field $\Delta G_\lambda = 0$, then we must have

$$\sum \nu_j[r_\lambda^{(Cj)}] - \sum \nu_i[r_\lambda^{(Ci)}] = 0,$$

where $[r_\lambda^{(Cj)}] \equiv \text{grad}\,\mu_\lambda^{(j)}/(\Delta\mathscr{G}_C/\Lambda_C)$, e.g.

Concentration Cells ("Gentle Agitation")

We can also use the methods evolved for treating concentration fields to treat electrochemical cells with transference. We can handle electrochemical cells that do not have concentration-dependent terms in the cell reaction in a straightforward fashion. Consider now a cell such as $Pb(s)|PbCl_2(m)|AgCl(s)$, $Ag(s)$, the potential difference of which is concentration-dependent. Although we cannot make the reaction

$$\tfrac{1}{2}Pb(s) + AgCl(s) = \tfrac{1}{2}PbCl_2(m) + Ag(s) \tag{13.13}$$

take place at a steady rate between terminal parts (all at temperature T) of a system (the concentration of the solute changes continuously during the course of the reaction), we can make the reaction

$$\tfrac{1}{2}Pb(s) + AgCl(s) + \frac{55}{2m}\,H_2O(g) = Ag(s) + \text{solution}(\tfrac{1}{2}PbCl_2 + \frac{55}{2m}\,H_2O) \tag{13.14}$$

take place in such a manner. In Figure 13–2 let P be the vapor pressure of water over a solution of molality m with respect to $PbCl_2$. By suitable operation of the electric engine e, we can send a steady current of $\dot{n}$ Faradays per second through the lead chloride solution causing the reaction described in Eq. (13.14) to take place in a steady manner; thus

$$\begin{aligned}\Theta &= -\frac{\dot{G}(\text{system})}{T} + \frac{\dot{W}_0}{T}\\ &= -\frac{1}{T}\{\dot{n}^{(1)}\mu^{(1)} + \tfrac{1}{2}\dot{n}\mu^{(2)} + \dot{n}\mu^{(\mathrm{Ag})} - \tfrac{1}{2}\dot{n}\mu^{(\mathrm{Pb})} - \dot{n}\mu^{(\mathrm{AgCl})} + \dot{n}^{(g)}\mu^{(g)}\}\\ &\qquad + \frac{\dot{W}_e}{T} + \frac{\dot{\theta}N}{T}\\ &= \frac{\dot{n}}{T}\left\{\frac{\dot{W}_e}{\dot{n}} - \frac{55}{2m}(\mu^{(1)} - \mu^{(g)}) - [\tfrac{1}{2}\mu^{(2)} + \mu^{(\mathrm{Ag})} - \tfrac{1}{2}\mu^{(\mathrm{Pb})} - \mu^{(\mathrm{AgCl})}]\right\} + \frac{\dot{\theta}N}{T}\\ &= Y_1\Omega_1 + Y_2\Omega_2,\end{aligned} \tag{13.15}$$

where $\dot{W}_e$ is the rate of supply of work to the electric engine in order to maintain the current $\dot{n}$ through the system, $\dot{\theta}N$ is the rate at which work is being dissipated by the torque-driven stirring motor, the superscript g refers to the gas phase, the superscripts 1 and 2 refer to the components (water and lead chloride, respectively) of the solution phase, $\dot{n}^{(g)} + \dot{n}^{(1)} = 0$, and $\dot{n}^{(1)} = (55/2m)\dot{n}$; the series of terms inside the square brackets in the third form of Eq. (13.15) is just the change in the Gibbs function $\Delta G(13)$ associated with the reaction given in Eq. (13.13). To find the condition for no flow of current in the circuit, we must perform the operation $(\delta/\tilde{\delta}\dot{n})_{T,\ldots}$ on Eq. (13.15). There is some uncertainty as to whether we should hold $\dot{\theta}$ or N constant in the $\delta/\tilde{\delta}\dot{n}$

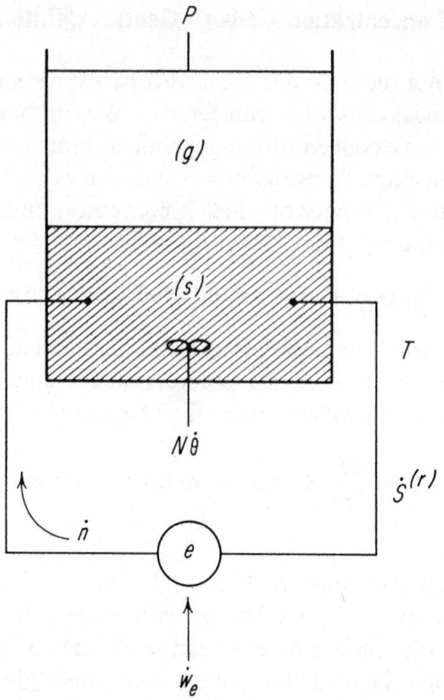

Figure 13–2. The cell Pb(*s*)|$PbCl_2$(*m*)|AgCl(*s*),Ag(*s*). An aqueous solution of molality *m* in $PbCl_2$ is in contact with water vapor at pressure *P*. Work is supplied to (or received from) an electric engine *e* at the rate $\dot{W}_e$ so as to maintain a current of $\dot{n}$ Faradays/sec through the system. The solution is stirred gently by a torque-driven motor, the work done by the stirring motor being given by $N\dot{\theta}$, with *N* being the applied torque and $\dot{\theta}$ being the velocity of rotation (angular) of the stirring propeller.

operation;* in this chapter the uncertainty is of no consequence since I assume in each case that $(\delta(\dot{\theta}N)/\tilde{\delta}\dot{n})_{T,\ldots} \approx 0$.

If we use assumption IV and the assumption just mentioned, we get

$$-\Delta G(13) = F\Delta\psi, \tag{13.16}$$

since at equilibrium $\mu^{(1)} = \mu^{(g)}$ and $(\delta\dot{W}_e/\tilde{\delta}\dot{n})_{T,\ldots} = -F\Delta\psi$, with *F* being the Faraday and $\Delta\psi$ being the potential difference of the cell in the limit of vanishing current. Equation (13.16) is, of course, a standard result; I produce it here merely to show how concentration-dependent cells are handled by steady-flow methods.

* See the *special fields* section of the Appendix.

Concentration Cells with Transference ("Gentle Agitation")

Consider now a concentration cell with transference (Figure 13–3). If we cause a steady current of $\dot{n}$ Faradays per second to pass through the cell by supplying work at the rate $\dot{W}_e$ to the electric engine e, then we have

$$\Theta = -\frac{1}{T}\{\dot{n}_\alpha^{(1)}\mu_\alpha^{(1)} + \dot{n}_\alpha^{(g)}\mu_\alpha^{(g)} + \dot{n}_\alpha^{(2)}\mu_\alpha^{(2)} + \dot{n}_\beta^{(1)}\mu_\beta^{(1)} + \dot{n}_\beta^{(g)}\mu_\beta^{(g)} + \dot{n}_\beta^{(2)}\mu_\beta^{(2)}\} + \frac{\dot{W}_e}{T} + \frac{\dot{\theta}_\alpha N_\alpha}{T} + \frac{\dot{\theta}_\beta N_\beta}{T}, \quad (13.17)$$

where I have neglected kinetic energy terms. $\dot{\theta}_\omega N_\omega$ is the work of "gentle agitation" supplied by the torque-driven stirring motor at ω so as to keep the solution part at ω nearly uniform in composition; the partial pressures of

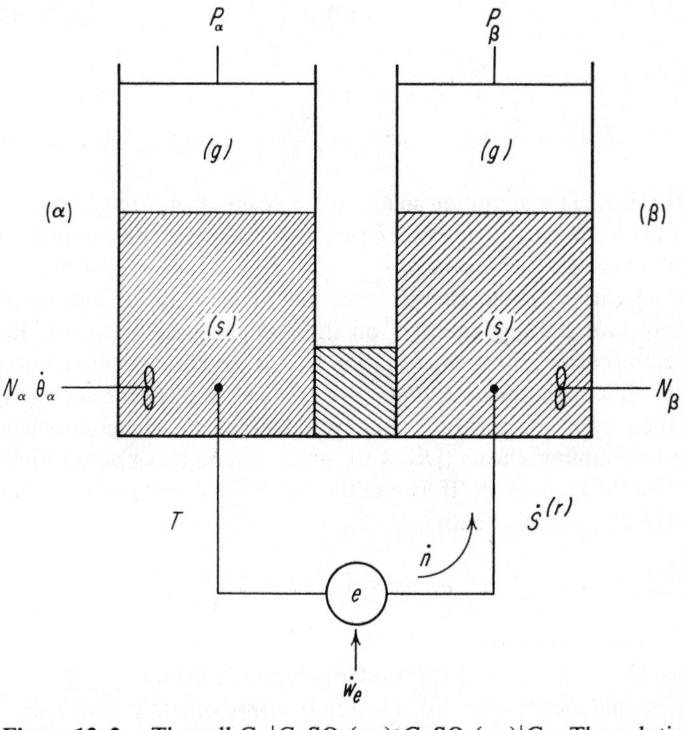

Figure 13–3. The cell Cu|$CuSO_4(m_\alpha)$:$CuSO_4(m_\beta)$|Cu. The solutions at α and β are connected by a porous membrane; each solution is subjected to "gentle agitation." The pressures P_α and P_β are saturated vapor pressures of water as appropriate to the molalities (m) of the solutions. An electric engine e is used to maintain a steady current through the system.

component 1 (water) over the solutions are P_α and P_β. I assume that because of the agitation $\mu_\omega^{(1)} = \mu_\omega^{(g)}$. Let $\dot{n}_\omega^{(L)} \equiv \dot{n}_\omega^{(1)} + \dot{n}_\omega^{(g)}$ represent the rate of influx of component 1 into the solution part at ω due to flow across the porous membrane (link), then the steady state is characterized by

$$\dot{n}_\alpha^{(2)} + \dot{n}_\beta^{(2)} = 0 \quad \text{and} \quad \dot{n}_\alpha^{(L)} + \dot{n}_\beta^{(L)} = 0. \tag{13.18}$$

We can now write Eq. (13.17) as

$$\begin{aligned} \Theta &= -\left\{\dot{n}_\alpha^{(L)}\left(\frac{\mu_\alpha^{(1)} - \mu_\beta^{(1)}}{T}\right) + \dot{n}_\alpha^{(2)}\left(\frac{\mu_\alpha^{(2)} - \mu_\beta^{(2)}}{T}\right)\right\} + \dot{n}\left(\frac{\dot{W}_e}{\dot{n}T}\right) + \dot{\theta}_\alpha \frac{N_\alpha}{T} + \dot{\theta}_\beta \frac{N_\beta}{T} \\ &= Y_1\Omega_1 + Y_2\Omega_2 + Y_3\Omega_3 + Y_4\Omega_4 + Y_5\Omega_5. \end{aligned} \tag{13.19}$$

The application of the operation $(\delta/\bar{\delta}\dot{n})_{T,\Delta\mu^{(1)},\Delta\mu^{(2)},\ldots}$ to Eq. (13.19) [together with assumption IV, the assumption that $(\delta\dot{\theta}_\omega N_\omega/\bar{\delta}\dot{n})_{T,\ldots} \approx 0$, and the relation $(\delta\dot{W}_e/\bar{\delta}\dot{n})_{T,\ldots} = -F\Delta\psi$] leads to the relation

$$-F\Delta\psi = \left(\frac{\delta\dot{n}_\alpha^{(2)}}{\bar{\delta}\dot{n}}\right)_{T,\ldots}(\mu_\alpha^{(2)} - \mu_\beta^{(2)}) + \left(\frac{\delta\dot{n}_\alpha^{(L)}}{\bar{\delta}\dot{n}}\right)_{T,\ldots}(\mu_\alpha^{(1)} - \mu_\beta^{(1)}). \tag{13.20}$$

Let $(\delta\dot{n}_\alpha^{(2)}/\bar{\delta}\dot{n})_{T,\ldots} \equiv \tau_-/2$, then

$$-F\Delta\psi = \frac{\tau_-}{2}(\mu_\alpha^{(2)} - \mu_\beta^{(2)}) + \left(\frac{\delta\dot{n}_\alpha^{(L)}}{\bar{\delta}\dot{n}}\right)_{T,\ldots}(\mu_\alpha^{(1)} - \mu_\beta^{(1)}). \tag{13.21}$$

The usual (Hittorf) assumption made in this case is that $(\delta\dot{n}_\alpha^{(L)}/\bar{\delta}\dot{n})_{T,\ldots} = 0$; i.e., that there is no coupling between the flow of electric current and the flow of solvent across the membrane.

I showed earlier in the chapter that the steady flow of one *component* tends to produce a dragging effect on the stationary components. For the flow of electric current through a solution the positive and negative ions move in opposite directions, thus exerting more of a *shearing* effect than a dragging effect on the solvent molecules. It could well be the case that component flow gives rise to coupling effects ($[R] \neq 0$), whereas counteropposed ionic flow does not $[(\delta\dot{n}_\alpha^{(L)}/\bar{\delta}\dot{n})_{T,\ldots} = 0]$. If we use the Hittorf assumption in conjunction with Eq. (13.21), we get, finally,

$$-F\Delta\psi = \frac{\tau_-}{2}(\mu_\alpha^{(2)} - \mu_\beta^{(2)}). \tag{13.22}$$

Exercise 13–2. Show that for moderately dilute solutions $|\mu_\alpha^{(1)} - \mu_\beta^{(1)}| \ll |\mu_\alpha^{(2)} - \mu_\beta^{(2)}|$, and hence that Eq. (13.22) is approximately true even if the Hittorf assumption does not hold (provided that $(\delta\dot{n}_\alpha^{(L)}/\bar{\delta}\dot{n})_{T,\ldots}$ is not inordinately large).

Hint: Suppose that $m_\alpha^{(2)} = 0.1$ and $m_\beta^{(2)} = 1$, then the ratio of the molalities $m_\omega^{(2)}$ is 1:10 but the ratio of the mole fractions $X_\omega^{(1)}$ is only 56.55:55.65 or 1.016:1.

For the case we are considering (copper electrodes in a copper sulfate solution) the classical thermodynamic treatment [1] yields

$$-F\,\Delta\psi = \int_{\beta}^{\alpha} \frac{t_-}{2}\,d\mu^{(2)}, \tag{13.23}$$

where t_- is the Hittorf transference number of the anion. The classical result and our result are approximately equivalent if we identify τ_- with the average Hittorf transference number of the anion over the concentration range m_β to m_α.

An Example

Perhaps an example will help clarify some of the conceptions thus far introduced. Consider the situation indicated schematically in Figure 13–4. An aqueous solution of copper sulfate contains copper electrodes a fixed distance Λ_{Cu} apart and has two liquid–vapor interfaces a distance Λ_{vap} apart. Let us apply a potential difference $\Delta\psi$ to the copper electrodes via an electric engine e so as to set up a steady current of electricity through the solution. For such a steady state it follows that

$$0 = -\dot{G}(\text{system}) = T\Theta - \dot{W}_0, \tag{13.24}$$

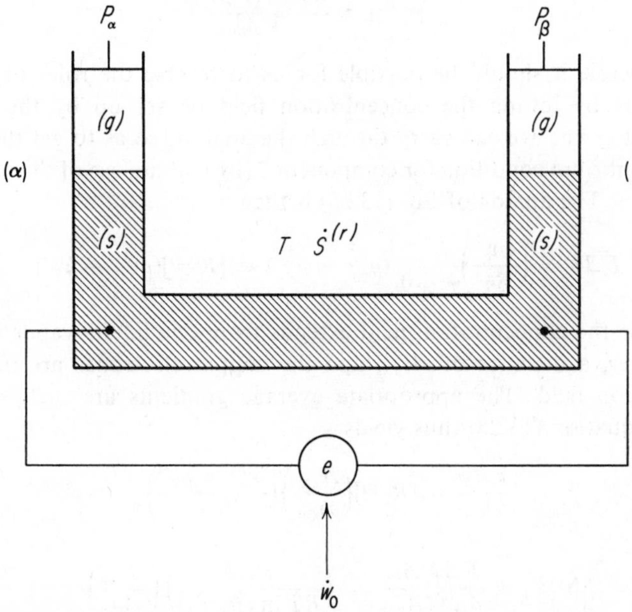

Figure 13–4. Copper electrodes in a copper sulfate solution. The electric engine e receives work at the rate $\dot{W}_0$ and maintains a steady electric current through the solution.

where the number of Faradays of electricity passing through the solution per second is $\dot{n}$, and $\dot{W}_0$ is the rate at which work is supplied to the electric engine; i.e., $\dot{W}_0 = \dot{n}F\Delta\psi$.* If, now, we keep $\Delta\psi$ constant and if we cause a steady current of solvent to pass through the solution by varying the pressures P_α, P_β, we have (neglecting kinetic energy terms)

$$\begin{aligned}\Theta &= -\dot{n}_\alpha^{(g)}\left(\frac{\mu_\alpha^{(g)} - \mu_\beta^{(g)}}{T}\right) + \dot{n}\,\frac{F\Delta\psi}{T} \\ &= Y_1\Omega_1 + Y_2\Omega_2. \end{aligned} \tag{13.25}$$

Our application of the operation $(\delta/\tilde{\delta}\dot{n}_\alpha^{(g)})_{T,\Delta\psi}$ to Eq. (13.25) and our use of assumption IV lead to the relation

$$\mu_\alpha^{(g)} - \mu_\beta^{(g)} = \left(\frac{\delta\dot{n}}{\tilde{\delta}\dot{n}_\alpha^{(g)}}\right)_{T,\Delta\psi} F\Delta\psi \equiv [R^{(21)}]F\Delta\psi, \tag{13.26}$$

where I have labeled the solvent component 1, have labeled the copper sulfate component 2, and have indicated by the superscript on the $[R]$ coefficient that the concentration field has been set up by a flow related to component 2. In the present case the concentration field is set up between the copper electrodes so the appropriate gradients are $\Delta\mu^{(g)}/\Lambda_{\text{Cu}}$ and $\Delta\psi/\Lambda_{\text{Cu}}$. Thus, in this case, $[r^{(21)}] \equiv [R^{(21)}](\Lambda_{\text{Cu}}/\Lambda_{\text{Cu}}) = [R^{(21)}]$ and

$$[r^{(21)}] \approx \frac{RT\ln(P_\alpha/P_\beta)}{F\Delta\psi}. \tag{13.27}$$

In principle it should be possible for us to reverse the roles of the two components by letting the concentration field be set up by the flow of component 1, and we can carry through the analysis so as to get the migrational equilibrium condition for component 2 (by making use of the operation $(\delta/\tilde{\delta}\dot{n})_{T,\Delta\mu^{(1)}}$). The analog of Eq. (13.26) is then

$$F\Delta\psi = \left(\frac{\delta\dot{n}_\alpha^{(g)}}{\tilde{\delta}\dot{n}}\right)_{T,\Delta\mu^{(1)}} (\mu_\alpha^{(g)} - \mu_\beta^{(g)}) \equiv [R^{(12)}](\mu_\alpha^{(g)} - \mu_\beta^{(g)}). \tag{13.28}$$

In this case the concentration field extends from one liquid–vapor interface to the other, a distance of Λ_{vap}, and the copper electrodes are inside the concentration field. The appropriate average gradients are $\Delta\mu^{(g)}/\Lambda_{\text{vap}}$ and $\Delta\psi/\Lambda_{\text{Cu}}$. Equation (13.28) thus yields

$$\frac{F\Delta\psi}{\Lambda_{\text{Cu}}} = [R^{(12)}]\left(\frac{\Lambda_{\text{vap}}}{\Lambda_{\text{Cu}}}\right)\left(\frac{\mu_\alpha^{(g)} - \mu_\beta^{(g)}}{\Lambda_{\text{vap}}}\right) \tag{13.29}$$

or

$$[r^{(12)}] = \frac{F\Delta\psi/\Lambda_{\text{Cu}}}{\Delta\mu^{(g)}/\Lambda_{\text{vap}}} = \left(\frac{F\Delta\psi}{RT\ln(P_\alpha/P_\beta)}\right)\left(\frac{\Lambda_{\text{vap}}}{\Lambda_{\text{Cu}}}\right). \tag{13.30}$$

* We must establish a convention about the direction of electric current flow. The sign of $\Delta\psi = \psi' - \psi''$ depends on our sign convention for the direction of electric current flow.

The work of a previous section implies that

$$[r^{(12)}][r^{(21)}] \approx 1 \tag{13.31}$$

if the coefficients are computed for two states such that $\Delta\mu^{(g)}/\Lambda_{\text{vap}}$ for Eq. (13.30) is the same as $F\Delta\psi/\Lambda_{\text{Cu}}$ for Eq. (13.27)* and the temperature and the average composition of the solutions are the same.

Although in principle we can test Eq. (13.31) experimentally, it is unlikely that we can measure the coefficient $[r^{(12)}]$ with any ease due to the extreme slowness of the diffusion process in solutions. It is quite likely that in order to test relations of the types (13.3) and (13.31) it will be necessary to go to 3-component systems so that two sets of electrodes can be inserted into the solution and two different potential differences applied. Then if we call the species participating in the two electrode reactions components 2 and 3, it should be possible for us to determine experimentally whether the relations

$$[r_{\lambda}^{(23)}][r_{\lambda}^{(32)}] \approx 1 \tag{13.32}$$

and

$$\sum_{i=1}^{3} \langle X^{(i)} \rangle [r_{\lambda}^{(3i)}] = 0 \quad \text{(say)} \tag{13.33}$$

hold.

Reference

1. G. N. Lewis and M. Randall, *Thermodynamics*, second edition (edited by K. S. Pitzer and G. Brewer) (McGraw-Hill Book Company, New York, 1961), Chapter 24.

* In Eq. (13.27) divide the numerator and the denominator of the fraction by Λ_{Cu}.

14

Migrational Equilibrium in Polycurrent Fields

General Remarks

The problems of migrational equilibrium that I have dealt with thus far have been problems pertaining to monocurrent fields; i.e., the system* has been the site of a single steady current of heat $\dot{Q}$, of a chemical component $\dot{n}_k$, of an electric current I, or the site of a steady chemical reaction consuming $\dot{\xi}$ reaction measures per unit time. The steady current in each case had associated with it a gradient in an intensive property, and the problem was to determine the migrational equilibrium condition in the particular gradient field. For the set of current variables $\dot{Q}$, $\dot{n}_k$, $\dot{n}_j$, I, $\dot{\xi}$ the various monocurrent effects are related to coefficients of the type $\delta(\text{current}_1)/\bar{\delta}(\text{current}_2)$: $\delta\dot{Q}/\bar{\delta}\dot{n}_k$, thermomolecular pressure effect; $\delta\dot{Q}/\bar{\delta}I$, thermocouple; $\delta\dot{Q}/\bar{\delta}\dot{\xi}$, reaction equilibrium in a polythermal field; $\delta\dot{n}_k/\bar{\delta}\dot{n}_j$, concentration field; $\delta\dot{n}_k/\bar{\delta}I$, concentration field with transference; $\delta\dot{n}_k/\bar{\delta}\dot{\xi}$, reaction equilibrium in a concentration field; $\delta I/\bar{\delta}\dot{\xi}$, relation between the Gibbs free energy change and the potential difference for a cell.

Consider the case now where there are two or more independent currents traversing the system* and we seek a migrational equilibrium condition in such a polycurrent field. Let us represent a heat current by $\dot{Q}$ and let J_i stand generally for any of the currents $\dot{n}_k$, $\dot{n}_j$, I, or $\dot{\xi}$; also let us use the notation (*independent current*$_1$, *independent current*$_2$)/*current with respect to which*

* In the state of migrational equilibrium.

migrational equilibrium is sought to describe bicurrent fields. Bicurrent effects, then, are either of the form $(\dot{Q}, J_1)/J_2$ or $(J_1, J_2)/J_3$. For the first case we describe the phenomena in terms of the quantities $[S]$ and $[R^{(12)}] \equiv \delta J_1/\bar{\delta} J_2$, where we adapt the $[S]$ quantity to the new context; for the second case the appropriate quantities are $[R^{(13)}] \equiv \delta J_1/\bar{\delta} J_3$ and $[R^{(23)}] \equiv \delta J_2/\bar{\delta} J_3$.

To illustrate the general procedure, I investigate two cases of the type $(\dot{Q}, J_1)/J_2$; I analyzed the type $(\dot{Q}, \dot{n}_k)/I$ in a previous chapter in discussing the initial potential difference of thermocells.

Polythermal Concentration Field

The situation that I propose to investigate is indicated schematically in Figure 14–1. A 2-component MIX region communicates with terminal parts containing pure components 1 and 2 in each of two heat reservoirs kept at temperatures T_α and T_β; the MIX region functions as a link between the two heat reservoirs; and we maintain a steady flow of component 1 from *a* to *b*. Our problem is to find the migrational equilibium condition for component 2 in the polythermal concentration field.

In the usual manner I superimpose a steady flow of component 2 on the flows of heat and of component 1 and then pass to the limit of vanishing flow

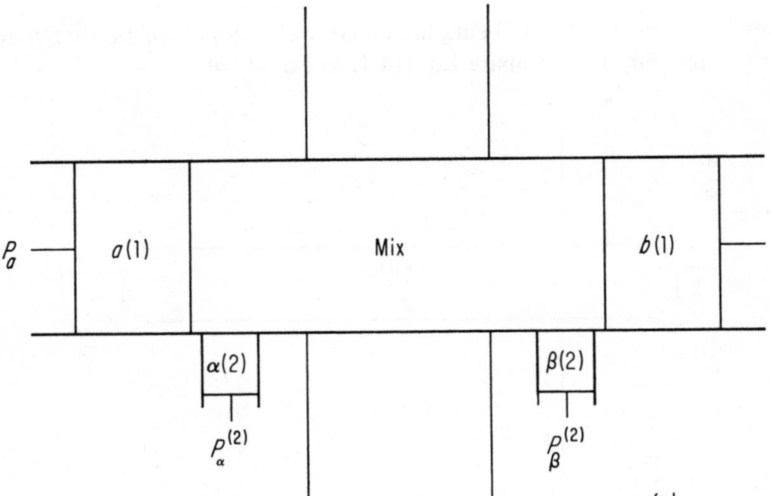

Figure 14–1. Steady flow of heat and component 1 through a 2-component MIX region; arbitrary linkage.

of component 2 via a sequence of steady-flow states, keeping $\mathscr{G}_a$, $\mathscr{G}_b$, T_α, T_β, $\langle T(\alpha\beta)\rangle$ constant. Equation (6.39) yields in this case*

$$\left(\frac{\delta \dot{G}_a}{\tilde{\delta}\dot{n}_\alpha^{(2)}}\right)_{\Omega'} + \left(\frac{\delta \dot{G}_b}{\tilde{\delta}\dot{n}_\alpha^{(2)}}\right)_{\Omega'} + \mu_\alpha^{(2)} - \mu_\beta^{(2)} + \left(\frac{\delta \dot{q}(\alpha\beta)}{\tilde{\delta}\dot{n}_\alpha^{(2)}}\right)_{\Omega'}$$
$$+ T_\alpha\left\{\left(\frac{\delta \dot{S}_\alpha(\text{in})}{\tilde{\delta}\dot{n}_\alpha^{(2)}}\right)_{\Omega'} - \left(\frac{\delta \dot{S}_\alpha(\text{out})}{\tilde{\delta}\dot{n}_\alpha^{(2)}}\right)_{\Omega'}\right\}$$
$$+ T_\beta\left\{\left(\frac{\delta \dot{S}_\beta(\text{in})}{\tilde{\delta}\dot{n}_\alpha^{(2)}}\right)_{\Omega'} - \left(\frac{\delta \dot{S}_\beta(\text{out})}{\tilde{\delta}\dot{n}_\alpha^{(2)}}\right)_{\Omega'}\right\} = 0. \quad (14.1)$$

As the component-flows either initiate or terminate in each heat reservoir, we may formally write the last two terms on the left-hand side of Eq. (14.1) in terms of $\dot{S}_\omega(\text{in})$ with the sign of the term being taken care of by the signs of the quantities $\dot{n}_z$ and $\dot{n}_\omega^{(2)}$; thus let

$$\left(\frac{\delta \dot{S}_\omega(\text{in})}{\tilde{\delta}\dot{n}_\alpha^{(2)}}\right)_{\Omega'} \equiv [S_z]\left(\frac{\delta \dot{n}_z}{\tilde{\delta}\dot{n}_\alpha^{(2)}}\right)_{\Omega'} + [S_\omega^{(2)}]\left(\frac{\delta \dot{n}_\omega^{(2)}}{\tilde{\delta}\dot{n}_\alpha^{(2)}}\right)_{\Omega'}; \quad (14.2)$$

it follows then that

$$[R_\alpha^{(12)}](\mathscr{G}_a - \mathscr{G}_b) + \mu_\alpha^{(2)} - \mu_\beta^{(2)} + T_\alpha\{[R_\alpha^{(12)}][S_a] + [S_\alpha^{(2)}]\}$$
$$- T_\beta\{[R_\alpha^{(12)}][S_b] + [S_\beta^{(2)}]\} - [h(\beta\alpha)] = 0 \quad (14.3)$$

and that

$$[R_\alpha^{(12)}]\{[\mathscr{G}_a] - [\mathscr{G}_b]\} + [G_\alpha^{(2)}] - [G_\beta^{(2)}] = 0, \quad (14.4)$$

where $\mathscr{G} \equiv \mu + \mathscr{K}$ with $\mathscr{K}$ being the molar macroscopic kinetic energy and $[R_\alpha^{(12)}] \equiv (\delta\dot{n}_a/\tilde{\delta}\dot{n}_\alpha^{(2)})_{\Omega'}$. Compare Eq. (14.4) to Eq. (4.10).

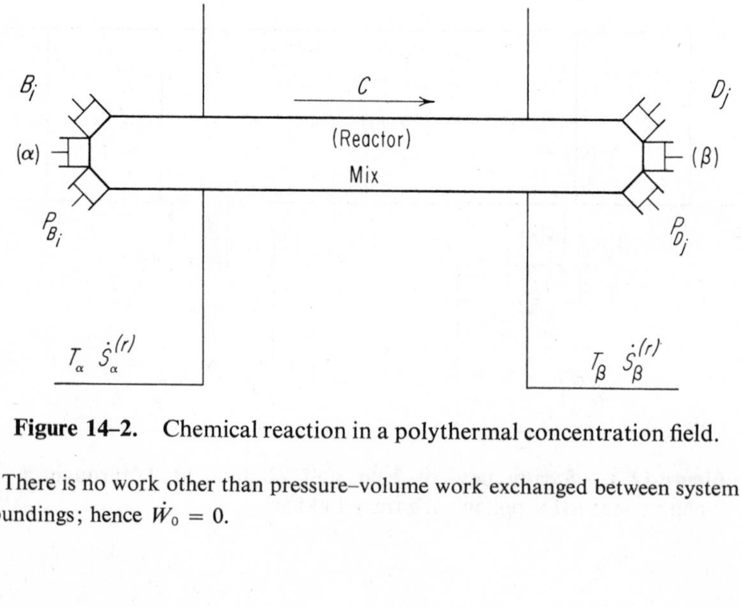

Figure 14–2. Chemical reaction in a polythermal concentration field.

* There is no work other than pressure–volume work exchanged between system and surroundings; hence $\dot{W}_0 = 0$.

Assumption IV implies that

$$[R_\alpha^{(12)}][S_a] + [S_\alpha^{(2)}] - [R_\alpha^{(12)}][S_b] - [S_\beta^{(2)}] = [s(\beta\alpha)]. \tag{14.5}$$

Consider now a chemical reaction in a polythermal concentration field. In Figure 14–2 let a reaction-neutral component (C) flow between terminal parts at α and β, and let reactants B_i communicate with the MIX region at α and let products D_j communicate similarly at β. Let the chemical reaction be represented by

$$\sum \nu_i B_i = \sum \nu_j D_j, \tag{14.6}$$

and let $\dot{\xi}$ reaction measures per second flow from reactants to products ($\dot{\xi} = -\dot{n}_i/\nu_i = \dot{n}_j/\nu_j$); then a set of equations analogous to Eqs. (14.1) to (14.4) holds:

$$\left(\frac{\delta\dot{G}_\alpha^{(C)}}{\delta\dot{\xi}}\right)_{\Omega'} + \left(\frac{\delta\dot{G}_\beta^{(C)}}{\delta\dot{\xi}}\right)_{\Omega'} - \sum \nu_i\mu_\alpha^{(B_i)} + \sum \nu_j\mu_\beta^{(D_j)} + T_\alpha\left(\frac{\delta\dot{S}_\alpha(\text{in})}{\delta\dot{\xi}}\right)_{\Omega'} + T_\beta\left(\frac{\delta\dot{S}_\beta(\text{in})}{\delta\dot{\xi}}\right)_{\Omega'} + \left(\frac{\delta\dot{q}}{\delta\dot{\xi}}\right)_{\Omega'} = 0, \tag{14.7}$$

$$\left(\frac{\delta\dot{S}_\alpha(\text{in})}{\delta\dot{\xi}}\right)_{\Omega'} \equiv [S_\alpha^{(C)}]\left(\frac{\delta\dot{n}_\alpha^{(C)}}{\delta\dot{\xi}}\right)_{\Omega'} + \sum [S_\alpha^{(B_i)}]\left(\frac{\delta\dot{n}_\alpha^{(B_i)}}{\delta\dot{\xi}}\right)_{\Omega'} \quad \text{(e.g.),} \tag{14.8}$$

$$[R_\alpha^{(C)}]\{[\mathscr{G}_\alpha^{(C)}] - [\mathscr{G}_\beta^{(C)}]\} + \sum \nu_j[G_\beta^{(D_j)}] - \sum \nu_i[G_\alpha^{(B_i)}] = 0, \tag{14.9}$$

with $[R_\alpha^{(C)}] \equiv (\delta\dot{n}_\alpha^{(C)}/\delta\dot{\xi})_{\Omega'}$.

Exercise 14–1. In Figure 14–3 let there be a 2-component metal amalgam phase in contact with mercury vapor at two temperatures T_α, T_β and let the amalgam be traversed by a steady electric current I. Analyze the situation according to the principles we have established and display the migrational equilibrium condition in terms of the coefficient $[R_\alpha^{(I)}] \equiv (\delta I/\delta\dot{n}_\alpha^{(g)})_{\Delta\psi,T_\alpha,T_\beta,\langle T\rangle}$, employing "gentle agitation" at α and β if necessary. Comment on the physical interpretation of the $[R_\alpha^{(I)}]$ coefficient and on the likelihood that the coefficient is significantly different from zero.

Catalog of Binary Effects

Instead of concentrating on the currents traversing a system, we can consider the gradients in intensive properties induced by the various flows through the system; we can consider one gradient to be the "cause" of some of

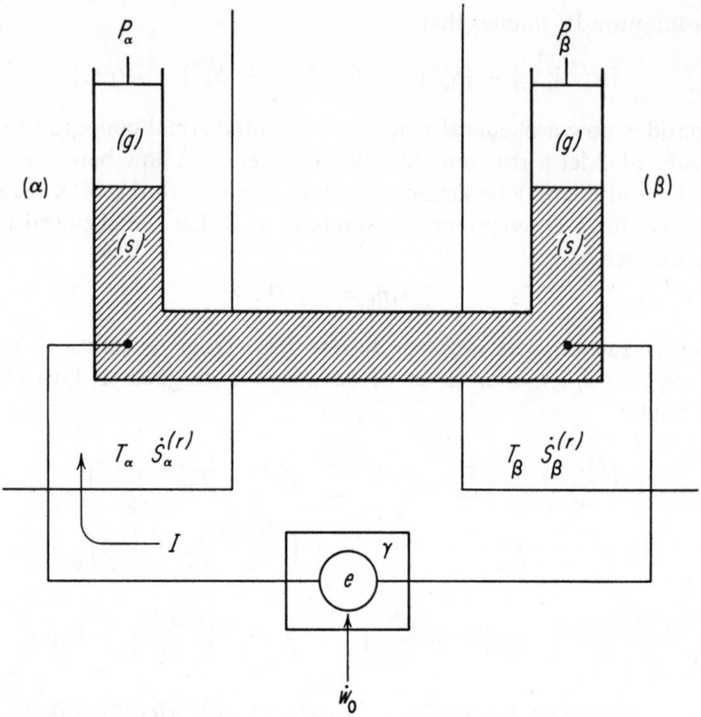

Figure 14–3. Metal amalgam in contact with mercury vapor and traversed by a steady electric current I in a polythermal field; e—an electric engine receiving work at the rate $\dot{W}_0$ and maintaining a potential difference $\Delta\psi$; "gentle agitation" at α and β if necessary.

the other gradients and we can call the ratio of two such gradients an "effect." If we take the set of variables T, P, φ, ψ, μ_2, $\mu_3, \ldots, \mu_\nu$ (X_2, $X_3, \ldots, X_\nu$)—temperature, pressure, gravitational potential, electric potential, $\nu - 1$ concentration variables, either chemical potentials μ_i or mole fractions X_i—then the various binary steady-state effects (if we omit ordinary thermostatic effects such as osmotic pressure and the piezoelectric effect) together with the appropriate migrational equilibrium conditions are as follows:

grad P/grad T—thermopiestic effect, $[G] = \text{const.}$
grad φ/grad T—thermogravitational effect, $[G] + M\varphi = \text{const.}$
grad ψ/grad T—thermoelectric effect, $[G] + zF\psi = \text{const.}$
grad X_i/grad T—thermoconcentration effect (Soret effect), $[G_i] = \text{const.}$
grad μ_i/grad T—thermocomposition effect, $[G_i] + [R][\mathcal{G}_k] = \text{const.}$
grad μ_i/grad P—piezocomposition effect, $\mu_i + [R]\mathcal{G}_k = \text{const.}$

grad μ_i/grad φ—gravicomposition effect, $\mu_i + M\varphi + [R]\mathscr{G}_k = \text{const.}$
grad μ_i/grad ψ—electrocomposition effect, $\mu_i + zF\psi + [R]\mathscr{G}_k = \text{const.}$
grad μ_i/grad μ_k—chemicomposition effect, $\mu_i + [R]\mathscr{G}_k = \text{const.}$

where M is the molecular weight, z is the "valence charge," and for those effects involving grad μ_i there is interaction between a concentration field involving a flowing component and another field (thermal, piestic, gravitational etc.).

PART III. COMMENTS

15

Conclusion

General Remarks

I have shown that nonequilibrium situations involving stationary states and steady-rate processes can be handled in an entirely thermodynamic fashion; I needed only the concepts *heat*, *work*, *energy*, and concepts derived therefrom. The various bracketed quantities that I introduced are perfectly good *thermodynamic* quantities that give us the means whereby to describe pertinent features of irreversible processes; these quantities, however, are characteristic of the complete system (contents plus container) being analyzed. Here, then, is a dilemma of nonequilibrium thermodynamics: we can easily and rigorously describe nonequilibrium situations in terms of general (bracketed) thermodynamic quantities; the quantities that we so use, however, are generally apparatus-dependent. We may accept this dilemma as a challenge. Can we in each case so devise a series of experiments as to be able to extrapolate the phenomena to an apparatus-independent limit? Thus far experimenters have given this matter but little attention—the thermomolecular pressure case and the forced vaporization case being the only two cases where an apparatus-independent limit has been established *experimentally*.* Of course, for engineering purposes it is no great tragedy if quantities prove to be apparatus-dependent, provided that such quantities depend only on general parameters of the apparatus (tube diameters, thermal conductivity of the wall material, etc.).

* In the thermomolecular pressure case, the Knudsen equation represents an apparatus-independent low-pressure limiting equation with a straightforward kinetic theory interpretation.

Although we tend to look upon the apparatus-dependence of the steady-state thermodynamic quantities as a nuisance, to be circumvented by suitable extrapolation procedures, from another point of view this apparatus-dependence is a characteristic and distinguishing feature of nonequilibrium thermodynamics. In (equilibrium) thermostatics we talk about walls and constraints when discussing a given system or process; our discussion, however, usually deals with but the functional characteristics, in the context of the thermostatic language, of the walls and constraints; and we avoid, as much as possible, saying anything about their physical structure. In nonequilibrium thermodynamics we continue to concern ourselves with walls and constraints, but now we must go into more detail concerning these items and their influence on the process being studied. Although we avoid giving gratuitous detail to our walls and constraints, we find, nevertheless, that their properties enter more explicitly into the discussions of nonequilibrium thermodynamics than they do into the discussions of thermostatics (see, e.g., the discussion of linkage-classes at the end of Chapter 5). It is, after all, matters of this sort that make steady states different from static ones.

The Assumptions I–IV

Consider again the basic assumptions I–IV in the light of the many analyses that we have carried through. Assumptions I and II are quite clear and of general validity. We may phrase assumptions III and IV thus:

(III) We find the condition of migrational equilibrium with respect to a given quantity in a field with ν independent steady currents by inducing a steady flow of the given quantity between terminal parts, keeping constant an appropriate set of variables, and observing the behavior of the system in the $(\nu + 1)$ current field as it approaches the original state (with ν currents) via a sequence of steady states.

(IV) If a system that is the site of $\nu + 1$ steady (independent) currents converges via a sequence of steady states on a state involving only ν steady currents in such a way that the affinities conjugate to the ν nonvanishing currents are maintained constant, then the state with ν currents is a state of minimum rate of entropy production relative to the (steady) states with $\nu + 1$ currents.

There is, of course, a dual form of the preceding statement with the roles of currents and affinities reversed. Although assumption III seems to be of general validity, the form in which I have heretofore stated assumption IV is one of restricted range: I have made no allowance for the presence of magnetic or centrifugal fields. I include a brief discussion of these *special fields* in the Appendix.

I now wish to make some additional remarks about the rate of entropy production and about assumption IV. We get an explicit resolution of the rate of entropy production into currents and affinities by eliminating a current between the First Law energy balance equation and the equation $\Theta = \dot{S}(\text{system}) + \dot{S}(\text{surroundings})$. In the case of a monothermal field we always eliminate the quantity $\dot{Q}^{(r)}$ to obtain the equation

$$\Theta = -\dot{G}(\text{system})T^{-1} + \dot{W}_0 T^{-1} = -\sum \dot{n}_i \mathscr{G}_i T^{-1} + \sum Y_{0x} \mathscr{F}_{0x} T^{-1}.$$

In a polythermal field we usually have several currents that can be eliminated between the basic pair of equations; thus we wind up with a set of equivalent resolutions of the rate of entropy production into currents and affinities. As an example, consider the thermomolecular pressure effect (Figure 5–1). The two basic equations are Eqs. (5.6) and (5.7):

$$\dot{n}_\alpha \Delta\bar{H} + \dot{Q}_\alpha^{(r)} + \dot{Q}_\beta^{(r)} + \dot{q} = 0, \tag{5.6}$$

$$\Theta = \dot{n}_\alpha \Delta\bar{S} + \frac{\dot{Q}_\alpha^{(r)}}{T_\alpha} + \frac{\dot{Q}_\beta^{(r)}}{T_\beta} + \frac{\dot{q}}{\langle T\rangle}, \tag{5.7}$$

where $\Delta\bar{Z} \equiv \bar{Z}_\alpha - \bar{Z}_\beta$. Upon eliminating one current at a time between Eqs. (5.6) and (5.7), we get the following set of resolutions of Θ into currents and affinities:

$$\Theta = \dot{n}_\alpha\left(\Delta\bar{S} - \frac{\Delta\bar{H}}{T_\beta}\right) + \dot{Q}_\alpha^{(r)}\left(\frac{1}{T_\alpha} - \frac{1}{T_\beta}\right) + \dot{q}\left(\frac{1}{\langle T\rangle} - \frac{1}{T_\beta}\right) \tag{15.1}$$

$$= \dot{n}_\alpha\left(\Delta\bar{S} - \frac{\Delta\bar{H}}{T_\alpha}\right) + \dot{Q}_\beta^{(r)}\left(\frac{1}{T_\beta} - \frac{1}{T_\alpha}\right) + \dot{q}\left(\frac{1}{\langle T\rangle} - \frac{1}{T_\alpha}\right) \tag{15.2}$$

$$= \dot{n}_\alpha\left(\Delta\bar{S} - \frac{\Delta\bar{H}}{\langle T\rangle}\right) + \dot{Q}_\alpha^{(r)}\left(\frac{1}{T_\alpha} - \frac{1}{\langle T\rangle}\right) + \dot{Q}_\beta^{(r)}\left(\frac{1}{T_\beta} - \frac{1}{\langle T\rangle}\right) \tag{15.3}$$

$$= \dot{Q}_\alpha^{(r)}\left(\frac{1}{T_\alpha} - \frac{\Delta\bar{S}}{\Delta\bar{H}}\right) + \dot{Q}_\beta^{(r)}\left(\frac{1}{T_\beta} - \frac{\Delta\bar{S}}{\Delta\bar{H}}\right) + \dot{q}\left(\frac{1}{\langle T\rangle} - \frac{\Delta\bar{S}}{\Delta\bar{H}}\right). \tag{15.4}$$

Note the following things about the set of relations (15.1) to (15.4). If we are interested in the condition of migrational equilibrium with respect to mass flow ($\dot{n}_\alpha = 0$), we will not use Eq. (15.4). In addition, we will tend not to use relation (15.3) because of its inconvenience in the case of full-flux linkage. We are left then with the two remaining resolutions (15.1) and (15.2).

We *could* combine these two expressions to get a resultant expression that is more symmetric in the indices α and β:

$$\Theta = \dot{n}_\alpha\left(\Delta\bar{S} - \frac{\Delta\bar{H}}{T_m}\right) + \tfrac{1}{2}(\dot{Q}_\alpha^{(r)} - \dot{Q}_\beta^{(r)})\left(\frac{1}{T_\alpha} - \frac{1}{T_\beta}\right) + \dot{q}\left(\frac{1}{\langle T\rangle} - \frac{1}{T_m}\right), \quad (15.5)$$

where $T_m^{-1} \equiv \frac{1}{2}(T_\alpha^{-1} + T_\beta^{-1})$, but at the cost of having to consider the combination $\frac{1}{2}(\dot{Q}_\alpha^{(r)} - \dot{Q}_\beta^{(r)})$ as a *single current.*

I prefer *not* to deal with combinations such as Eq. (15.5), and I feel that the separate resolutions of Θ (Eqs. 15.1 to 15.4) are each equally valid. I also feel that the range of validity of the *petit* principles of entropy production (Chapter 3) is the same for each member of this set of equations. In this regard consider the relation $(\delta\Omega_1/\tilde{\delta} Y_1)_{\Omega',\beta} > 0$ for Eqs. (15.1) and (15.2). For Eq. (15.1) we have, as we saw in Chapter 5,

$$(\delta\Omega_1/\tilde{\delta} Y_1)_{\Omega',\beta} = -T_\beta^{-1}\{\bar{V}_\alpha - T_\alpha(\partial\bar{V}_\alpha/\partial T_\alpha)_{P_\alpha} + T_\beta(\partial\bar{V}_\alpha/\partial T_\alpha)_{P_\alpha}\}(\delta P_\alpha/\tilde{\delta}\dot{n}_\alpha)_{\beta,T_\alpha,\langle T\rangle},$$

whereas for Eq. (15.2) we have $(\delta\Omega_1/\tilde{\delta} Y_1)_{\Omega',\beta} = -T_\alpha^{-1}\bar{V}_\alpha(\delta P_\alpha/\tilde{\delta}\dot{n}_\alpha)_{\beta,T_\alpha,\langle T\rangle}$. Thus the condition $(\delta\Omega_1/\tilde{\delta} Y_1)_{\Omega',\beta} > 0$ leads directly to the condition of stability $(\delta P_\alpha/\tilde{\delta}\dot{n}_\alpha)_{\beta,T_\alpha,\langle T\rangle} < 0$ in the case of Eq. (15.2); in Eq. (15.1), however, we obtain the condition of stability $(\delta P_\alpha/\tilde{\delta}\dot{n}_\alpha)_{\beta,T_\alpha,\langle T\rangle} < 0$ only if the quantity in the braces { } is positive. We saw in Chapter 5 that it is difficult to decide *a priori* about the sign of { } for all physically compatible pairs of states α,β subject to the migrational equilibrium constraint. Now it is conceivable that for some pair or pairs of states α,β (migrational equilibrium constraint) the quantity { } might be negative; in such circumstances we should have the range of validity of the relation $(\delta\Omega_1/\tilde{\delta} Y_1)_{\Omega',\beta} > 0$ depending on the choice of current-affinity representation for Θ: a lucky choice of current-affinity representation would give us an unrestricted range of validity for the relation $(\delta\Omega_1/\tilde{\delta} Y_1)_{\Omega',\beta} > 0$, whereas an unlucky choice would give us a restricted range of validity for the equivalent relation. Now I maintain that all of the representations (15.1) to (15.4) are equally valid with respect to the *petit* principles of entropy production; consequently I maintain that the quantity { } *must* be positive for all physically compatible pairs of states α,β subject to the migrational equilibrium constraint.

The preceding considerations are pertinent to the *grand* principles of entropy production as well as to the *petit* principles. I mentioned in Chapter 5 that the *grand* principle $(\partial\Omega_i/\partial Y_i)_{\Omega',\sigma} > 0$ might be of limited validity. I now wish to discuss the dependence of the rate of entropy production on the currents or the affinities and the implications of this dependence for the range of validity of the *grand* principle just mentioned. Consider the thermomolecular pressure case once more (full-flux linkage). The rate of entropy production Θ is fully determined when the two states α and β are given; i.e., $\Theta = \Theta(T_\alpha, P_\alpha, T_\beta, P_\beta) = \Theta(\alpha, \beta)$. Now take state β as the reference thermostatic state and write $\dot{n}_\alpha = \dot{n}_\alpha(T_\alpha, P_\alpha, \beta)$, $\dot{Q}_\alpha^{(r)} = \dot{Q}_\alpha^{(r)}(T_\alpha, P_\alpha, \beta)$. In order to invert these relations so as to get $T_\alpha = T_\alpha(\dot{n}_\alpha, \dot{Q}_\alpha^{(r)}, \beta)$, $P_\alpha = P_\alpha(\dot{n}_\alpha, \dot{Q}_\alpha^{(r)}, \beta)$ and $\Theta = \Theta(\dot{n}_\alpha, \dot{Q}_\alpha^{(r)}, \beta)$, we must have a nonvanishing value for the Jacobian of the transformation; i.e., $\partial(\dot{n}_\alpha, \dot{Q}_\alpha^{(r)})/\partial(T_\alpha, P_\alpha) \neq 0$. The Jacobian of the transformation has the value

$$\frac{\partial(\dot{n}_\alpha, \dot{Q}_\alpha^{(r)})}{\partial(T_\alpha, P_\alpha)} = \left(\frac{\partial \dot{n}_\alpha}{\partial T_\alpha}\right)_{\beta,P_\alpha}\left(\frac{\partial \dot{Q}_\alpha^{(r)}}{\partial P_\alpha}\right)_{\beta,T_\alpha} - \left(\frac{\partial \dot{n}_\alpha}{\partial P_\alpha}\right)_{\beta,T_\alpha}\left(\frac{\partial \dot{Q}_\alpha^{(r)}}{\partial T_\alpha}\right)_{\beta,P_\alpha}$$

$$= -\left(\frac{\partial \dot{n}_\alpha}{\partial P_\alpha}\right)_{\beta,T_\alpha}\left(\frac{\partial \dot{Q}_\alpha^{(r)}}{\partial T_\alpha}\right)_{\beta,P_\alpha}\left[1 - \left(\frac{\partial P_\alpha}{\partial T_\alpha}\right)_{\beta,\dot{n}_\alpha}\left(\frac{\partial P_\alpha}{\partial T_\alpha}\right)^{-1}_{\beta,\dot{Q}_\alpha^{(r)}}\right]. \quad (15.6)$$

Although the factor $(\partial \dot{n}_\alpha/\partial P_\alpha)_{\beta,T_\alpha}$ is certainly nonvanishing and the factor $(\partial \dot{Q}_\alpha^{(r)}/\partial T_\alpha)_{\beta,P_\alpha}$ is probably nonvanishing, it is difficult to say anything definite about the remaining factor [ ]. Thus, although the current form of the rate of entropy production $\Theta = \Theta(\dot{n}_\alpha, \dot{Q}_\alpha^{(r)}, \beta)$ is intuitively very reasonable, we cannot be sure that the shift from $\Theta = \Theta(\alpha, \beta)$ to $\Theta = \Theta(\dot{n}_\alpha, \dot{Q}_\alpha^{(r)}, \beta)$ will always proceed smoothly and unambiguously.

The case is clearer if we deal with the affinity form of the rate of entropy production $\Theta = \Theta(\Omega_1, \Omega_2, \beta)$. The Jacobian of the transformation now has the value

$$\frac{\partial(\Omega_1, \Omega_2)}{\partial(T_\alpha, P_\alpha)} = -\frac{1}{T_\alpha^2 T_\beta}\left\{\bar{V}_\alpha - T_\alpha\left(\frac{\partial \bar{V}_\alpha}{\partial T_\alpha}\right)_{P_\alpha} + T_\beta\left(\frac{\partial \bar{V}_\alpha}{\partial T_\alpha}\right)_{P_\alpha}\right\}, \quad (15.7)$$

and the Jacobian vanishes when the quantity in the braces { } has the value zero. Thus, when the quantity { } has the value zero, not only does the *grand* principle $(\partial\Omega_1/\partial\dot{n}_\alpha)_{\beta,T_\alpha} > 0$ fail for Eq. (15.1), but even the simple shift from $\Theta = \Theta(\alpha, \beta)$ to $\Theta = \Theta(\Omega_1, \Omega_2, \beta)$ becomes ambiguous. I argued earlier that the *petit* principles of entropy production for ordinary steady state situations were valid for any of the equivalent current-affinity representations of Θ; I now argue that to secure a maximum range of validity for the *grand* principles of entropy production we should (if possible) choose a current-affinity representation of Θ and a thermostatic reference state such that neither of the two Jacobians of transformation* can vanish. If we can make such a choice, it may be that then the *grand* principles of entropy production, as well as the *petit* principles, for ordinary steady-state situations will be of unlimited validity.

The Stability Problem for Steady States

Consider the following statement:

(A) A steady state has minimum rate of entropy production *relative to transient states* with the same boundary conditions.

* The transformation of Θ to the current form or to the affinity form.

Statement A and the verbal statement of assumption IV seemingly refer to two different physical situations; statement A is Prigogine's well-known theorem [1–4] about the stability of a steady state relative to a class of transient states.

Prigogine's Theorem

Prigogine and his coworkers [3, 5, 6] have shown that for a certain class of transient states* (i) close to (thermostatic) equilibrium, statement A holds, (ii) far away from equilibrium, statement A is not generally true. The procedure followed in their analysis is to consider a system in a steady state and, by instantaneous step-function forcing, to change the boundary conditions of the system, thereafter holding the new boundary conditions constant. The properties of the system are studied as it adjusts to the new set of boundary conditions. The system thus starts out in a steady state and then drifts through a series of *transient states* toward some final state compatible with the new boundary conditions. The rate of entropy production in the final state is compared to the rate of entropy production in the *transient states*. Prigogine and coworkers have shown that far away from equilibrium for systems with time-independent boundary conditions (i) the rate of entropy production in the final state need not have extremum properties relative to the rate of entropy production in the transient states, and (ii) the final state may not be a steady state at all—the system may oscillate or circulate about some average configuration. Denbigh [7] and Klein [8] have also pointed out the limitations of Prigogine's theorem.

This sort of stability problem (steady state versus related transient states) has been of concern to a number of people; thus Bak [9] and Ono [10] have published excellent overviews of the present status of the stability problem, and Li [4] has sought to approach the stability question by defining a thermokinetic potential and examining its extremum properties. What is being sought is a steady-state analog of the thermostatic criterion of equilibrium, so let us take a moment to review that thermostatic criterion.

The condition of equilibrium for an isolated system in thermostatics is that the entropy of the system be a maximum. In making use of the entropy-maximum principle, we must find a class of states with which to compare the equilibrium state, and that poses something of a problem since the entropy function is only defined for equilibrium states. The way out of the dilemma is

* If we wish to talk about rates of change of thermodynamic quantities in *transient states*, we must make extra, far-reaching assumptions about the local thermodynamic state at an arbitrary point in the system and about the description of that state in terms of thermostatic functional forms (see Chapter 11 of the book cited in reference [1] and page 93 of the book cited in reference [3]).

to consider the virtual states to which the equilibrium state is to be compared as equilibrium states also, but *more constrained* equilibrium states than the one that we are investigating [11, 12]. What we do in effect is to associate with a nonequilibrium situation a constrained equilibrium state that approximates the actual gradients in temperature, composition, etc., through the use of a sufficient number of partitioning adiabatic or diathermal walls. The entropy-maximum principle then compares the class of constrained equilibrium states associated with the actual nonequilibrium states to the (unconstrained) final equilibrium state.

Consider, for example, the following case. Divide an isolated system into two equal parts (α, β) by a fixed, rigid adiabatic partition and consider all states such that $U_\alpha + U_\beta =$ constant. The state of maximum entropy for the given situation is then the equilibrium state that subsists in the absence of the adiabatic partition [11, 12]. Mathematically the situation is as follows.

Let ΔS represent the difference in entropy between the equilibrium state and a nearby, more constrained state; i.e.,

$$\Delta S = \Delta S_\alpha + \Delta S_\beta \tag{15.8}$$

subject to the constraint that

$$\Delta U_\alpha + \Delta U_\beta = 0. \tag{15.9}$$

The two subsystems (α, β) being of constant volume, we may develop each of the quantities ΔS_α and ΔS_β into a Taylor's series in terms of the appropriate quantity ΔU_α or ΔU_β; thus we have

$$\begin{aligned}\Delta S &= \frac{\partial S_\alpha}{\partial U_\alpha}\Delta U_\alpha + \tfrac{1}{2}\frac{\partial^2 S_\alpha}{\partial U_\alpha^{\,2}}(\Delta U_\alpha)^2 + \cdots + \frac{\partial S_\beta}{\partial U_\beta}\Delta U_\beta + \tfrac{1}{2}\frac{\partial^2 S_\beta}{\partial U_\beta^{\,2}}(\Delta U_\beta)^2 + \cdots \\ &= \left(\frac{1}{T_\alpha} - \frac{1}{T_\beta}\right)\Delta U_\alpha - \tfrac{1}{2}\left(\frac{1}{T_\alpha^{\,2}C_V(\alpha)} + \frac{1}{T_\beta^{\,2}C_V(\beta)}\right)(\Delta U_\alpha)^2 + \cdots. \end{aligned} \tag{15.10}$$

Since the equilibrium state is to be the state of maximum entropy, we require that the coefficient of ΔU_α vanish and that the coefficient of $(\Delta U_\alpha)^2$ be negative. We thus get the results $T_\alpha = T_\beta$, and $C_V > 0$: at equilibrium the temperature is uniform throughout the system and the heat capacity at constant volume is positive.* Upon generalizing this procedure, we obtain the conditions of equilibrium—T, P, $\mu^{(i)}, \ldots$, each uniform throughout the system—and the conditions of intrinsic stability—$C_V > 0$, $(\partial V/\partial P)_T < 0, \ldots$.

In seeking a steady-state analog of the thermostatic entropy-maximum principle, Prigogine [3] and others [1, 2, 4, 9, 10] have reckoned the rate of entropy production for a given state, steady or nonsteady, by applying the Gibbs relation $T\,dS = dU + P\,dV - \sum \mu^{(i)}\,dn^{(i)}$ in a local form to each and every point (gradient-bearing or nongradient-bearing) of the system. This

* At equilibrium $C_V(\alpha) = C_V(\beta) = \tfrac{1}{2}C_V(\text{total system})$.

local form application of the Gibbs relation to gradient-bearing systems constitutes a new definition of entropy for nonequilibrium systems.*

In terms of this new entropy definition the Prigogine theorem (statement A) holds near thermostatic equilibrium, but further away from equilibrium Prigogine's theorem fails and has to be replaced by a more elaborate evolution principle [3, 5, 6, 13].

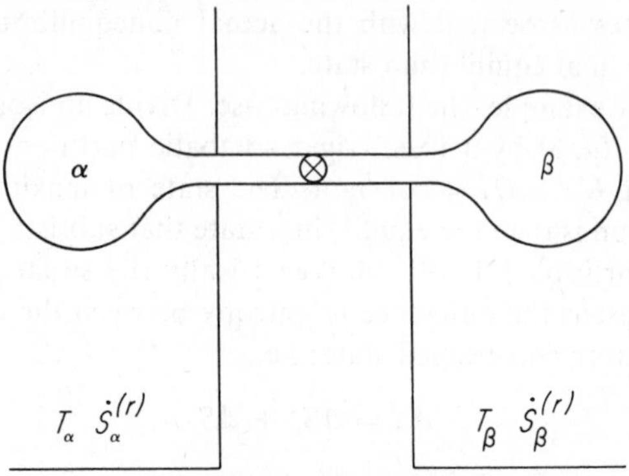

Figure 15–1. Thermomolecular pressure effect, schematic; full-flux linkage.

I now wish to show that statement A reduces to a special case of assumption IV for those cases for which Prigogine's theorem is valid and that for those cases for which Prigogine's theorem is not valid the failure is due largely to the new entropy definition, there being alternative ways of developing a steady-state stability principle. Consider yet again the thermomolecular pressure case (full-flux linkage) as indicated in Figure 15–1. Let two separately thermostatted bulbs (α, β) be connected by an efficiently insulated capillary tube and let the tube have a stopcock halfway between the bulbs. With the stopcock closed, fill the bulbs with the gas in question; wait a few minutes, and then open the stopcock. In general, upon the stopcock being opened, the gas migrates from one bulb to the other until eventually a state of migrational equilibrium is reached. Prigogine's theorem (statement A) says that from the time the stopcock is opened to the final establishment of migrational equilibrium the rate of entropy production for the system steadily decreases, reaching its minimum in the state of migrational equilibrium. Now if the capillary tube offers a high resistance to the flow of the gas, then the bulbs at α and β function nearly as terminal parts of the system, and the system effectively drifts through a sequence of steady states; i.e., over a small time interval the changes in thermodynamic quantities in the bulbs are much larger than the analogous changes in the capillary, and the changes in the

* See the earlier footnote devoted to this point on page 170.

bulbs are approximately proportional to the rates of mass flow into or out of the bulbs:

$$\dot{n}_\alpha(t) + \dot{n}_\beta(t) \approx 0, \tag{15.11}$$

$$\Theta(t) \approx \dot{n}_\alpha(t)\bar{S}_\alpha(t) + \dot{n}_\beta(t)\bar{S}_\beta(t) + \frac{\dot{Q}_\alpha^{(r)}(t)}{T_\alpha} + \frac{\dot{Q}_\beta^{(r)}(t)}{T_\beta}, \tag{15.12}$$

at a given instant of time t. If we assume that the behavior in time of the system is approximately equivalent to motion along a sequence of steady states toward a state of migrational equilibrium such that $\dot{n}_\omega = 0$—i.e., if we assume that upon replacing the walls of the bulbs by cylinder-and-piston arrangements such that $P_\alpha = P_\alpha(t)$ and $P_\beta = P_\beta(t)$, we should have $\dot{n}_\omega \approx \dot{n}_\omega(t)$, $\Theta \approx \Theta(t)$, etc.—then clearly statement A becomes just a special case of assumption IV.

Consider now the following point. The rate of entropy production is well defined in a steady state, the entropy changes in reservoirs or in terminal parts of the system being calculable according to classically approved recipes. In nonsteady states (transient states) the rate of entropy production is undefined in the classical sense. The considerations of Prigogine [3, 5, 6, 13] for nonsteady states are based on the acceptance of the local-form Gibbs relation for all points of a nonequilibrium system; i.e., Prigogine defines a rate of entropy production in a nonsteady state via a certain thermostatic functional form. Now there are several ways of defining a rate of entropy production for nonsteady states. By analogy to what we do in thermostatics—where we associate a constrained equilibrium state with each nonequilibrium state in order to be able to speak of an entropy-maximum principle—we can associate a "more constrained" steady state with each transient state, the "more constrained" steady state approximating the gradient distributions and current fluctuations of the transient state. We can then compare the rate of entropy production in the associated "more constrained" steady states to that of the final state (less constrained steady state) upon which the transient states converge for given boundary constraints.

Consider by way of example the simple heat conduction case (Figure 11–1). Let the system start out in the state $T_a = T_b = T_\beta$ and then instantaneously make the change $T_a \to T_\alpha$. The system will drift through a series of transient states ($\dot{Q}_\alpha^{(r)\prime} + \dot{Q}_\beta^{(r)\prime} \neq 0$) toward a final steady state ($\dot{Q}_\alpha^{(r)} + \dot{Q}_\beta^{(r)} = 0$), and the temperature distribution along the bar $T'(\lambda)$ will gradually change over to the distribution $T(\lambda)$ characteristic of the steady state.* Now let us associate with each transient state a "more constrained" steady state as indicated schematically in Figure 15–2. For this "more constrained" steady state we have

$$\dot{Q}_\alpha^{(r)} + \dot{Q}_\beta^{(r)} + \dot{Q}_x^{(r)} = 0 \tag{15.13}$$

* I am using primes to distinguish transient-state quantities from steady-state quantities.

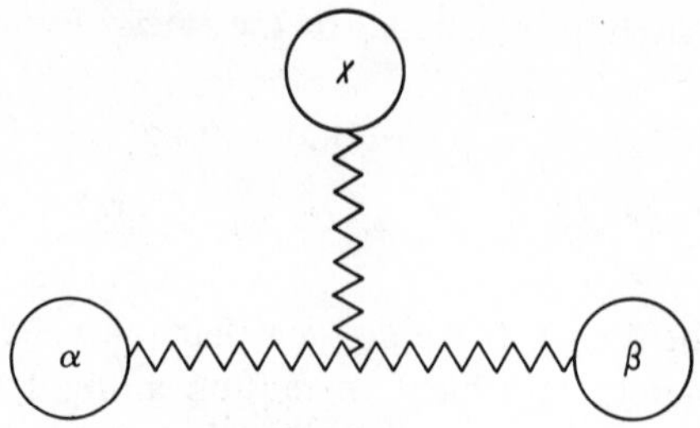

Figure 15–2. The "more constrained" steady state associated with a given transient state in the linkage.

and

$$\begin{aligned}\Theta &= \frac{\dot{Q}_{\alpha}^{(r)}}{T_{\alpha}} + \frac{\dot{Q}_{\beta}^{(r)}}{T_{\beta}} + \frac{\dot{Q}_{x}^{(r)}}{T_{x}} \\ &= \dot{Q}_{\alpha}^{(r)}\left(\frac{1}{T_{\alpha}} - \frac{1}{T_{\beta}}\right) + \dot{Q}_{x}^{(r)}\left(\frac{1}{T_{x}} - \frac{1}{T_{\beta}}\right).\end{aligned} \tag{15.14}$$

Now let us choose the temperature T_x and the point of attachment of the x-reservoir such that $-\dot{Q}_x^{(r)} = \dot{Q}_\alpha^{(r)} + \dot{Q}_\beta^{(r)} \approx \dot{Q}_\alpha^{(r)\prime} + \dot{Q}_\beta^{(r)\prime}$ and $T(\lambda) \approx T'(\lambda)$. With respect to these "more constrained" steady states that approximate (in some respects) the properties of the actual transient states, we can say that the final state ($\dot{Q}_\alpha^{(r)} + \dot{Q}_\beta^{(r)} = 0$) is the state of minimum rate of entropy production since, according to assumption IV,

$$\left(\frac{\delta\Theta}{\bar{\delta}\dot{Q}_x^{(r)}}\right)_{T_\alpha, T_\beta} = 0, \quad \left(\frac{\delta^2\Theta}{\bar{\delta}(\dot{Q}_x^{(r)})^2}\right)_{T_\alpha, T_\beta} > 0 \tag{15.15}$$

and

$$\Theta(\dot{Q}_\alpha^{(r)}, \dot{Q}_x^{(r)} = 0, \beta) < \Theta(\dot{Q}_\alpha^{(r)}, \dot{Q}_x^{(r)} \neq 0, \beta) \tag{15.16}$$

for fixed T_α, T_β.

Thus statement A can be given an unlimited range of validity if we interpret it to mean that the rate of entropy production in the (final) steady state is to be compared to that of the "more constrained" steady states associated with the transient states in question. By coupling together assumption IV and the concept of the "more constrained" steady state associated with a fluctuation state or with a transient state, we arrive at a generally valid entropy production-minimum principle that plays a role for ordinary steady states analogous to that played by the entropy-maximum principle for static states.

Oscillating or Circulating States

Now what of the possibility that a given system, for a given set of boundary constraints, may not settle down into a steady state but may perhaps circulate or oscillate about some average configuration [3]? To illustrate the point, consider again the simple heat conduction case (Figure 11–1). Suppose that the $\alpha\beta$ link does not merely transmit energy from the α

reservoir to the β reservoir (assume $T_\alpha > T_\beta$), but that it periodically stores up and releases energy as well; i.e., suppose that no matter how long we wait it will still be true that $\dot{Q}_\alpha^{(r)} + \dot{Q}_\beta^{(r)} = f(t)$, where $f(t)$ is some periodically varying function of the time. What effect would such a situation have on our basic thermodynamic considerations?

We are familiar with just this sort of thing in equilibrium thermostatics. We know that our macroscopic thermostatic quantities show fluctuations in time and that what we actually measure are time averages of the given quantities: the period of a fluctuation is usually very short compared to the time taken by an experimental measurement so we obtain a value that is an average over many fluctuation cycles. It is to the time-averaged values of our macroscopic quantities that we apply the laws of thermodynamics.

Of course, we do the same thing in steady-state thermodynamics: our steady currents show fluctuations in time and we merely arrange to average our current measurements over many fluctuation cycles. If the fluctuations are small in magnitude, of the order of experimental error, the averaging procedure is usually taken for granted. If the fluctuations are of a spectacular order of magnitude [3], we need to remind ourselves that thermodynamics concerns itself with the average, long-term trends in the macroscopic properties of systems. Thus for the hypothetical heat conduction case, it is still true that, over the long-term, energy flows on the average from reservoir α to reservoir β. Let me express this observation somewhat more formally. I define the time average $\langle Z \rangle_t$ of a macroscopic quantity Z via the relation

$$\langle Z \rangle_t \equiv \frac{1}{t_2 - t_1} \int_{t_1}^{t_2} Z(t)\, dt, \tag{15.17}$$

where the interval of time $t_2 - t_1 \equiv \Delta t$ is to be taken large compared to the period of fluctuation in question.* Now, regardless of the scale of the fluctuations, oscillations, or circulations, I maintain that the fundamental relations†

$$\langle \Theta \rangle_t = \sum \langle Y_i \rangle_t \Omega_i, \tag{15.18}$$

$$\left(\frac{\delta \langle \Theta \rangle_t}{\delta \langle Y_k \rangle_t}\right)_{\Omega'} = 0, \quad \left(\frac{\delta^2 \langle \Theta \rangle_t}{\delta \langle Y_k \rangle_t^2}\right)_{\Omega'} > 0, \tag{15.19}$$

* If in doubt, let $|\Delta t| \rightarrow \infty$.

† Note the following points. The entropy associated with material in the terminal parts of the system or in reservoirs adjoined to the system is well defined in the classical sense, whereas the entropy associated with material in the gradient parts of the system is not. The ambiguity in the entropy concept for the gradient parts of the system, however, is immaterial in the following two cases: (i) in a steady state the rate of change of the entropy of a gradient part, *no matter how that entropy is defined*, is just exactly zero; (ii) in an oscillating or circulating state, we may make the time-average rate of change of the entropy of a gradient part, *no matter how that entropy is defined*, approach zero as closely as we please by averaging over a sufficiently long time interval.

are valid in terms of the time-averaged quantities. For the hypothetical heat conduction case we have, then, the relations

$$\langle \dot{Q}_{\alpha}^{(r)} \rangle_t + \langle \dot{Q}_{\beta}^{(r)} \rangle_t = 0, \tag{15.20}$$

$$\langle \Theta \rangle_t = \frac{\langle \dot{Q}_{\alpha}^{(r)} \rangle_t}{T_\alpha} + \frac{\langle \dot{Q}_{\beta}^{(r)} \rangle_t}{T_\beta}$$

$$= \langle \dot{Q}_{\alpha}^{(r)} \rangle_t \left(\frac{1}{T_\alpha} - \frac{1}{T_\beta} \right), \tag{15.21}$$

$$0 = \left(\frac{\delta \langle \Theta \rangle_t}{\delta \langle \dot{Q}_{\alpha}^{(r)} \rangle_t} \right)_\beta = \left(\frac{1}{T_\alpha} - \frac{1}{T_\beta} \right). \tag{15.22}$$

On the average, over a long period of time, there will be a net transfer of energy between reservoirs α and β unless $T_\alpha = T_\beta$.

Now what of the entropy production-minimum principle of the previous section? I showed in that section that a steady state is stable relative to an "instantaneous" fluctuation of the system by computing the rate of entropy production via the "more constrained" steady-state technique. We must remember, however, that "instantaneous" in macroscopic thermodynamics means a time interval short on the human scale but long enough on the microscopic scale so that the system shall have undergone many microscopic fluctuation cycles. The time scale in macroscopic thermodynamics is based on the minimum time needed to measure to a given degree of accuracy* the macroscopic thermodynamic properties of the system. If the period of the microscopic fluctuations is short, the macroscopic time scale will also be short and we may speak of the "instantaneous" properties of the system. If we are dealing with oscillating or circulating systems, it will take a certain minimum time of observation to establish average properties such as $\langle \dot{Q}_{\omega}^{(r)} \rangle_t$ to a desired degree of accuracy; time intervals much shorter than this minimum time of observation will not have any *macroscopic thermodynamic* significance. Hence for oscillating or circulating systems we may say that the final *average* state for given boundary conditions is stable *relative to fluctuations averaged over the thermodynamic time scale appropriate to these systems*: if over the appropriate time interval we find that $\langle \dot{Q}_{\alpha}^{(r)} \rangle_t' + \langle \dot{Q}_{\beta}^{(r)} \rangle_t' \neq 0$ for the hypothetical heat conduction case, we then associate with this average fluctuation state an averaged version of the situation shown in Figure 15–2 such that $-\langle \dot{Q}_{x}^{(r)} \rangle_t = \langle \dot{Q}_{\alpha}^{(r)} \rangle_t + \langle \dot{Q}_{\beta}^{(r)} \rangle_t \approx \langle \dot{Q}_{\alpha}^{(r)} \rangle_t' + \langle \dot{Q}_{\beta}^{(r)} \rangle_t'$ and $\langle \Theta \rangle_t = \langle \dot{Q}_{\alpha}^{(r)} \rangle_t (T_\alpha^{-1} - T_\beta^{-1}) + \langle \dot{Q}_{x}^{(r)} \rangle_t (T_x^{-1} - T_\beta^{-1})$; and we find that

$$\langle \Theta \rangle_t (\langle \dot{Q}_{x}^{(r)} \rangle_t = 0) < \langle \Theta \rangle_t (\langle \dot{Q}_{x}^{(r)} \rangle_t \neq 0)$$

for fixed T_α, T_β.†

* To determine $\langle \dot{Q}_{\omega}^{(r)} \rangle_t$, e.g., to an order of accuracy of 0.1% takes a longer observation time (more fluctuation cycles must be averaged over) than it does to determine $\langle \dot{Q}_{\omega}^{(r)} \rangle_t$ to 1.0%, and so on.

† For some interesting comments on time scales in thermodynamics, see page 107 of the book cited in reference [3], pp. 146–148 of the book cited in reference [4] of Chapter 3, and the last chapter of the book by Van Rysselberghe [14].

The general validity of the entropy production-minimum principle for ordinary situations then hinges on our recognition of an appropriate time scale for a given thermodynamic system and on our using, in the formulation of the principle, quantities that are averaged over the characteristic time scale of the system. Fluctuating or oscillating systems, then, present us with no fundamental *thermodynamic* problems; the larger the scale of the fluctuation, the longer the time interval over which we average. Although the really spectacular fluctuations or oscillations pose no *thermodynamic* problems, they do challenge our statistical mechanical abilities: we shall, of course, be greatly interested in the detailed structure of the fluctuations or oscillations and in elucidating the underlying microscopic causes of the phenomenon [3].

Quasi-Steady States

In establishing the conditions of migrational equilibrium, I have thus far always used states that are rigorously steady; now, of course, the same general techniques will work for quasi-steady states as well. If we can treat a system as temporally drifting through a sequence of (essentially) steady states, the situation is quasi-steady and we can handle it by our standard methods.

In a given steady state the currents Y_i are interconnected via the First Law energy balance equation and via a set of mass balance (stoichiometric) relations. We may say that the currents Y_i are subject to a set of *constraints*, and we may express the equations of constraint in the form $f_k(Y_i) = 0$, $k = 1, 2, \ldots$. In the case of the thermomolecular pressure effect, for example, the equations of constraint are $\dot{n}_\alpha \overline{H}_\alpha + \dot{n}_\beta \overline{H}_\beta + \dot{Q}_\alpha^{(r)} + \dot{Q}_\beta^{(r)} + \dot{q} = 0$ and $\dot{n}_\alpha + \dot{n}_\beta = 0$. Now it is the steady-state equations of constraint plus the relation $\dot{Z}(\text{system}) = \sum \overline{Z}_i \dot{n}_i$ for the rate of change of a thermodynamic property Z of the system, the sum being over the terminal parts of the system, that enable us to transform the expression for the rate of entropy production into the form $\Theta = \sum_i Y_i \Omega_i$.

If a state is to be quasi-steady, then the equations of constraint (as they would hold in the steady state) must be nearly satisfied, i.e., $f_k(Y_i) \approx 0$; and the rate of change of a thermodynamic property Z of the system must be nearly expressible as $\sum \overline{Z}_i \dot{n}_i$, i.e., $\dot{Z}(\text{system}) - \sum \overline{Z}_i \dot{n}_i \approx 0$. Formally, then, the conditions of quasi-steadiness are

$$\frac{|f_k(Y_i)|}{\sum_i |\lambda_k^{(i)} Y_i|} \ll 1 \qquad k = 1, 2, \ldots, \tag{15.23}$$

and

$$\frac{|\dot{Z}(\text{system}) - \sum \overline{Z}_i \dot{n}_i|}{\sum |\overline{Z}_i \dot{n}_i|} \ll 1, \tag{15.24}$$

where $f_k(Y_i) \equiv \sum_i \lambda_k^{(i)} Y_i$.

What I am saying in Eqs. (15.23) and (15.24) is this: characteristic sums that add up rigorously to zero in the steady state must add up to values that are small compared to the individual terms of the sums if the state in question is to be considered quasi-steady.

"Continuous" versus "Discontinuous" Systems

The analyses that we have carried out have all been of the global type; i.e., we have analyzed finite *systems* rather than local effects at single points in space. This global versus local dichotomy has also been referred to in the literature as a *continuous* versus *discontinuous* one.* Now the global form of analysis is the more appropriate one for describing experiments: we rarely *measure* a flux or a gradient; instead we measure a total current and divide by an area or we measure a finite difference between two spatial points and divide by the distance between the points. At those points where we measure a property of the system we assume that the property is well defined; i.e., we assume that we make contact with the system at a terminal part. We can accommodate some spatial operations in the global formalism: see the treatment of concentration fields (Chapters 4 and 13) and the treatment of the radiation field (Chapter 12). The global formulation has the advantage that properties of the total system are known: in the concentration field, e.g., we perform the operation grad while keeping the average concentration of certain components constant; in the radiation field we perform the operation grad while keeping certain bounding temperatures constant. Whereas the global formulation readily yields conservation relations of the form $[Z] =$ constant, the corresponding local form relations are not at all apparent. For the experimenter, then, the global formulation is the more natural, the more operational one.

Statistical Mechanics of the Steady State

Of course, we cannot remain satisfied with a purely macroscopic treatment of steady states; ultimately we must develop a satisfactory statistical mechanics of the steady state to form a bridge between the properties of atoms and molecules and the measurable (time-averaged) properties of steady-state systems. Now the statistical mechanical structure that we strive to erect will depend on our view of the thermodynamics of the steady state. Thus, e.g., the statistical considerations of Boltzmann, culminating in the H-theorem, have a distinctly different flavor from the statistical considerations of Gibbs,

* See Chapters 4 and 5 of the book cited in reference [1] and Chapter 5 of the book cited in reference [3].

which culminated in the "thermodynamic analogies." Now much of the statistical work to date has aimed at justifying and generalizing the Onsager reciprocal relations and, hence, has been (in the thermodynamic sense) rather narrowly conceived. I hope that I have shown in this book that a wider, richer conception of the thermodynamics of steady states is called for and that the statistical explication of the language of steady-state thermodynamics is an exciting and challenging task.

For the interested reader I list a few references spanning a spectrum of approaches to the problem of applying statistical mechanics to nonequilibrium situations [15–17]; I find the work of Cox [15] especially interesting.

Final Comments

Now *any* thermodynamic formalism (devised for equilibrium states or for irreversible processes) is largely a language for describing experiments and for correlating the results of those experiments; a good formalism, therefore, should be *operational* and *natural*—it should be couched in terms of (idealized) laboratory operations. I feel that we have seen in the preceding pages the development of just such a formalism—a formalism entirely classical in spirit, easy of application, and laboratory oriented.

The task of bringing to fruition the potentialities inherent in the application of thermodynamics to nonequilibrium situations lies with the experimentalist; the interesting work is still largely to be done. We need renewed, informed experimentation—experimentation conducted in such a way as to yield well-defined results expressible in terms of a simple, operational language. While we remain in the macroscopic domain, let us preserve the full generality and rigor of the thermodynamic way of doing things. Let us not limit ourselves to near-equilibrium situations, and let us make no appeals (at this stage) to the principle of microscopic reversibility.

After we have learned what to expect at the macroscopic level, *then*, by all means, let us try to explain such behavior statistically in terms of atoms and molecules.

References

1. S. de Groot, *Thermodynamics of Irreversible Processes* (North-Holland Publishing Company, Amsterdam, 1951), Chapter 10.
2. S. de Groot and P. Mazur, *Non-Equilibrium Thermodynamics* (North-Holland Publishing Company, Amsterdam, 1962), Chapter 5.
3. I. Prigogine, *Introduction to the Thermodynamics of Irreversible Processes*, second edition (John Wiley and Sons, New York, 1961), Chapters 6 and 7.
4. J. C. M. Li, *J. Appl. Phys.*, **33**, 616 (1962).

5. P. Glansdorff, *Molecular Phys.*, **3**, 277 (1960).
6. P. Glansdorff and I. Prigogine, *Physica*, **30**, 351 (1964).
7. K. Denbigh, *Trans. Faraday Soc.*, **48**, 389 (1952).
8. M. J. Klein, *Proceedings of the International Symposium on Transport Processes in Statistical Mechanics—Brussels 1956* (I. Prigogine, editor) (Interscience Publishers, New York, 1958), p. 311.
9. T. A. Bak, *Advances in Chemical Physics* (I. Prigogine, editor), Vol. III (Interscience Publishers, New York, 1961), p. 33.
10. S. Ono, *ibid.*, p. 267.
11. L. Tisza, *Annals Phys.*, **13**, 1 (1961).
12. H. B. Callen, *Thermodynamics* (John Wiley and Sons, New York, 1960).
13. I. Prigogine and P. Glansdorff, *Physica*, **31**, 1242 (1965).
14. P. Van Rysselberghe, *Thermodynamics of Irreversible Processes* (Hermann, Paris, and Blaisdell Publishing Co., New York, 1963), Chapter 15.
15. R. T. Cox, *Statistical Mechanics of Irreversible Change* (The Johns Hopkins Press, Baltimore, 1955).
16. H. N. V. Temperley, *Proceedings of the International Symposium on Transport Processes in Statistical Mechanics—Brussels 1956* (I. Prigogine, editor) (Interscience Publishers, New York, 1958), p. 45.
17. I. Prigogine, *Statistical Mechanics of Irreversible Processes* (John Wiley and Sons, New York, 1962).

APPENDIXES

Appendix A

Supplementary Discussions

Thermotics: The Science of Heat

In recent years there has been evidence of increasing dissatisfaction with the use of the word "thermodynamics" to describe (practically) the entire field of the science of heat. It has often been remarked that the classical material collected under the title *thermodynamics* would be more aptly described by the title *thermostatics* [1, 2], and there seems to be a growing sentiment for restricting the word "thermodynamics" to its literal signification, i.e., to the motional aspects of the science of heat or to those aspects for which time variation is important—aspects which are prominently displayed in this book and in the discipline entitled *thermodynamics of irreversible processes*.*

I wish to point out the existence of a word that can readily do the work that the word "thermodynamics" formerly did, thus freeing "thermodynamics" for its new, restricted usage: the word that I wish to call attention to is "thermotics." (Brønsted's word† "energetics" would be equally good or perhaps even better; however, as used at present, the word "energetics" carries with it the connotation of the Brønsted formalism and thus has become a highly specialized word.)

"Thermotics" is a word of good Greek origin meaning *the science of heat* and having obvious affinities to a large fraction of the words in a scientist's vocabulary. The *Oxford English Dictionary* indicates that the use of "thermotics" in written English antedates the use of "thermodynamic"

* See the preface of this book and references [5–9] in that preface.

† See reference [1] of Chapter 1.

and "thermodynamics" by some ten to twenty years (1837 versus 1849 and 1854, respectively). However, "thermotics" seems not to have taken hold, and since at least the time of Gibbs, "thermodynamics" has been the word customarily used by writers on the subject. In light of the discussion in the first paragraph it seems worthwhile to attempt to revive and to popularize the use of the word "thermotics," since through its agency we can establish a logical and satisfactory nomenclature.

In line with the foregoing I recommend that the general science of heat be called *thermotics* and that the well-known laws be referred to as the First, Second, and Third Laws of Thermotics. We can conveniently subdivide thermotics into *thermo-statics*, *thermo-staedics*, and *thermo-dynamics*. Thermo-statics pertains to the ordinary, classical equilibrium aspects of thermotics; thermo-dynamics pertains to those aspects for which time variation is important; and thermo-staedics pertains to aspects that are temporally steady or stationary. I write "thermo-staedics" with *ae* instead of *ea* to indicate that the pronunciation should be "-stē′dĭks" so as to keep it phonetically distinct from "-statics." We may speak of the *state* of a thermotic system as static, staedic, or dynamic. All thermotic *processes* are *dynamic*, but under special circumstances we may call processes *quasi-static* or *quasi-staedic* if they involve a change from a well-defined initial state to a well-defined final state along a path that can be considered (approximately) as a locus of proper static or staedic states, respectively.

I have written the subdivisions of thermotics (thermo-statics, etc.) with a hyphen so as to give visual warning of special usage. If we rigidly adhere to this convention, we can make allowance for the use (if such usage is still desired) of the unhyphenated form of the word "thermodynamics" in the old sense to cover all those aspects of the science of heat amenable to analysis via the concept of *equilibrium state function.*

We may indicate subfields of the general science of heat (the overlap or intersection of the science of heat with another science) by placing the appropriate adjective in front of the word "thermotics"; thus, e.g., we may speak of chemical or electrical thermotics, and it would seem appropriate to label the statistical approach to the science of heat as *statistical thermotics* [3]. Lastly, that part of the kinetic theory of gases that ordinarily finds its way into textbooks on heat we could aptly call *molecular thermotics.*

Nonlinear Current-Affinity Relations

Within the limitations mentioned earlier (no magnetic fields, etc.; see the next section on Special Fields), we can apply assumption IV and its dual to current-affinity relations of any complexity to get relations among the phenomenological coefficients. Consider the general current-affinity relation (relative to a fixed thermostatic reference state σ)

$$Y_i = \sum_j L_{ij}\Omega_j + \frac{1}{2!}\sum_j\sum_k L_{ijk}\Omega_j\Omega_k + \frac{1}{3!}\sum_j\sum_k\sum_m L_{ijkm}\Omega_j\Omega_k\Omega_m + \cdots; \quad \text{(A.1)}$$

in actual practice it is customary to lump together all the terms of a given type, $\Omega_j{}^a\Omega_k{}^b\Omega_m{}^c \ldots$ say, with a single coefficient $L_{ijkm\ldots}$. For the case of two currents and two affinities Eq. (A.1) takes the form, if we stop with terms of the second degree,

$$Y_1 = L_{11}\Omega_1 + L_{12}\Omega_2 + \tfrac{1}{2}L_{111}\Omega_1{}^2 + L_{112}\Omega_1\Omega_2 + \tfrac{1}{2}L_{122}\Omega_2{}^2, \quad \text{(A.2)}$$

$$Y_2 = L_{21}\Omega_1 + L_{22}\Omega_2 + \tfrac{1}{2}L_{211}\Omega_1{}^2 + L_{212}\Omega_1\Omega_2 + \tfrac{1}{2}L_{222}\Omega_2{}^2. \quad \text{(A.3)}$$

The application of assumption IV and its dual to Eqs. (A.2) and (A.3) leads, after much tedious algebra [4], to the following relations:

$$L_{12} = L_{21}, \quad \text{(A.4)}$$

$$L_{122} = L_{212}, \quad \text{(A.5)}$$

$$L_{112} = L_{211}, \quad \text{(A.6)}$$

$$L_{12}L_{222} = L_{22}L_{212}, \quad \text{(A.7)}$$

$$L_{21}L_{111} = L_{11}L_{112}, \quad \text{(A.8)}$$

$$L_{11}L_{122} = L_{12}L_{112}, \quad \text{(A.9)}$$

$$L_{22}L_{211} = L_{21}L_{212}, \quad \text{(A.10)}$$

where each of the L coefficients has been treated as a function of the thermostatic reference state (σ) only. Now the set of relations (A.4) to (A.10) is highly restrictive: there are seven equations of constraint connecting ten coefficients, and for the case $L_{12} \neq 0$ the relation

$$L_{222} = \left(\frac{L_{22}{}^2}{L_{11}L_{12}}\right)L_{111} \quad \text{(A.11)}$$

follows from the equations of constraint. But it is physically implausible to expect a relation between L_{111} and L_{222}; hence actual physical situations satisfying all seven of Eqs. (A.4) to (A.10) are either very rare or nonexistent.

Furthermore, for currents and affinities as defined in this text it should be the case that reversal of all the affinities in a given ordinary situation results in the exact reversal of all the currents; i.e., the transformation $\Omega_i \to -\Omega_i$ for all i should result in the relations $Y_i \to -Y_i$ for all i. The foregoing implies, then, that in the general expansion (Eq. A.1), only terms of odd degree should appear (the coefficients of terms of even degree are to be set identically equal to zero). The simplest nonlinear current-affinity relation should then be one involving first-order and third-order terms only. If we write equations analogous to Eqs. (A.2) and (A.3) with terms of first degree and third degree only and if we apply assumption IV, we get ten equations of constraint connecting twelve coefficients; and a number of physically implausible relations follow. Thus the restriction to terms of odd degree in Eq. (A.1) does not appreciably change the situation.

It seems, then, that outside of the linear current-affinity region we must either give up the entropy-production principle (assumption IV) or show that the expansion in Eq. (A.1), with constant coefficients, is generally invalid. Consider for a moment the linear current-affinity region; it is possible to write simple current-affinity relations in this region because the thermodynamic affinities are proportional to the true physical forces: for small values of the gradient, the (isothermal) gradient of a chemical potential is proportional to the gradient of a pressure or to the gradient of a concentration; the gradient of reciprocal temperature is proportional to the gradient of temperature, and so on. The proportionality between the thermodynamic affinities and the physical forces, however, normally holds for only a small part of the region where the physical laws are linear; outside of this *overlap region* the physical laws are still linear, but the current-affinity relations are not expressible in the form (A.1) with constant coefficients.

As an example consider the heat conduction case discussed in Chapter 11 (see Figure 11–1). Let the average temperature $\langle T\rangle \equiv \frac{1}{2}(T_\alpha + T_\beta)$ characterize the thermostatic reference state, and let the state of steady heat flow be characterized by $\langle T\rangle$ and $\Delta T \equiv T_\alpha - T_\beta$. The appropriate linear physical law is, then,

$$\dot{Q}_\alpha^{(r)} = -M_{11}(\langle T\rangle)\,\Delta T, \tag{A.12}$$

where $M_{11} = \kappa(\langle T\rangle)B/\Lambda$; and the current-affinity relation is

$$\begin{aligned}\dot{Q}_\alpha^{(r)} &= L_{11}\left(\frac{1}{T_\alpha} - \frac{1}{T_\beta}\right)\\ &= -\frac{L_{11}\,\Delta T}{\langle T\rangle^2\{1 - \frac{1}{4}(\Delta T/\langle T\rangle)^2\}}\end{aligned} \tag{A.13}$$

From Eqs. (A.12) and (A.13) it follows that

$$L_{11} = M_{11}\langle T\rangle^2\left\{1 - \frac{1}{4}\left(\frac{\Delta T}{\langle T\rangle}\right)^2\right\} \tag{A.14}$$

and that the overlap region is defined by the condition $(\Delta T/\langle T\rangle)^2 \ll 1$. In the overlap region we can treat L_{11} as effectively a function of $\langle T\rangle$ only; outside the overlap region, however, we must consider L_{11} to be a function of both $\langle T\rangle$ and ΔT. Now suppose we try to improve things by letting L_{11} equal

$M_{11}\langle T\rangle^2$ and by extending Eq. (A.13) to include a term quadratic in $(T_\alpha^{-1} - T_\beta^{-1})$. We should then find that

$$L_{111} = \frac{1}{2} M_{11}\, \Delta T \langle T\rangle^2 \left\{1 - \frac{1}{4}\left(\frac{\Delta T}{\langle T\rangle}\right)^2\right\}, \tag{A.15}$$

and the situation would be worse instead of better. On the other hand, if we were to set L_{11} equal to $M_{11}\langle T\rangle^2$, L_{111} equal to zero, and were to extend Eq. (A.13) to include a cubic term, we should find that

$$L_{1111} = -\frac{3}{2} M_{11}\langle T\rangle^4 \left\{1 - \frac{1}{4}\left(\frac{\Delta T}{\langle T\rangle}\right)^2\right\}^2; \tag{A.16}$$

and, although the situation would not be worse than in the linear case, neither would it be better: for L_{1111} to be effectively a function of $\langle T\rangle$ only, it would be necessary for the condition $(\Delta T/\langle T\rangle)^2 \ll 1$ to be satisfied. However, if the given condition were satisfied, then the linear current-affinity relation would be quite adequate and there would be no need for the extra complication of the cubic term.

Perhaps I can make the matter clearer by considering the relation between ΔT and $\Omega_1 \equiv (T_\alpha^{-1} - T_\beta^{-1})$:

$$\Omega_1 = -\frac{\Delta T}{\langle T\rangle^2 - (\frac{1}{2}\Delta T)^2}. \tag{A.17}$$

Hence

$$\Delta T = \frac{2}{\Omega_1}\{1 - [1 + (\Omega_1\langle T\rangle)^2]^{1/2}\} \tag{A.18}$$

and

$$\Delta T = -\Omega_1\langle T\rangle^2 + \frac{1}{4}\Omega_1^3\langle T\rangle^4 - \frac{1}{8}\Omega_1^5\langle T\rangle^6 + \cdots$$
$$0 \leqslant (\Omega_1\langle T\rangle)^2 < 1. \tag{A.19}$$

The condition $|\Omega_1\langle T\rangle| < 1$ is equivalent to the condition $|\Delta T/\langle T\rangle| < 0.83$. Inside the range $0 \leqslant |\Delta T/\langle T\rangle| < 0.83$, then, we can write Eq. (A.12) as

$$\dot{Q}_\alpha^{(r)} = M_{11}\langle T\rangle^2\Omega_1 - \left(\frac{1}{3!}\right)\frac{3}{2} M_{11}\langle T\rangle^4\Omega_1^3 + \left(\frac{1}{5!}\right) 15 M_{11}\langle T\rangle^6\Omega_1^5 - \cdots. \tag{A.12a}$$

There are two things to note about Eq. (A.12a): (i) Equation (A.12a) is equivalent to Eq. (A.12) only if we use the full infinite series expression; if we cut off the series in Eq. (A.12a) after a finite number of terms, then the coefficient of the last term will depend on ΔT and, in fact, will contain $\{1 - \frac{1}{4}(\Delta T/\langle T\rangle)^2\}$ as a factor. (ii) If $|\Delta T/\langle T\rangle| > 0.83$, it is impossible to express Eq. (A.12) as a power series in Ω_1. By way of example consider the case of stainless steel in the temperature range 5–50°K, a range over which the thermal conductivity of the steel is very nearly a linear function of the temperature [5]. If we take 27.5°K as our midpoint and take temperature intervals ΔT about this point, then for the range $0 \leqslant |\Delta T/\langle T \rangle| \leqslant 1.63$ Eq. (A.12) is a fairly good representation of the facts; yet for the part of the range $0.83 < |\Delta T/\langle T \rangle| \leqslant 1.63$ it is not possible to express $\dot{Q}_\alpha^{(r)}$ as a power series in Ω_1 (with constant coefficients).

The current-affinity relations for other physical situations behave in a manner analogous to that of the heat conduction case.

The conclusions that I draw from the preceding discussion are the following:

(i) The entropy-production principle (assumption IV) holds for *all* ordinary steady-state situations.

(ii) For the thermodynamic currents and affinities as defined in Chapter 3 it is correct to write linear current-affinity relations with (effectively) constant coefficients (coefficients that are functions of the thermostatic reference state variables only) in the overlap region.

(iii) Outside the overlap region it is in general not possible to express the currents as powers of the affinities with constant coefficients.*

Special Fields

The considerations that I have thus far advanced hold for ordinary situations—i.e., situations not involving magnetic or centrifugal fields. In the presence of the two special fields some modification of the heretofore standard procedure is required. The reversal of the direction of a magnetic field **B** or of a centrifugal field $\dot{\boldsymbol{\theta}}$ sometimes leads to a distinguishably different state of the system (due to the presence of Lorentz or Coriolis forces [7, 8]). If we let **f** stand indifferently for either of the special field vectors **B** or $\dot{\boldsymbol{\theta}}$, then we must in general distinguish between properties of the system in state **f** and properties of the system in state −**f**. In the presence of a magnetic or centrifugal field,

* J. C. M. Li (see reference [4] of Chapter 15) has proposed a situation that seems to allow the application of Eqs. (A.2) and (A.3) with constant coefficients; his L coefficients (there are a few arithmetical errors in Li's derivation) satisfy Eqs. (A.4) to (A.7) and (A.10) but not Eqs. (A.8) and (A.9). Li's analysis, however, seems to be overidealized: the steady diffusion of hydrogen and nitrogen through an iron membrane at a rate sufficiently large to require higher-order terms in the current-affinity relations will certainly generate a temperature difference between the interfaces where the gases dissolve and evaporate; hence the simple isothermal Fick's law expression will not be adequate to describe the process. Also, the assumption of gas-solution equilibrium at each gas–membrane interface becomes increasingly invalid as the rate of diffusion increases. Thus Li's analysis of his example is incomplete, and his present results have no bearing on points (i) and (iii) above. See also the discussion of Rastogi, Srivastava, and Singh [6].

then, the assumption analogous to assumption IV for ordinary situations is that

$$\left(\frac{\delta\,\Theta(\mathbf{f})}{\tilde{\delta}\,Y_k}\right)_{\Omega',\mathbf{f}} + \left(\frac{\delta\,\Theta(-\mathbf{f})}{\tilde{\delta}\,Y_k}\right)_{\Omega',-\mathbf{f}} = 0,$$

$$\left(\frac{\delta^2\,\Theta(\mathbf{f})}{\tilde{\delta}\,Y_k^{\,2}}\right)_{\Omega',\mathbf{f}} + \left(\frac{\delta^2\,\Theta(-\mathbf{f})}{\tilde{\delta}\,Y_k^{\,2}}\right)_{\Omega',-\mathbf{f}} > 0. \tag{A.20}$$

I refer to Eq. (A.20) as assumption IV.S. If we multiply Eq. (A.20) through by the factor $\frac{1}{2}$, then we may state assumption IV.S thus:

(IV.S) If in the presence of a magnetic or centrifugal field we average the rates of entropy production (steady-state situations) for two opposed directions of the field vector **f**, then the *average rate of entropy production* in an affine sequence of steady states with $\nu + 1$ currents tends to a minimum for the state with ν currents.

The quantities that are averaged in assumption IV.S are the quantities $\Theta(Y_k, \Omega', \sigma, \mathbf{f})$ and $\Theta(Y_k, \Omega', \sigma, -\mathbf{f})$; i.e., we compare the rate of entropy production in two states that have the same value of Y_k, of Ω_i $(i \neq k)$, the same reference state σ, and reversed directions of the field vector **f**.

In the region of linear current-affinity relations Eq. (A.20) implies that

$$\frac{L_{ik}(\mathbf{f})}{L_{kk}(\mathbf{f})} + \frac{L_{ik}(-\mathbf{f})}{L_{kk}(-\mathbf{f})} = \frac{L_{ki}(\mathbf{f})}{L_{kk}(\mathbf{f})} + \frac{L_{ki}(-\mathbf{f})}{L_{kk}(-\mathbf{f})}. \tag{A.21}$$

Equation (A.21) is weaker than, but compatible with, the Onsager relations for special fields [7–9]:

$$L_{ik}(\mathbf{f}) = L_{ki}(-\mathbf{f}). \tag{A.21a}$$

Exercise A–1. Show that in the linear current-affinity region the Onsager relations (Eq. A.21a) imply that

$$\left(\frac{\delta\,\Theta}{\tilde{\delta}\,Y_k}\right)_{Y',\mathbf{f}} = \left(\frac{\delta\,\Theta}{\tilde{\delta}\,Y_k}\right)_{Y',-\mathbf{f}}.$$

There is a class of special field situations governed by a more stringent entropy-production principle than that of Eq. (A.20). For effects that vanish with the field **f**, I introduce the following extra assumption:

(IV.SX) The relation $0 = \delta\Theta/\tilde{\delta}\,Y_k$ holds for special field effects that vanish with the field **f** provided that (i) field-inducing currents (electric currents in solenoids and currents associated with angular motion) are kept constant, and (ii) currents that couple with the field **f** are kept constant.

I rationalize assumption IV.SX somewhat in the following manner. Even in equilibrium thermodynamics, magnetic fields have their puzzling aspects; the differential element of work in magnetic systems has an unusual form [10, 11]: $\int \mathbf{H}\cdot d\mathbf{B}\, dV$ instead of $\int \mathbf{B}\cdot d\mathbf{H}\, dV$—the roles of the intensive and extensive factors being just the reverse of usual. Magnetic energy is in some ways analogous to kinetic energy [10]; hence it is not too surprising to find magnetic fields and centrifugal fields lumped together into a common class of "odd" variables [7]. Since for magnetic systems the intensive and extensive variables play reversed roles (relative to the usual case), we would expect that for steady-state situations involving magnetic or centrifugal fields there should be some reversal of the roles of currents and affinities; assumption IV.SX shows that such is indeed the case for those effects that vanish with the field **f**.

In order to make clear the physical significance of assumption IV.SX, I work out a number of examples; the cases that I consider are the equilibrium centrifuge, the Hall effect, the Nernst effect, the Righi–Leduc effect, and the Ettingshausen effect.

The Equilibrium Centrifuge

In the equilibrium centrifuge the tangential velocity of the fluid in the rotating container varies with the distance from the axis of rotation, so we are really dealing with a problem of migrational equilibrium in a velocity field. It is well known in the study of mechanics that a system rotating with a constant angular velocity $\dot{\boldsymbol{\theta}}$ is equivalent to a static system with an imposed centrifugal force, the force having as its potential the expression $-\frac{1}{2}mr^2\dot{\boldsymbol{\theta}}^2$, where m is the mass of the particle acted upon and r is the distance from the axis of rotation. In Chapter 4 I considered a general potential field in which the potential energy per gram of material was φ, and we reached the conclusion that for migrational equilibrium in such a field it is necessary that the condition

$$\mu + M\varphi = \text{constant} \tag{A.22}$$

be satisfied at each point in the field, M being the molecular weight and μ being the chemical potential of the substance in question. We expect, then, that the condition for migrational equilibrium in the centrifuge is that [12]

$$\mu - \tfrac{1}{2}Mr^2\dot{\boldsymbol{\theta}}^2 = \text{constant}. \tag{A.23}$$

The problem at hand is to derive Eq. (A.23) by considering a sequence of steady-flow states in the centrifugal field (1-component fluid).

Consider now the schematic version of a centrifuge shown in Figure A–1; the axis of rotation is perpendicular to the plane of the diagram. Suppose that there are two terminal parts (α, β) at distances r_α and r_β from the axis of rotation, and suppose that the pressures P_α and P_β are maintained by devices

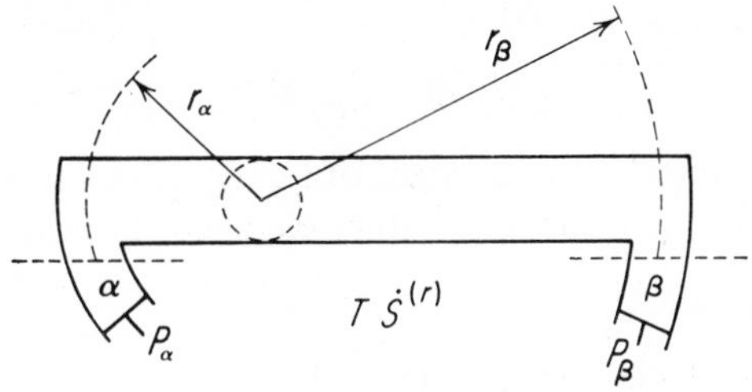

Figure A–1. Schematic version of a centrifuge.

coupled to the walls of the containing vessel. The apparatus is rigidly fixed to a shaft that is subjected to an external torque N, thus bringing about the necessary rotation. Let us assume that all the walls, shafts, etc., are of metal and are good thermal conductors; let us also assume that some stationary metallic part of the apparatus is in contact with a heat bath of temperature T. All exchanges of heat between the system and the surroundings are to take place by conduction through the metallic parts of the apparatus and are to be registered eventually in the heat reservoir of temperature T.

For the case of constant angular velocity $\dot{\boldsymbol{\theta}}$ and steady exchange of mass between the terminal parts ($\dot{n}_\alpha + \dot{n}_\beta = 0$), we have (see Eq. 4.1)

$$\Theta = -\frac{1}{T}\sum \mathcal{G}_i \dot{n}_i + \frac{\dot{W}_0}{T} = -\dot{n}_\alpha \frac{\mathcal{G}_\alpha - \mathcal{G}_\beta}{T} + \dot{\boldsymbol{\theta}}\frac{N}{T}$$
$$= Y_1\Omega_1 + Y_2\Omega_2. \tag{A.24}$$

For small rates of transfer (so as to minimize the frictional dissipation in transferring the mass from part α to part β) the relation

$$N\dot{\boldsymbol{\theta}} = \dot{\boldsymbol{\theta}}\frac{d(\mathcal{I}\dot{\boldsymbol{\theta}})}{dt} + T\Theta, \tag{A.25}$$

where $\mathcal{I}$ is the moment of inertia of the system about the axis of rotation, is valid. We can combine Eqs. (A.24) and (A.25) to get

$$\dot{n}_\alpha(\mathcal{G}_\alpha - \mathcal{G}_\beta) = \dot{\boldsymbol{\theta}}\frac{d(\mathcal{I}\dot{\boldsymbol{\theta}})}{dt}, \tag{A.26}$$

where $\mathcal{G} = \mu + \mathcal{K} = \mu + \frac{1}{2}Mr^2\dot{\boldsymbol{\theta}}^2$, the translational kinetic energy generated in transferring mass from one terminal part to the other being neglected.

The application of the operation $(\delta/\tilde{\delta}\dot{n}_\alpha)_{T,\dot{\boldsymbol{\theta}}}$ (assumption IV.SX.i) to Eq. (A.26) yields

$$\mu_\alpha + \mathcal{K}_\alpha - (\mu_\beta + \mathcal{K}_\beta) = \dot{\boldsymbol{\theta}}^2\left(\frac{\delta(d\mathcal{I}/dt)}{\tilde{\delta}\dot{n}_\alpha}\right)_{T,\dot{\boldsymbol{\theta}}}$$
$$= \dot{\boldsymbol{\theta}}^2\left(\frac{\delta(\dot{n}_\alpha M r_\alpha^2 + \dot{n}_\beta M r_\beta^2)}{\tilde{\delta}\dot{n}_\alpha}\right)_{T,\dot{\boldsymbol{\theta}}}$$
$$= Mr_\alpha^2\dot{\boldsymbol{\theta}}^2 - Mr_\beta^2\dot{\boldsymbol{\theta}}^2; \tag{A.27}$$

but $\mathscr{K} = \frac{1}{2}Mr^2\dot{\theta}^2$, so

$$\mu_\alpha - \tfrac{1}{2}Mr_\alpha^2\dot{\theta}^2 = \mu_\beta - \tfrac{1}{2}Mr_\beta^2\dot{\theta}^2. \tag{A.28}$$

Thus we have produced the equivalent of Eq. (A.23) by steady-flow methods, and assumption IV.SX.i was a necessary element of our derivation.

Exercise A–2. Show that for the case

$$\Theta = Y_1\Omega_1 + Y_2\Omega_2$$

the following implication holds for linear current-affinity relations:

$$0 = \left(\frac{\delta\Theta}{\delta Y_1}\right)_{Y_2} \rightarrow K_{12} = -K_{21} \quad (\text{and } L_{12} = -L_{21}).$$

Transverse Thermomagnetic and Galvanomagnetic Effects

The transverse thermomagnetic and galvanomagnetic effects refer to the coupling of crossed currents of heat or electricity in the presence of a magnetic field. The coupling effects vanish with the magnetic field, hence assumption IV.SX.ii applies to each of them. In the form of my general discussion and in the definitions of the various coefficients, I follow the treatment given by Bridgman [13]. The system of interest is a homogeneous isotropic metallic plate of rectangular section with length Λ, breadth b, and thickness d, together with some auxiliary loops and engines. Figure A–2 shows the orientation of the plate relative to a set of Cartesian axes. A magnetic field of magnitude B_z, pointing in the z-direction, spans a part of the metallic plate; and currents of heat or electricity flow in the x-direction and in the

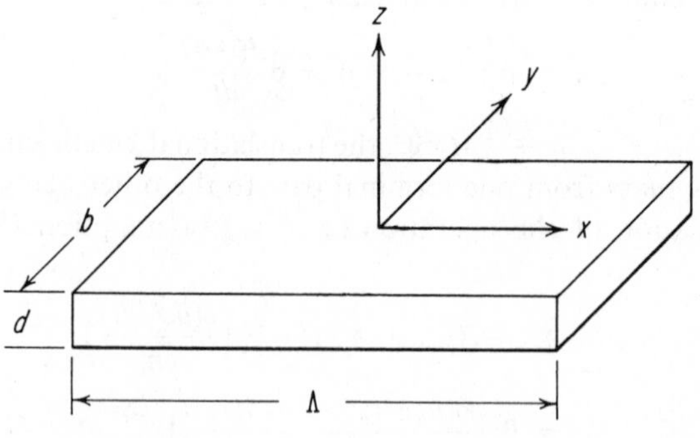

Figure A–2. Homogeneous isotropic metallic plate of rectangular section—length Λ, breadth b, thickness d.

y-direction. The appropriate coefficient in each case is proportional to the product of $-(\delta\Omega_x/\tilde{\delta} Y_y)_{Y_x}$ and d/B_z. The assumption that $0 = (\delta\Theta/\tilde{\delta} Y_y)_{Y_x}$ implies that $K_{xy} = -K_{yx}$ (and $L_{xy} = -L_{yx}$) in the linear current-affinity region.

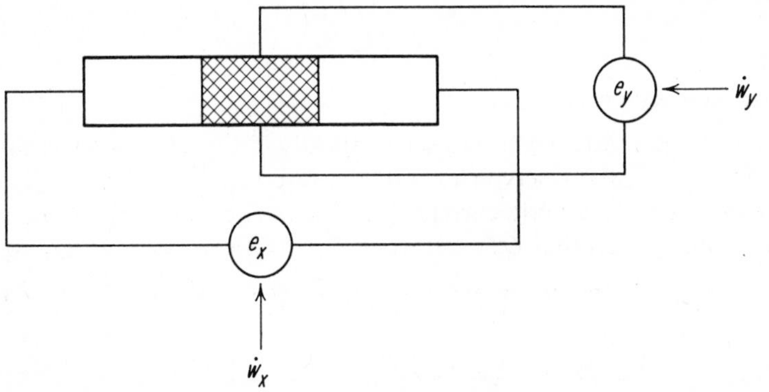

Figure A–3. The Hall effect. The cross-hatched part of the metal plate represents the region spanned by the magnetic field B_z. Electric engines at e_x and e_y maintain electric currents I_x and I_y through the metal plate.

THE HALL EFFECT

Consider the situation shown in Figure A–3: the electric engines e_x and e_y cause the electric currents I_x and I_y to flow through the metal plate; the cross-hatched part of the figure shows the region spanned by the magnetic field B_z; and the entire system is in a thermostat of temperature T. For a fixed magnetic field B_z and steady currents I_x and I_y we have

$$\dot{U}(\text{system}) = -\dot{Q}^{(r)} + \dot{W}_x + \dot{W}_y = 0 \tag{A.29}$$

and

$$\Theta = \frac{\dot{Q}^{(r)}}{T} = I_x \frac{\Delta\psi_x}{T} + I_y \frac{\Delta\psi_y}{T} = Y_1\Omega_1 + Y_2\Omega_2, \tag{A.30}$$

where, e.g., $\dot{W}_x \equiv I_x \Delta\psi_x$ for a given convention regarding the direction of current flow. The application of the operation $(\delta/\tilde{\delta} I_y)_{T,I_x}$ (assumption IV.SX.ii) to Eq. (A.30) leads to the relation

$$\frac{\Delta\psi_y}{I_x} = -\left(\frac{\delta\,\Delta\psi_x}{\delta I_y}\right)_{T,I_x}. \tag{A.31}$$

The Hall coefficient Γ_H is defined by [13]

$$\Gamma_H \equiv \frac{d}{B_z}\left(\frac{\Delta\psi_y}{I_x}\right)_{I_y=0}; \tag{A.32}$$

hence

$$\Gamma_H = -\frac{d}{B_z}\left(\frac{\delta\,\Delta\psi_x}{\delta I_y}\right)_{T,I_x}, \tag{A.33}$$

or, in the linear current-affinity region,

$$\Gamma_H = -\frac{TK_{12}d}{B_z}. \tag{A.34}$$

THE NERNST EFFECT

Consider the situation shown schematically in Figure A–4. Heat flows by conduction from the reservoir at α to the reservoir at β, and the engine e_y maintains a steady electric current I_y in the y-direction. Let us choose the temperature T_γ such that $\dot{Q}_\gamma^{(r)} = 0$ when $I_y = 0$. In the steady state we have

$$\dot{U}(\text{system}) = -\dot{Q}_\alpha^{(r)} - \dot{Q}_\beta^{(r)} - \dot{Q}_\gamma^{(r)} + \dot{W}_y = 0 \tag{A.35}$$

and

$$\begin{aligned}\Theta &= \frac{\dot{Q}_\alpha^{(r)}}{T_\alpha} + \frac{\dot{Q}_\beta^{(r)}}{T_\beta} + \frac{\dot{Q}_\gamma^{(r)}}{T_\gamma} \\ &= \dot{Q}_\alpha^{(r)}\left(\frac{1}{T_\alpha} - \frac{1}{T_\beta}\right) + I_y\frac{\Delta\psi_y}{T_\beta} + \dot{Q}_\gamma^{(r)}\left(\frac{1}{T_\gamma} - \frac{1}{T_\beta}\right) \\ &= Y_1\Omega_1 + Y_2\Omega_2 + Y_3\Omega_3. \end{aligned} \tag{A.36}$$

The operation $(\delta/\tilde{\delta}I_y)_{\dot{Q}_\alpha^{(r)},T_\beta,T_\gamma}$ is of the form $(\delta/\tilde{\delta}Y_2)_{Y_1,\Omega_3}$; hence the application of this operation to Eq. (A.36) (assumption IV.SX.ii) leads to the relation

$$\frac{\Delta\psi_y}{\dot{Q}_\alpha^{(r)}} = -T_\beta\left(\frac{\delta\Omega_1}{\tilde{\delta}Y_2}\right)_{Y_1,\Omega_3}, \tag{A.37}$$

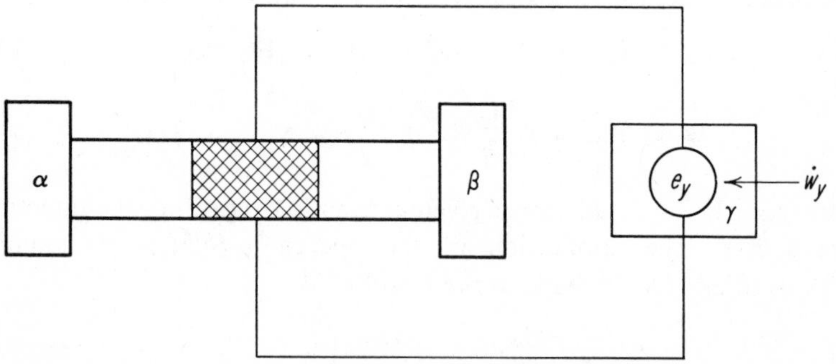

Figure A–4. The Nernst effect. The cross-hatched part represents the region spanned by the magnetic field B_z. α, β, γ—heat reservoirs at temperatures T_α, T_β, T_γ, respectively. The electric engine e_y maintains a current I_y in the y-direction. The temperature T_γ is chosen such that $\dot{Q}_\gamma^{(r)} = 0$ when $I_y = 0$; $T_\alpha > T_\beta$.

where I have assumed that $(\delta\dot{Q}_{\gamma}^{(r)}/\tilde{\delta}I_y)_{\dot{Q}_{\alpha}^{(r)},T_\beta,T_\gamma} \approx 0$. In the limiting path used in obtaining Eq. (A.37), I have treated the currents $\dot{Q}_{\alpha}^{(r)}$ and $\dot{Q}_{\gamma}^{(r)}$ unsymmetrically. The current $\dot{Q}_{\gamma}^{(r)}$ mainly represents work dissipation in the form of joule heat and frictional effects in the engine e_y; the dissipation occurs at the place γ, and hence $\dot{Q}_{\gamma}^{(r)}$ is a current that is *not* expected to couple with the magnetic field. On the other hand the current $\dot{Q}_{\alpha}^{(r)}$ represents (mainly) a heat flow from α to β through the magnetic field; hence coupling of $\dot{Q}_{\alpha}^{(r)}$ with the magnetic field *is* expected. Assumption IV.SX.ii, then—$\dot{Q}_{\alpha}^{(r)}$ coupling, $\dot{Q}_{\gamma}^{(r)}$ noncoupling—dictates that the form of the limiting path be $(\delta/\tilde{\delta}Y_2)_{Y_1,\Omega_3}$.

The Nernst coefficient Γ_N is defined [13] by

$$\Gamma_N \equiv \frac{\kappa d}{B_z}\left(\frac{\Delta\psi_y}{\dot{Q}_{\alpha}^{(r)}}\right)_{I_y=0}, \tag{A.38}$$

where κ is the coefficient of thermal conductivity; hence

$$\Gamma_N = -T_\beta\left(\frac{\kappa d}{B_z}\right)\left(\frac{\delta\Omega_1}{\tilde{\delta}Y_2}\right)_{Y_1,\Omega_3}, \tag{A.39}$$

or, in the linear current-affinity region,

$$\Gamma_N = -T_\beta\left(\frac{|K|_{21}}{K_{33}}\right)\left(\frac{\kappa d}{B_z}\right), \tag{A.40}$$

where $|K|_{21}$ is the cofactor of element K_{21} in the determinant of the matrix of coefficients K_{ij}.

It has been suggested that a thermal converter (Chapter 10) based on the Nernst effect may ultimately prove to be practical [14].

Exercise A–3. Show that for the case

$$\Theta = Y_1\Omega_1 + Y_2\Omega_2 + Y_3\Omega_3$$

the following implication holds in the linear current-affinity region:

$$0 = \left(\frac{\delta\Theta}{\tilde{\delta}Y_2}\right)_{Y_1,\Omega_3} \leftarrow K_{12} = -K_{21},\ K_{13} = -K_{31},\ K_{23} = K_{32}.$$

THE RIGHI–LEDUC EFFECT

Consider the situation shown in Figure A–5. Heat flows from the reservoir at α to the reservoir at β. There is to be a second heat flow in the y-direction. In order to manipulate easily the two independent heat currents, let that in the y-direction be driven by a radiation turbine (Chapter 12). Let the two areas of dimensions Δd be insulated against heat losses except for two diametrically opposed spots that connect to hollow, flexible tubes with

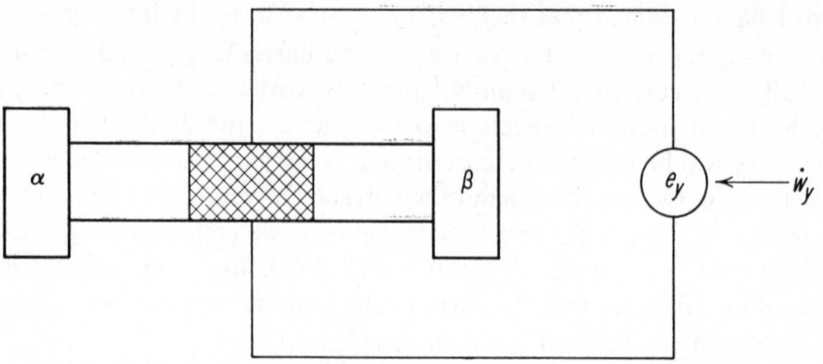

Figure A–5. The Righi–Leduc effect. The cross-hatched part represents the region spanned by the magnetic field. α, β—heat reservoirs at temperatures T_α, T_β, with $T_\alpha > T_\beta$. The engine e_y is a radiation turbine, its blades sweeping out a volume $\dot{V}_y$ per second.

perfectly reflecting walls. The flexible, perfectly reflecting tubes connect to opposite sides of a radiation turbine e_y; the perfectly reflecting blades of the turbine sweep out a volume $\dot{V}_y$ per second. In the steady state, then,

$$\dot{U}(\text{system}) = -\dot{Q}_\alpha^{(r)} - \dot{Q}_\beta^{(r)} + \dot{W}_y = 0 \tag{A.41}$$

and

$$\begin{aligned}\Theta &= \frac{\dot{Q}_\alpha^{(r)}}{T_\alpha} + \frac{\dot{Q}_\beta^{(r)}}{T_\beta} = \dot{Q}_\alpha^{(r)}\left(\frac{1}{T_\alpha} - \frac{1}{T_\beta}\right) + \dot{V}_y\left(\frac{\dot{W}_y}{\dot{V}_y T_\beta}\right)\\ &= Y_1\Omega_1 + Y_2\Omega_2.\end{aligned} \tag{A.42}$$

The application of the operation $(\delta/\bar{\delta}\dot{V}_y)_{\dot{Q}_\alpha^{(r)},T_\beta}$ to Eq. (A.42) (assumption IV.SX.ii) leads to

$$\frac{1}{\dot{Q}_\alpha^{(r)}T_\beta}\left(\frac{\delta\dot{W}_y}{\bar{\delta}\dot{V}_y}\right)_{\dot{Q}_\alpha^{(r)},T_\beta} = -\left(\frac{\delta\Omega_1}{\bar{\delta}Y_2}\right)_{Y_1,\beta} \tag{A.43}$$

since lim $(\dot{W}_y/\dot{V}_y)$ as $\dot{V}_y \to 0 \equiv \delta\dot{W}_y/\bar{\delta}\dot{V}_y$. By analogy to Eq. (12.15) we should be able to factorize the quantity $(\delta\dot{W}_y/\bar{\delta}\dot{V}_y)_{Y_1,\beta}$ into the form $(\delta\dot{W}_y/\bar{\delta}\dot{V}_y)_{Y_1,\beta} = \Delta s\,\Delta T_y$; we can then rewrite Eq. (A.43) as

$$\frac{\Delta T_y}{\dot{Q}_\alpha^{(r)}} = -\frac{T_\beta}{\Delta s}\left(\frac{\delta\Omega_1}{\bar{\delta}Y_2}\right)_{Y_1,\beta}. \tag{A.44}$$

The Righi–Leduc coefficient Γ_{R-L} is defined [13] by

$$\Gamma_{R-L} \equiv \frac{\kappa d}{B_z}\left(\frac{\Delta T_y}{\dot{Q}_\alpha^{(r)}}\right)_{\dot{V}_y=0}; \tag{A.45}$$

hence

$$\Gamma_{R-L} = -\frac{T_\beta}{\Delta s}\left(\frac{\kappa d}{B_z}\right)\left(\frac{\delta\Omega_1}{\bar{\delta}Y_2}\right)_{Y_1,\beta}, \tag{A.46}$$

or, in the linear current-affinity region,

$$\Gamma_{R-L} = -\frac{K_{12}T_\beta \kappa d}{B_z \Delta s}, \tag{A.47}$$

where κ is the coefficient of thermal conductivity.

THE ETTINGSHAUSEN EFFECT

Consider the case shown schematically in Figure A–6. The engine e_x maintains a steady electric current I_x in the x-direction, and the radiation turbine at e_y drives a heat current in the y-direction (see the discussion of the radiation turbine in the treatment of the Righi–Leduc effect). A thermostat keeps the ends of the metal plate and the engine e_x at temperature T. In the steady state we have

$$\dot{U}(\text{system}) = -\dot{Q}^{(r)} + \dot{W}_x + \dot{W}_y = 0 \tag{A.48}$$

and

$$\begin{aligned}\Theta = \frac{\dot{Q}^{(r)}}{T} &= \frac{\dot{W}_x}{T} + \frac{\dot{W}_y}{T} \\ &= \frac{1}{T}\left\{I_x \Delta\psi_x + \dot{V}_y\left(\frac{\dot{W}_y}{\dot{V}_y}\right)\right\} \\ &= Y_1\Omega_1 + Y_2\Omega_2.\end{aligned} \tag{A.49}$$

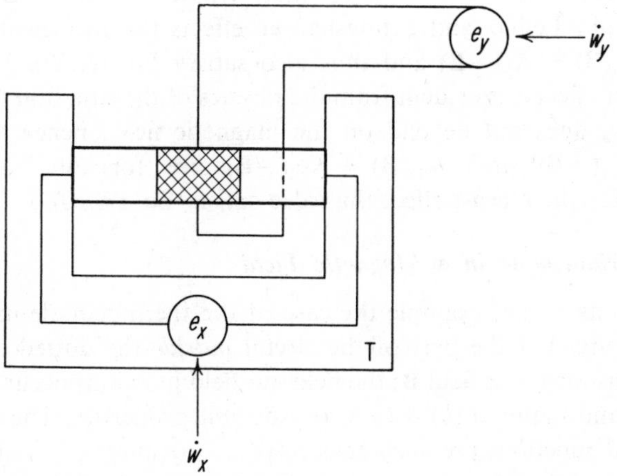

Figure A–6. The Ettingshausen effect. The cross-hatched part represents the region spanned by the magnetic field. The electric engine e_x maintains a current I_x in the x-direction. The engine e_y is a radiation turbine, its blades sweeping out a volume $\dot{V}_y$ per second. The two areas of dimensions bd and the engine e_x are maintained at temperature T.

The application of the operation $(\delta/\tilde{\delta}\dot{V}_y)_{T,I_x}$ to Eq. (A.49) (assumption IV.SX.ii) yields (see the discussion of the Righi–Leduc effect)

$$\frac{1}{I_x}\left(\frac{\delta \dot{W}_y}{\tilde{\delta}\dot{V}_y}\right)_{T,I_x} = \frac{\Delta s\, \Delta T_y}{I_x} = -\left(\frac{\delta\, \Delta\psi_x}{\tilde{\delta}\dot{V}_y}\right)_{T,I_x}. \tag{A.50}$$

The Ettingshausen coefficient Γ_E is defined [13] by

$$\Gamma_E \equiv \frac{d}{B_z}\left(\frac{\Delta T_y}{I_x}\right)_{\dot{V}_y=0}. \tag{A.51}$$

Hence,

$$\Gamma_E = -\left(\frac{d}{B_z\, \Delta s}\right)\left(\frac{\delta\, \Delta\psi_x}{\tilde{\delta}\dot{V}_y}\right)_{T,I_x}, \tag{A.52}$$

or, in the region of linear current-affinity relations,

$$\Gamma_E = -\frac{TK_{12}\, d}{B_z\, \Delta s}. \tag{A.53}$$

REMARK

In the linear current-affinity region each of the thermomagnetic and galvanomagnetic effects satisfies the condition $K_{12} = -K_{21}$ *in the given magnetic field*; i.e.,

$$K_{12}(\mathbf{B}) = -K_{21}(\mathbf{B}). \tag{A.54}$$

It is also true for each of the effects that* $K_{12}(\mathbf{B}) = -K_{12}(-\mathbf{B})$; hence for the Hall, Righi–Leduc, and Ettingshausen effects the coefficients satisfy the relations $K_{ij}(\mathbf{B}) = K_{ji}(-\mathbf{B})$ and thus also satisfy Eq. (A.20). For the case of the Nernst effect it is evident from the physics of the situation that $K_{13} = 0$ and that K_{23} does not depend on the magnetic field; hence the relations $K_{13}(\mathbf{B}) = K_{31}(-\mathbf{B})$ and $K_{23}(\mathbf{B}) = K_{32}(-\mathbf{B})$ are formally satisfied; the coefficients for the Nernst effect thus also satisfy Eq. (A.20).

The Thermocouple in a Magnetic Field

Consider as a final example the case of the thermocouple in a magnetic field. In Figure A–7 the part of the circuit *outside* the dotted circle is in a homogeneous magnetic field **B**; the field–no-field junctions occur in reservoirs 10 and 60; and material (*b*) is to have isotropic properties. The effects at the field–no-field junctions are such that $\{\delta(\dot{Q}_{10}^{(r)} + \dot{Q}_{60}^{(r)})/\tilde{\delta}I\}_{T_\alpha,\ldots} = 0$. Since the thermoelectric effect does not vanish with the magnetic field, we cannot use assumption IV.SX and we must fall back on Eq. (A.20). In the linear current-affinity region it can be shown† that Eq. (A.21a) implies that

* See Chapter 13 of the book cited in reference [8].

† See page 145 of the book cited in reference [2] and Chapter 13 of the book cited in reference [8].

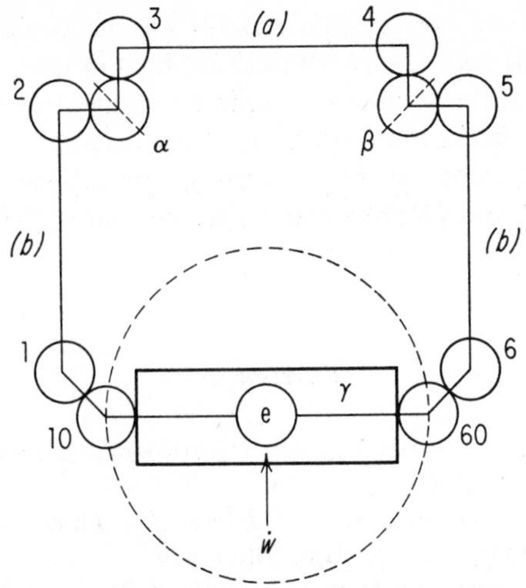

Figure A–7. Thermocouple in a magnetic field. The part of the circuit *outside* the dotted circle is in a homogeneous magnetic field **B**. The field–no-field junctions occur in thermostats 10 and 60; the rest of the figure is the same as Figure 9–1.

$d\,\Delta\psi(\mathbf{B})/dT = \pi(-\mathbf{B})/T$. The working assumption for arbitrary steady-state situations, then, is that the relations

$$\left(\frac{\partial\,\Delta\psi(\mathbf{B})}{\partial T_\beta}\right)_{T_\alpha,\mathbf{B}} = \frac{\pi_\beta^{(ab)}(-\mathbf{B})}{T_\beta}, \tag{A.55}$$

$$0 = [c_\beta^{(a)}(\mathbf{B})] - [c_\beta^{(b)}(\mathbf{B})] + T_\beta\left(\frac{\partial(\pi_\beta^{(ab)}(-\mathbf{B})/T_\beta)}{\partial T_\beta}\right)_{T_\alpha,-\mathbf{B}}, \tag{A.56}$$

$$T_\beta\left(\frac{\partial^2\,\Delta\psi(\mathbf{B})}{\partial {T_\beta}^2}\right)_{T_\alpha,\mathbf{B}} = [c_\beta^{(b)}(\mathbf{B})] - [c_\beta^{(a)}(\mathbf{B})], \tag{A.57}$$

are rigorously true for the thermocouple in a magnetic field.

Exercise A–4. Show that Eqs. (A.55) to (A.57) and Eq. (9.7) lead to the relations

$$\left(\frac{\partial\pi_\beta^{(ab)}(\mathbf{B})}{\partial T_\beta}\right)_{T_\alpha,\mathbf{B}} = \left(\frac{\partial\pi_\beta^{(ab)}(-\mathbf{B})}{\partial T_\beta}\right)_{T_\alpha,-\mathbf{B}}$$

and

$$-\Delta(\pi_\beta^{(ab)}/T_\beta) = \Delta\{[c_\beta^{(a)}] - [c_\beta^{(b)}]\},$$

where $\Delta Z \equiv Z(\mathbf{B}) - Z(-\mathbf{B})$.

If material (a) as well as material (b) has isotropic properties, then $\pi_{\omega}^{(ab)}(\mathbf{B}) = \pi_{\omega}^{(ab)}(-\mathbf{B})$ and Eqs. (9.10) to (9.12) hold in the given field with the proviso that the Seebeck potential difference, the Peltier heats, and the Thomson coefficients are each functions of the magnetic field **B**. If material (a) has anisotropic properties, bismuth being a prime example, then we have to use Eqs. (A.55) and (A.56) since it may be that $\pi_{\omega}^{(ab)}(\mathbf{B}) \neq \pi_{\omega}^{(ab)}(-\mathbf{B})$ in such cases [15].

References

1. E. A. Guggenheim, *Thermodynamics* (North-Holland Publishing Company, Amsterdam, 1950), p. 1.
2. S. de Groot, *Thermodynamics of Irreversible Processes* (North-Holland Publishing Company, Amsterdam, 1951), p. 1.
3. D. ter Haar, *Elements of Statistical Mechanics* (Rinehart and Company, New York, 1954), p. xvii.
4. M. L. Lieberman, M.S. Thesis, Illinois Institute of Technology (1963).
5. *American Institute of Physics Handbook* (McGraw-Hill Book Company, New York, 1957), p. **4**–77.
6. R. P. Rastogi, R. C. Srivastava, and K. Singh, *Trans. Faraday Soc.*, **61**, 854 (1965).
7. D. Fitts, *Nonequilibrium Thermodynamics* (McGraw-Hill Book Company, New York, 1962), p. 154.
8. S. de Groot and P. Mazur, *Non-Equilibrium Thermodynamics* (North-Holland Publishing Company, Amsterdam, 1962), Chapter 4.
9. L. Onsager, *Phys. Rev.*, **38**, 2265 (1931).
10. A. Sommerfeld, *Electrodynamics* (Academic Press, Publishers, New York, 1952), pp. 27 and 28.
11. E. A. Guggenheim, *Thermodynamics* (North-Holland Publishing Company, Amsterdam, 1950), pp. 374 and 375.
12. L. Landau and E. Lifshitz, *Statistical Physics* (Addison-Wesley Publishing Company, Reading, Mass., 1958), p. 74.
13. P. W. Bridgman, *The Thermodynamics of Electrical Phenomena in Metals and a Condensed Collection of Thermodynamic Formulas* (Dover Publications, New York, 1961), Chapter 7.
14. S. W. Angrist, *Direct Energy Conversion* (Allyn and Bacon, Boston, 1965), Chapter 9.
15. R. Wolfe and G. Smith, *Phys. Rev.*, **129**, 1086 (1963).

Appendix B

Glossary of Terms

(*Number following definition indicates page where term is first used.*)

affine sequence—a sequence of steady states all of which have the same values for a set of affinities Ω', 7, 28.

bitherm or **bithermal relation**—a form of the equation of correlation for the thermomolecular pressure effect, 55.

canonical set of steady currents—currents that are time derivatives of extensive thermodynamic quantities, 26.

energetics—Brønsted's reformulation of the principles of thermodynamics, 3.

equation of correlation—the "equation of state" for the thermomolecular pressure effect, 54.

forced vaporization—steady vaporization of a liquid *without boiling*, 13.

full-flux linkage—a linkage functioning as a lossless heat conductor, 51.

global property—a property of the entire system, to be distinguished from a local property; thus, e.g., the resistance of a length of wire is a global property whereas the resistivity at a point along the wire is a local property, 32.

gradient part—a part of the system that contains gradients in intensive variables, 6.

grand **principles of entropy production**—principles asserted to hold for any value of a certain current; to be distinguished from *petit* principles of entropy production, 33.

link or **linkage**—a part of the system connecting two terminal parts in separate thermostats, 47.

local property—property at a point of the system; to be distinguished from a global property, 32.

migrational equilibrium—a chemical species is said to be in migrational equilibrium in a spatial field if there is no macroscopic tendency for the given species to migrate from one place in the field to another, 10.

monothermal process—a process in which the entire system is in heat communication with a single external heat reservoir during the process, 8.

ordinary steady-state situation—one not involving magnetic or centrifugal fields, 26.

overlap region—a range of conditions for which the pertinent physical laws are linear and for which the thermodynamic affinities are proportional to the physical forces, 186.

partial-flux linkage—a linkage functioning as a heat conductor with some lateral heat losses, 51.

***petit* principles of entropy production**—principles asserted to hold at a point where a certain current vanishes; to be distinguished from *grand* principles of entropy production, 33.

polythermal process—a process in which the terminal parts of the system are separately in heat communication with heat reservoirs of temperatures T_i during the process, 8.

quasi-static process—sequence of equilibrium states, 5.

quasi-steady process—sequence of steady states, 5.

special steady-state situation—one involving magnetic or centrifugal fields, 26.

static state—equilibrium state, 5.

stationary part—a part of the system the state of which remains pointwise invariant in time, 6.

terminal part—a part of the system that is spatially uniform with respect to the intensive variables, 6.

thermal converter—a device of the heat-to-work type, 122.

thermo-dynamics—aspects of thermotics for which time variation is important, 184.

thermo-staedics—aspects of thermotics that are temporally steady or stationary, 184.

thermostatics—ordinary equilibrium thermodynamics.

thermo-statics—ordinary, classical equilibrium aspects of thermotics, 184.

thermotics—the science of heat, 183.

zero-flux linkage—a theoretical construct used to maintain a fixed temperature gradient in a linkage during steady-flow operations, 51.

Appendix C

Answers to Selected Exercises

2–2 By hypothesis we have

$$\ln \frac{P}{P_0} = -\dot{\xi}^{(i)}[N^{(i)}] = -\dot{\xi}^{(k)}[N^{(k)}] = \cdots$$

for a given setting of the pressure. Averaging the terms on each side of this equation for the m pressure settings, we get

$$\left\langle \ln \frac{P}{P_0} \right\rangle = -\langle \dot{\xi}^{(i)}[N^{(i)}] \rangle = -\langle \dot{\xi}^{(k)}[N^{(k)}] \rangle = \cdots .$$

Since we are taking the $[N]$ coefficients as constant for each tube, we have, e.g.,

$$\langle \dot{\xi}^{(i)}[N^{(i)}] \rangle = \langle \dot{\xi}^{(i)} \rangle [N^{(i)}],$$

and consequently

$$\langle \dot{\xi}^{(i)} \rangle [N^{(i)}] = \langle \dot{\xi}^{(k)} \rangle [N^{(k)}] = \cdots .$$

If we now write the basic equation $\ln P = \ln P_0 - \dot{\xi}^{(i)}[N^{(i)}]$ in the form

$$\ln P = \ln P_0 - \theta^{(i)} \langle \dot{\xi}^{(i)} \rangle [N^{(i)}],$$

the m data points for the ith tube, when plotted as $\ln P$ versus $\theta^{(i)}$, will lie on a straight line of slope $-\langle \dot{\xi}^{(i)} \rangle [N^{(i)}]$. The other tubes give straight-line plots of exactly the same slope. Since the data points from all the tubes lie on straight lines of the same slope and since each straight line passes through the point $(0, \ln P_0)$, all the data fall on a single straight line when plotted in the form $\ln P$ versus $\theta^{(i)}$.

2–4 At the melting temperature $\mu(*)_{sol} - \mu(*)_{liq} = 0$; hence

(i) $$\mu_{sol} - \mu_{liq} = \mu_{sol} - \mu(*)_{sol} - (\mu_{liq} - \mu(*)_{liq})$$
$$= \int_{T*}^{T} (\bar{S}_{liq} - \bar{S}_{sol})\, dT > 0$$

as $\bar{S}_{liq} - \bar{S}_{sol} > 0$ at the melting point and in a neighborhood of the melting point. Similarly,

(ii) $$\mu_{sol} - \mu_{liq} = \mu(*)_{sol} - \mu_{liq} = \mu(*)_{liq} - \mu_{liq}$$
$$= \int_{T*}^{T} \bar{S}_{liq}\, dT > 0.$$

From Eq. (2.16) it follows that

(i) $$RT[N]_{mel}\, \dot{n}_{liq} = \mu_{sol} - \mu_{liq}$$
$$= \int_{T*}^{T} (\bar{S}_{liq} - \bar{S}_{sol})\, dT \approx \Delta\bar{H}(*)_{mel} \int_{T*}^{T} d\ln T$$
$$= T*\, \Delta\bar{S}(*)_{mel} \ln \frac{T}{T*};$$

hence

$$\frac{T*}{T} \ln \frac{T}{T*} \approx \dot{n}_{liq}\left(\frac{R[N]_{mel}}{\Delta\bar{S}(*)_{mel}}\right).$$

From Eq. (2.15) it follows that

(ii) $$RT[N]_{mel}\, \dot{n}_{liq} - (T* - T)\bar{S}_{sol} = \mu_{sol} - \mu_{liq} = \mu(*)_{liq} - \mu_{liq}$$
$$= \int_{T*}^{T} \bar{S}_{liq}\, dT = \langle\bar{S}_{liq}\rangle(T - T*);$$

hence

$$\frac{\Delta T}{T} = \dot{n}_{liq}\left(\frac{R[N]_{mel}}{\langle\bar{S}_{liq}\rangle - \bar{S}_{sol}}\right) \approx \dot{n}_{liq}\left(\frac{R[N]_{mel}}{\Delta\bar{S}(*)_{mel}}\right).$$

Finally, observe that

$$\frac{T*}{T} \ln \frac{T}{T*} = \frac{T*}{T} \ln\left(1 + \frac{\Delta T}{T*}\right)$$
$$= \frac{T*}{T}\left(\frac{\Delta T}{T*} - \frac{1}{2}\left(\frac{\Delta T}{T*}\right)^2 + \cdots\right)$$
$$\approx \frac{\Delta T}{T}.$$

2–5 For the case considered, Eq. (2.28) takes the form

$$\ln \mathcal{Q} = \ln K - [N_V]\dot{C}_D.$$

Let* $\mathcal{Q} \equiv K + \Delta$, then

$$\ln\left(1 + \frac{\Delta}{K}\right) = -[N_V](k_f C_B - k_b C_D) = -[N_V]k_b C_D\left(\frac{K}{\mathcal{Q}} - 1\right)$$
$$= [N_V]k_b C_D\left\{\frac{\Delta/K}{1 + (\Delta/K)}\right\}.$$

* Remember that $\mathcal{Q} = C_D/C_B$, $K = C_D^{(eq)}/C_B^{(eq)} = k_f/k_b$, and that $\dot{C}_D = k_f C_B - k_b C_D$.

Close to equilibrium we have $(\Delta/K) \ll 1$, $\ln\{1 + (\Delta/K)\} \approx \Delta/K$, and consequently

$$[N_V] \approx \frac{1}{k_b C_D^{(\text{eq})}}.$$

3–1 Since in the linear current-affinity region

$$\left(\frac{\partial Y_k}{\partial \Omega_j}\right)_{\Omega',\sigma} = L_{kj},$$

Eq. (3.31) is simply a statement of the Onsager reciprocal relations $L_{kj} = L_{jk}$.

From Eq. (3.33) we see that, in the linear current-affinity region,

$$\left(\frac{\partial^2 \Theta}{\partial Y_k^{\,2}}\right)_{\Omega',\sigma} = 2\left(\frac{\partial \Omega_k}{\partial Y_k}\right)_{\Omega',\sigma} = \frac{2}{L_{kk}} > 0,$$

since $L_{kk} > 0$ due to the positive definite character of Θ.

From the relations (for the linear current-affinity case)

$$\left(\frac{\partial \Omega_k}{\partial Y_k}\right)_{Y',\sigma} = K_{kk} > 0 \quad \text{and} \quad \left(\frac{\partial \Omega_k}{\partial Y_k}\right)_{\Omega',\sigma} = \frac{1}{L_{kk}} > 0$$

and the relation $L_{ij} = |K|_{ji}/|K|$ with $|K|$ being the determinant of the matrix of coefficients K_{ij} and $|K|_{ji}$ being the cofactor of element K_{ji} in the determinant $|K|$, we see that

$$\begin{aligned}\left(\frac{\partial \Omega_k}{\partial Y_k}\right)_{Y',\sigma} - \left(\frac{\partial \Omega_k}{\partial Y_k}\right)_{\Omega',\sigma} &= K_{kk} - \frac{|K|}{|K|_{kk}} \\ &= K_{kk}\left(1 - \frac{|K|}{K_{kk}|K|_{kk}}\right).\end{aligned}$$

The matrix of coefficients K_{ij} is symmetric for ordinary steady-state situations; hence (see reference [6]) $K_{kk}|K|_{kk} > |K| > 0$ and

$$\left(\frac{\partial \Omega_k}{\partial Y_k}\right)_{Y',\sigma} - \left(\frac{\partial \Omega_k}{\partial Y_k}\right)_{\Omega',\sigma} > 0.$$

See also the discussion in the *Explorations* section.

3–2 For fixed values of the affinities Ω_i $(i \neq k)$ the graph of Θ versus Y_k will be concave upward in the vicinity of the point $Y_k = 0$ and will have a minimum at that point. It follows then that on either side of the point $Y_k = 0$ the quantities Y_k and $(\partial \Theta/\partial Y_k)_{\Omega',\sigma}$ have the same sign; hence

$$Y_k(\partial \Theta/\partial Y_k)_{\Omega',\sigma} \geqslant 0.$$

4–2 The values of $(\Delta\psi/\Delta P)_{T,I=0}$ appear to be fairly constant for each set of data, the average values being 2.62 and 144 for the cellulose plug and the capillary, respectively; the linear relations (4.27) and (4.28) thus appear to describe the data adequately. From Eq. (4.22) we see that the expressions

$\dot{V}\,\Delta P$ and $I\,\Delta\psi$ must be expressed in the same energy units. If we select ergs for our energy unit, then when ΔP is expressed in centimeters of mercury, $\Delta\psi$ in millivolts, I in milliamperes, and $\dot{V}$ in cm^3 sec^{-1} Eq. (4.22) takes the form

$$\Theta = 13.6 \times 981\dot{V}\left(\frac{\Delta P}{T}\right) + 10I\left(\frac{\Delta\psi}{T}\right),$$

and Eq. (4.29) reduces to

$$\left|\left(\frac{\Delta\psi}{\Delta P}\right)_{T,I=0}\right| = \frac{13.6 \times 981}{10}\left|\left(\frac{\dot{V}}{I}\right)_{T,\Delta P=0}\right|.$$

For the cellulose plug, then (for the case $\Delta P = 0$),

$$\dot{V} = 10(13.6 \times 981)^{-1}\, 2.62I = 0.00196I.$$

(i) For a current of 1 ma, $\dot{V} = 0.00196$ cm^3 sec^{-1}.

(ii) For a volume flow of 1 cm^3 sec^{-1}, $I = 510$ ma.
For the glass capillary tube ($\Delta P = 0$)

$$\dot{V} = 10(13.6 \times 981)^{-1}\, 144I = 0.108I.$$

(i) For a current of 1 ma, $\dot{V} = 0.108$ cm^3 sec^{-1}.
(ii) For a volume flow of 1 cm^3 sec^{-1}, $I = 9.3$ ma.

5–2 (i) From the definition of the quantity $\langle[S]^\partial\rangle$ it follows that

$$-\langle[S]^\partial\rangle = \frac{\mu_\chi - \mu_\omega}{T_\chi - T_\omega}$$
$$= \frac{1}{T_\chi - T_\omega}\left\{\int_{T_\omega}^{T_\chi} - \left(\bar{S}_\omega + \bar{C}_P \ln\frac{T}{T_\omega}\right) dT + RT_\chi \int_{P_\omega}^{P_\chi} d\ln P\right\},$$

the first integral being taken at constant pressure and the second being taken at constant temperature (see reference [1] of Chapter 1, pp. 112 and 113).
(ii) Upon subtracting the expression for $\bar{S}_\chi - \langle[S]^\partial\rangle$ from that for $\bar{S}_\omega - \langle[S]^\partial\rangle$, we get

$$\bar{S}_\omega - \bar{S}_\chi = \bar{C}_P \ln\frac{T_\omega}{T_\chi} - R\ln\frac{P_\omega}{P_\chi}$$

which is the correct expression for an ideal gas.

5–4 Note that $P_\alpha = \frac{1}{2}(P_\alpha + P_\beta) + \frac{1}{2}(P_\alpha - P_\beta)$ and that

$$P_\beta = \tfrac{1}{2}(P_\alpha + P_\beta) - \tfrac{1}{2}(P_\alpha - P_\beta).$$

(i) Use Eq. (5.38).
(ii) The proper equation of the form (5.32) is just

$$\left\langle\frac{\bar{S}_\alpha - [S_\alpha]^\partial}{R}\right\rangle_\beta = \frac{\ln(P_\alpha/P_\beta)}{\ln(T_\alpha/T_\beta)}.$$

(iii) $$\left\{\frac{\bar{S}_\alpha - \langle[S]^\partial\rangle}{R}\right\} - \left\langle\frac{\bar{S}_\alpha - [S_\alpha]^\partial}{R}\right\rangle_\beta = \frac{\bar{C}_P}{R} - \frac{T_\beta}{T_\alpha - T_\beta}\left(\frac{\bar{C}_P}{R}\ln\frac{T_\alpha}{T_\beta} - \ln\frac{P_\alpha}{P_\beta}\right) - \frac{\ln(P_\alpha/P_\beta)}{\ln(T_\alpha/T_\beta)}.$$

For $P_\alpha/P_\beta = (T_\alpha/T_\beta)^{1/2}$ we get

$$\{\} - \langle\rangle = \frac{\bar{C}_P}{R} - \frac{1}{2} - \frac{T_\beta}{T_\alpha - T_\beta}\left\{\left(\frac{\bar{C}_P}{R} - \frac{1}{2}\right)\ln\frac{T_\alpha}{T_\beta}\right\}$$

and for $P_\alpha = P_\beta$ we get

$$\{\} - \langle\rangle = \frac{\bar{C}_P}{R} - \frac{T_\beta}{T_\alpha - T_\beta}\left\{\frac{\bar{C}_P}{R}\ln\frac{T_\alpha}{T_\beta}\right\}.$$

6–2 (i) If $(\partial[H_\omega]/\partial T_\omega)_\chi = [C_{\omega\omega}]$, then by Eqs. (6.9) and (6.10)

$$[C_{\omega\omega}] - [C_{\chi\omega}] - (\partial[h(\chi\omega)]/\partial T_\omega)_\chi = 0 \text{ and } [S_\omega]^\partial = [S_\omega].$$

But $[S_\omega]$ is in general a function of several of the intensive variables T_α, P_α, T_β, P_β, $\langle T\rangle$, whereas $[S_\omega]^\partial$ is a function of the ω state variables only; hence the relation $(\partial[H_\omega]/\partial T_\omega)_\chi = [C_{\omega\omega}]$ cannot have any general validity.

(ii) Set $(\partial[G_\alpha]/\partial T_\alpha)_{\beta,\langle T\rangle} = [C_{\beta\alpha}](1 - \langle T\rangle T_\beta^{-1})$ equal to $-[S_\alpha]$; then

$$[S_\alpha] = [C_{\beta\alpha}](\langle T\rangle T_\beta^{-1} - 1).$$

Now let

$$T_\alpha \to T_\beta\colon [S_\alpha(\beta)] = [S_\beta]^\partial = [C_{ba}(\beta)](\langle T\rangle T_\beta^{-1} - 1).$$

The right-hand side of this last equality is a function of $\langle T\rangle$, whereas the left-hand side is not; hence the relation $(\partial[G_\alpha]/\partial T_\alpha)_{\beta,\langle T\rangle} = -[S_\alpha]$ cannot be generally valid.

(iii) $(\partial[G_\alpha]^\partial/\partial T_\alpha)_{\beta,\langle T\rangle} = [C_{\alpha\alpha}]^\partial(1 - \langle T\rangle T_\alpha^{-1})$ is clearly a function of $\langle T\rangle$, whereas $[S_\alpha]^\partial$ is not; hence the relation $(\partial[G_\alpha]^\partial/\partial T_\alpha)_{\beta,\langle T\rangle} = -[S_\alpha]^\partial$ cannot have any general validity.

The proofs in parts (i) to (iii) all depend on the acceptance of assumption Q.

6–4 For the case considered, the relation $(\delta\Theta/\tilde{\delta}\Omega_2)_{Y_1,\beta} = 0$ implies that $(\partial\Theta/\partial T_\alpha)_{\dot{n}_\alpha,\beta}|_{T_\alpha = T_\beta} = 0$.

The application of this result to the relation

$$\Theta = \dot{n}_\alpha\left(\frac{\bar{H}_\beta - \bar{H}_\alpha}{T_\beta} + \bar{S}_\alpha - \bar{S}_\beta\right) + \dot{Q}_\alpha^{(r)}\left(\frac{1}{T_\alpha} - \frac{1}{T_\beta}\right)$$

yields

$$\bar{V}_\alpha\left(\frac{\partial P_\alpha}{\partial T_\alpha}\right)_{\dot{n}_\alpha,\beta}\Bigg|_{T_\alpha = T_\beta} = -\frac{\dot{Q}_\alpha^{(r)}}{T_\alpha\dot{n}_\alpha}\Bigg|_{T_\alpha = T_\beta} = -\frac{\dot{S}_\alpha^{(r)}}{\dot{n}_\alpha}\Bigg|_{T_\alpha = T_\beta}.$$

Upon passing to the limit $\dot{n}_\alpha \to 0$, the preceding relation implies that

$$\bar{S}_a(\beta) - [S_a(\beta)]^\partial = \bar{S}_a(\beta) - [S_a(\beta)]$$

and, hence, that $[S_a(\beta)]^\partial = [S_a(\beta)]$.

Since $[S_a(\beta)]^\partial = [S_b(\beta)]^\partial$ and $[S_a(\beta)] = [S_b(\beta)]$, it follows that

$$[S_b(\beta)]^\partial = [S_b(\beta)].$$

6–5 In Eq. (6.39) let $\dot{n} = \dot{n}_\alpha$, $\dot{W}_0 = 0$, $\mathscr{G}_\rho = \mu_\rho$ (there being no additional—kinetic, gravitational, etc.—forms of energy involved); then, if the mass flow is thought of as taking place in the α direction, it follows that

$$\mu_\alpha - \mu_\beta + T_\alpha\left(\frac{\delta \dot{S}_\alpha(\text{in})}{\delta \dot{n}_\alpha}\right)_{\Omega'} - T_\beta\left(\frac{\delta \dot{S}_\beta(\text{out})}{\delta \dot{n}_\alpha}\right)_{\Omega'} + \left(\frac{\delta \dot{q}(\alpha\beta)}{\delta \dot{n}_\alpha}\right)_{\Omega'} = 0$$

and

$$\mu_\alpha - \mu_\beta + T_\alpha[S_\alpha] - T_\beta[S_\beta] - [h(\beta\alpha)] = 0.$$

6–6 (i) Use Eq. (6.39) with the same conventions as in Ex. 6–5:

$$\mu_\alpha - \mu_\gamma + T_\alpha[S_\alpha] + T_\beta\{[S_\beta(\text{in})] - [S_\beta(\text{out})]\} - T_\gamma[S_\gamma] = 0.$$

Since the linkages are full-flux ones, it follows from assumption IV that

$$[S_\beta(\text{in})] = [S_\gamma] \quad \text{and} \quad [S_\beta(\text{out})] = [S_\alpha];$$

hence

$$[H_\alpha] - [H_\gamma] + T_\beta\{[S_\gamma] - [S_\alpha]\} = 0.$$

(ii) In Eq. (6.39) let $\dot{n} = \dot{n}_\chi$, $\dot{W}_0 = 0$, $\mathscr{G}_\rho = \mu_\rho$, etc.:

$$\mu_\alpha[R_{\alpha\chi}] + \mu_\beta[R_{\beta\chi}] + \mu_\gamma[R_{\gamma\chi}] + T_\alpha[S_\alpha][R_{\alpha\chi}] + T_\beta[S_\beta][R_{\beta\chi}] + T_\gamma[S_\gamma][R_{\gamma\chi}] + \left(\frac{\delta \dot{q}(\alpha\beta\gamma)}{\delta \dot{n}_\chi}\right)_{\Omega'} = 0$$

or

$$[R_{\alpha\chi}][H_\alpha] + [R_{\beta\chi}][H_\beta] + [R_{\gamma\chi}][H_\gamma] = [h(\psi\omega\chi)],$$

where $(\delta \dot{q}(\alpha\beta\gamma)/\delta \dot{n}_\chi)_{\Omega'} \equiv -[h(\psi\omega\chi)]$.

Equation (6.47) follows directly from Eq. (6.40). Equation (6.48) is a direct consequence of the relation $\dot{n}_\alpha + \dot{n}_\beta + \dot{n}_\gamma = 0$. Now set

$$[G_\omega] \equiv [H_\omega] - \langle T(\alpha\beta\gamma)\rangle[S_\omega];$$

then Eq. (6.50) follows from Eqs. (6.46) to (6.49).

8–1 Equation (5.38) is merely based on the definition $-\langle[S]^{\partial}\rangle \equiv \Delta\mu/\Delta T$; the definition is applicable to the present case also; hence, with some rearrangement, we get

$$\begin{aligned}\ln\frac{P_{\chi}}{P_{\omega}} &= \frac{\bar{C}_P^{(g)}}{R}\ln\frac{T_{\chi}}{T_{\omega}} + \frac{T_{\chi}-T_{\omega}}{T_{\chi}}\left\{\frac{\bar{S}_{\omega}^{(g)} - \langle[S]^{\partial}\rangle - \bar{C}_P^{(g)}}{R}\right\} \\ &= -\frac{(T_{\chi}^{-1} - T_{\omega}^{-1})}{R}\left\{\frac{T_{\chi}T_{\omega}}{T_{\chi}-T_{\omega}}\,\bar{C}_P^{(g)}\ln\frac{T_{\chi}}{T_{\omega}} \right. \\ &\quad \left. + T_{\omega}(\bar{S}_{\omega}^{(g)} - \langle[S]^{\partial}\rangle - \bar{C}_P^{(g)})\right\}.\end{aligned}$$

It follows then that

$$\langle[Q]^{\partial}\rangle = T_{\omega}\{\bar{S}_{\omega}^{(g)} - \langle[S]^{\partial}\rangle - \bar{C}_P^{(g)}\} + \frac{T_{\chi}T_{\omega}}{T_{\chi}-T_{\omega}}\,\bar{C}_P^{(g)}\ln\frac{T_{\chi}}{T_{\omega}}.$$

8–3 gas	$[Q]^{\partial}$	$\Delta\bar{H}$	$[Q^{(M)}]^{\partial}$
CO_2	−1800	−2800	+1000
N_2	−260	+100	−360
H_2	+100	+800	−700

All values are expressed in calories.

8–6 From Eq. (8.15) we have

$$\left(\frac{\partial \ln X_{\alpha}^{(1)}}{\partial T_{\alpha}}\right)_{\beta} = \frac{[Q_{\alpha}^{(1)}]^{\partial}}{RT_{\alpha}^{2}}$$

and

$$\begin{aligned}\int_{X_{\alpha}^{(1)}=X_{\alpha}^{(1)}}^{X_{\alpha}^{(1)}=X_{\beta}^{(1)}} d\ln X_{\alpha}^{(1)} &= \int_{T=T_{\alpha}}^{T=T_{\beta}} \frac{[Q_{\alpha}^{(1)}]^{\partial}}{RT^{2}}\,dT, \\ \ln\frac{X_{\beta}^{(1)}}{X_{\alpha}^{(1)}} &= -\frac{\langle[Q^{(1)}]^{\partial}\rangle}{R}\left(\frac{1}{T_{\beta}} - \frac{1}{T_{\alpha}}\right).\end{aligned}$$

We see then that

$$\begin{aligned}\langle[Q^{(1)}]^{\partial}\rangle &= T_{\alpha}T_{\beta}(T_{\beta}-T_{\alpha})^{-1}R\ln\frac{X_{\beta}^{(1)}}{X_{\alpha}^{(1)}} \\ &= -RT_{\alpha}T_{\beta}(T_{\alpha}-T_{\beta})^{-1}\ln\frac{T_{\alpha}}{T_{\beta}}\ln\frac{X_{\beta}^{(1)}}{X_{\alpha}^{(1)}}\left(\ln\frac{T_{\alpha}}{T_{\beta}}\right)^{-1} \\ &= RT_{r}\left\langle\frac{[Q^{(1)}]^{\partial}}{RT}\right\rangle \\ &= \langle[Q^{(1)}]^{\partial}\rangle_{r},\end{aligned}$$

where I have made use of Eqs. (8.24) to (8.26).

8–7 The fundamental relations

$$\dot{\xi}\{\sum \nu_j\bar{H}_j - \sum \nu_i\bar{H}_i\} + T_{\alpha}\dot{S}_{\alpha}^{(r)} + T_{\beta}\dot{S}_{\beta}^{(r)} + \dot{q}(\alpha\beta) = 0$$

and

$$\Theta = \dot{S}_{\alpha}^{(r)} + \dot{S}_{\beta}^{(r)} + \dot{s}(\alpha\beta) + \dot{\xi}\{\sum \nu_j\bar{S}_j - \sum \nu_i\bar{S}_i\},$$

where, e.g., $\bar{H}_i$ is short for $\bar{H}_{B_i}$, and the relation, e.g.,

$$\left(\frac{\delta\dot{S}_\alpha^{(r)}}{\delta\dot{\xi}}\right)_{\Omega'} \equiv \sum \nu_i(\bar{S}_i - [S_i])$$

allow us to write an equation of the form of Eq. (8.41).

10–3 In the limit $\dot{n}_\alpha \to 0$, Eq. (10.30) implies that

$$\bar{V}_\alpha\left(\frac{\partial P_\alpha}{\partial T_\alpha}\right)_{\beta,\dot{n}_\alpha=0} = -\left(\frac{\delta\dot{S}_\alpha^{(r)}}{\delta\dot{n}_\alpha}\right)_{\beta,T_\alpha} = \bar{S}_\alpha - [S_\alpha],$$

but

$$\bar{V}_\alpha\left(\frac{\partial P_\alpha}{\partial T_\alpha}\right)_{\beta,\dot{n}_\alpha=0} = \bar{S}_\alpha - [S_\alpha]^\partial.$$

The implication then is that $[S_\alpha] = [S_\alpha]^\partial$, but this is in general not true, since $[S_\alpha]^\partial = [S_\alpha(\alpha)] \neq [S_\alpha]$—see Eqs. (6.22) and (6.23). Equation (10.30) is thus unlikely to have any validity whatsoever.

11–1 For the first symmetry relation $\dot{Q}_{\mathrm{I}}^{(r)}(\text{old}) = \dot{Q}_{\mathrm{I}}^{(r)}(\text{new}_1)$, write

$$\dot{Q}_{\mathrm{I}}^{(r)}(\text{old}) = L_{11}\Omega_1 + L_{12}\Omega_2 + L_{13}\Omega_3,$$
$$\dot{Q}_{\mathrm{I}}^{(r)}(\text{new}_1) = L_{11}\Omega_1' + L_{12}\Omega_2' + L_{13}\Omega_3',$$

where $\Omega_i = T_i^{-1} - T_4^{-1}$, and I have used primes to distinguish "new$_1$" values of the affinities. It follows from the conditions of the problem that $\Omega_1' = \Omega_1 - \Omega_2$, $\Omega_2' = -\Omega_2$, $\Omega_3' = \Omega_3 - \Omega_2$; hence the relation $\dot{Q}_{\mathrm{I}}^{(r)}(\text{old}) = \dot{Q}_{\mathrm{I}}^{(r)}(\text{new}_1)$ implies that

$$-(L_{11} + L_{12} + L_{13}) = L_{12}$$

or

$$L_{13} = -(L_{11} + 2L_{12}).$$

The other symmetry relations can be treated in a similar manner.

11–2 From the symmetry of the case it follows that $\dot{Q}_1^{(r)} = \dot{Q}_2^{(r)}$ and hence that the two currents are not independent. Thus

$$\Theta = \dot{Q}_1^{(r)}\left(\frac{1}{T_1} - \frac{1}{T_4}\right) + \dot{Q}_2^{(r)}\left(\frac{1}{T_2} - \frac{1}{T_4}\right)$$
$$= (\dot{Q}_1^{(r)} + \dot{Q}_2^{(r)})\left(\frac{1}{T_{\mathrm{I}}} - \frac{1}{T_{\mathrm{IV}}}\right) = 2\dot{Q}_1^{(r)}\left(\frac{1}{T_{\mathrm{I}}} - \frac{1}{T_{\mathrm{IV}}}\right).$$

13–2 The numerical example in the hint adequately illustrates the point:

$$|\mu_\alpha^{(1)} - \mu_\beta^{(1)}| \approx 0.016RT,$$
$$|\mu_\alpha^{(2)} - \mu_\beta^{(2)}| \approx 2.3RT.$$

14–1 From the relations

$$\bar{H}_{\alpha}^{(g)}\dot{n}_{\alpha}^{(g)} + \bar{H}_{\beta}^{(g)}\dot{n}_{\beta}^{(g)} + \dot{Q}_{\alpha}^{(r)} + \dot{Q}_{\beta}^{(r)} + \dot{Q}_{\gamma}^{(r)} + \dot{q}(\alpha\beta) + \dot{q}(\beta\gamma) + \dot{q}(\alpha\gamma) = \dot{W}_0$$

and

$$\Theta = \bar{S}_{\alpha}^{(g)}\dot{n}_{\alpha}^{(g)} + \bar{S}_{\beta}^{(g)}\dot{n}_{\beta}^{(g)} + \dot{S}_{\alpha}^{(r)} + \dot{S}_{\beta}^{(r)} + \dot{S}_{\gamma}^{(r)} + \dot{\mathrm{s}}(\alpha\gamma) + \dot{\mathrm{s}}(\alpha\beta) + \dot{\mathrm{s}}(\beta\gamma),$$

it follows that [if we assume that (i) $\langle T(\alpha\beta)\rangle = \langle T(\beta\gamma)\rangle = \langle T(\alpha\gamma)\rangle$ (the linkages are exchanging heat with a common environment), that (ii)

$$(\delta\dot{Q}_{\gamma}^{(r)}/\tilde{\delta}\dot{n}_{\alpha}^{(g)})_{\Omega'} \approx 0,$$

and that (iii)

$$(\delta\dot{W}_0/\tilde{\delta}\dot{n}_{\alpha}^{(g)})_{\Omega'} = \Delta\psi(\delta I/\tilde{\delta}\dot{n}_{\alpha}^{(g)})_{\Omega'}]$$

$$[H_{\alpha}] - [H_{\beta}] - [h(\beta\alpha)] = [R_{\alpha}^{(I)}]\left\{\Delta\psi - \frac{\partial\dot{q}(\alpha\gamma)}{\partial I} - \frac{\partial\dot{q}(\beta\gamma)}{\partial I}\right\}$$

and

$$[S_{\alpha}] - [S_{\beta}] - [s(\beta\alpha)] + [R_{\alpha}^{(I)}]\left\{\frac{\partial\dot{\mathrm{s}}(\alpha\gamma)}{\partial I} + \frac{\partial\dot{\mathrm{s}}(\beta\gamma)}{\partial I}\right\} = 0,$$

where

$$\frac{\partial}{\partial I} \equiv \left(\frac{\partial}{\partial I}\right)_{\Omega'}\bigg|_{\dot{n}_{\alpha}^{(g)}=0}.$$

Since

$$\frac{\partial\dot{q}(\chi\omega)}{\partial I} = \langle T(\chi\omega)\rangle\frac{\partial\dot{\mathrm{s}}(\chi\omega)}{\partial I},$$

it follows that

$$[G_{\alpha}] - [G_{\beta}] = [R_{\alpha}^{(I)}]\,\Delta\psi.$$

If an amalgam is placed in a thermal field, the Soret effect builds up a concentration gradient along the temperature gradient. If, after Soret equilibrium is established, we pass a steady electric current through the amalgam, will the electric current cause any appreciable change in the Soret concentration gradient? Will the flow of electrons through the medium exert more of a dragging effect on one component than on the other? In view of the disparity in size and mass of the electron relative to the atoms of the amalgam, it seems unlikely that any selective dragging tendency will be observed. It seems plausible then that $[R_{\alpha}^{(I)}] \approx 0$; however, we can only find out for certain by performing the experiment.

A–1 In the linear current-affinity region it follows, if we make use of Eq. (A.21a), that

$$\begin{aligned}\left(\frac{\delta\Theta}{\tilde{\delta}Y_k}\right)_{Y',\mathbf{f}} &= \Omega_k + \sum_{i,i\neq k} Y_i\left(\frac{\delta\Omega_i}{\tilde{\delta}Y_k}\right)_{Y',\mathbf{f}}\\ &= \sum_{i,i\neq k} Y_i\{K_{ki}(\mathbf{f}) + K_{ik}(\mathbf{f})\}\\ &= \sum_{i,i\neq k} Y_i\{K_{ik}(-\mathbf{f}) + K_{ki}(-\mathbf{f})\}\\ &= \left(\frac{\delta\Theta}{\tilde{\delta}Y_k}\right)_{Y',-\mathbf{f}}.\end{aligned}$$

A–3 From the relations

$$\Theta = Y_1\Omega_1 + Y_2\Omega_2 + Y_3\Omega_3$$

and

$$\left(\frac{\delta\Theta}{\bar{\delta}Y_2}\right)_{Y_1,\Omega_3} = Y_1\left(\frac{\delta\Omega_1}{\bar{\delta}Y_2}\right)_{Y_1,\Omega_3} + \Omega_2 + \Omega_3\left(\frac{\delta Y_3}{\bar{\delta}Y_2}\right)_{Y_1,\Omega_3},$$

it follows, when $Y_2 = 0$, that

$$\begin{aligned}\left(\frac{\delta\Theta}{\bar{\delta}Y_2}\right)_{Y_1,\Omega_3} &= Y_1\left\{K_{12} + K_{21} + \left(\frac{\delta Y_3}{\bar{\delta}Y_2}\right)_{Y_1,\Omega_3}(K_{13} + K_{31})\right\} + Y_3(K_{23} - K_{32})\\ &= K_{33}^{-1}\{Y_1[K_{33}(K_{12} + K_{21}) - (K_{32}K_{13} + K_{31}K_{23})]\\ &\qquad + \Omega_3(K_{23} - K_{32})\}.\end{aligned}$$

Thus sufficient conditions for the vanishing of $(\delta\Theta/\bar{\delta}Y_2)_{Y_1,\Omega_3}$ are $K_{12} = -K_{21}$, $K_{13} = -K_{31}$, $K_{23} = K_{32}$; but the necessary conditions are only $K_{23} = K_{32}$, $K_{33}(K_{12} + K_{21}) - K_{32}(K_{13} + K_{31}) = 0$.

A–4 It follows from Eqs. (9.7) and (A.55) to (A.57) that

$$\begin{aligned}\frac{\pi_\beta^{(ab)}(-\mathbf{B})}{T} &= [c_\beta^{(a)}(\mathbf{B})] - [c_\beta^{(b)}(\mathbf{B})] + \frac{\pi_\beta^{(ab)}(\mathbf{B})}{T_\beta} + T_\beta\left\{\frac{\partial(\pi_\beta^{(ab)}(\mathbf{B})/T_\beta)}{\partial T_\beta}\right\}_{T_\alpha,\mathbf{B}}\\ &= -T_\beta\left\{\frac{\partial(\pi_\beta^{(ab)}(-\mathbf{B})/T_\beta)}{\partial T_\beta}\right\}_{T_\alpha,-\mathbf{B}} + \frac{\pi_\beta^{(ab)}(\mathbf{B})}{T_\beta} + T_\beta\left\{\frac{\partial(\pi_\beta^{(ab)}(\mathbf{B})/T_\beta)}{\partial T_\beta}\right\}_{T_\alpha,\mathbf{B}}\end{aligned}$$

and hence, that

$$\left(\frac{\partial\pi_\beta^{(ab)}(-\mathbf{B})}{\partial T_\beta}\right)_{T_\alpha,-\mathbf{B}} = \left(\frac{\partial\pi_\beta^{(ab)}(\mathbf{B})}{\partial T_\beta}\right)_{T_\alpha,\mathbf{B}}.$$

The other relation follows similarly from Eq. (A.56) and the result just established.

INDEX

Index